Short Guide Pergamon Museum

Collection of Classical Antiquities
Museum of Western Asiatic Antiquity

Max Kunze · Liane Jakob-Rost
Evelyn Klengel-Brandt
Joachim Marzahn · Ralf-B. Wartke

Staatliche Museen zu Berlin
Preußischer Kulturbesitz

Front cover   Hall I, Collection of
                     Classical Antiquities
**East Frieze of the Altar of Pergamon
(detail); Artemis fighting the giants**
164–156 B.C.
Marble; ht. (of the frieze) 2.30 m.
*The glance of the bow and arrow armed
goddess of the hunt, Artemis, is directed
at a naked, armed giant who may be
Otos. Between the pair, Artemis's hunting dog bites another giant in the neck to
death.*

Back cover   Gallery 11, Museum of
                    Western Asiatic Antiquity
Inside room of an Assyrian palace
*Gallery 11 of the Museum of Western
Asiatic Antiquity
Reconstruction on the basis of original
monuments from Nimrud, 9th century
B.C. (VAG 24, 1041, 939). The frescoes
from the palace of Tukulti-Ninurta I in
Tulul-al-'Aqar (13th century) were the
models for the mural painting.*

Pp. 2–3   Hall I, Collection of
                    Classical Antiquities
**Pergamon Altar
Reconstruction of the west side**
164–156 B.C.
Marble; ht. 9.66 m.
*The surface area of the altar measured
36.44 x 34.20 m. From the fifth step rises
a massive structure, separated into an
undecorated base and a frieze above,
2.30 m. tall, surmounted by a projecting
denticulate cornice. Only the open staircase cuts into this plinth and leads to a
columned hall with surrounds the entire
superstructure. The columns with their
moulded bases and Ionic capitals have a
remarkably delicate appearance. Crowning figures of gods, griffins, horses and
centaurs once stood above the column
shafts and the unfinished cyma.*

Collection of Classical Antiquities
Aphrodite   *1st floor, Gallery 6*
Middle of the 2nd century B.C.
Terracotta; ht. 37.6 cm.
*From Myrina; acquired in 1930 from the
von Heyl Collection, Darmstadt
Acc. no. 31272*
*This figure of Aphrodite is considered one
of the finest works made in workshops in
Asia Minor at the height of the Hellenistic
Period. Because the left leg is lost below
the knee and the hands are also missing,
the pose of the goddess cannot be reconstructed with certainty; perhaps she
turned her head toward Eros while holding a mirror in her hands. The figure's
charm is due to the contrasts it embodies:
the movement of the head is opposed to
that of the body and the nudity of the
upper torso contrasts with the con-
cealment of the body below the waist
under heavy drapery rendered in deeply
cut folds around the legs. The sensual
quality of the figure is emphasized by
the smooth areas of drapery which reveal
the feminine physique.*

Max Kunze

Classical art in the Pergamon Museum: Past and present

Fig. 1   *Hall I*
**East Frieze of the Altar of Pergamon
(detail); Zeus fighting the giants**
164–156 B.C.
Marble; ht. (of the frieze) 2.30 m.
*Zeus, the most important of the Olym-
pians who collected the clouds, sent the
rain and threw thunderbolts, accompanied by an eagle fights the leader of
the giants, Porphyrion, and two young
giants.*

Very few of today's visitors will be able
to remember that the display of
Classical antiquities was mounted in
three separate buildings before the outbreak of World War II and the resulting
closure of the museums. From the
grounds of a palace garden, the «Lustgarten,» the visitor entered the Old
Museum with its collection of Classical
sculpture; from there one could pass
directly into the New Museum, with its
comprehensive exhibition of ancient
minor arts. And from the New Museum
in turn, a passage gave access to Greek
and Roman architecture in the Pergamon
Museum, which was named after the
great altar from Pergamon that it housed.
Divided among the three buildings but all
on a single level and joined by passage-
ways, the entire complex enabled the
visitor who strolled through the galleries
to follow the development of Greek,
Roman, Etruscan and Cypriot art. The
declared intention of the two museums
with collections of Classical antiquities in
present-day Berlin – the Antikenmuseum
in Charlottenburg and the Pergamon
Museum – is now to bring their holdings
together again and to exhibit them in a
new, comprehensive exhibition integrated with the other archaeological collections on Museum Island with its rich
tradition, taking up the old conception of
the museum which had evolved over a
century.

The exhibition of Classical antiquities since 1830

In 1830 the first public museum in Berlin
opened; it served for more than a century
as the home of the collection of Classical
sculpture. This «Old Museum» was designed by the architect Carl Friedrich
Schinkel and built opposite the Schloß
am Lustgarten. The visitor entered the
museum at the point where Classical
statuary was exhibited in a rotunda; for
some years now ancient statuary depicting gods has once again been shown in
this domed hall. Over-lifesized statues of
deities – Roman copies after Greek
originals – are exhibited between the columns on the main level, while above in
the ambulatory there are lifesized and
smaller figures. Thus Schinkel's concep-

Fig. 1a   Hall I
Detail of the Great Frieze, Pergamon Altar; west side, north face of the open staircase
164–156 B.C.
Marble; ht. (of the frieze) 2.30 m.

The figures that decorate the wall flanking the staircase show how the mythological battle has been adapted to the architecture of the altar. The gods drive the giants up the steps into the furthest corner. To the north, marine gods dominate the battle; here they are Doris and Nereus, Oceanus and Tethys while in an analogous position opposite, Amphitrite and her son Triton are shown. The natural element of these gods, the ocean, is everywhere in evidence: wet garments cling to their bodies or fall in heavy folds, Nereus wears a fish skin on his head and Doris's boots are made of fish skin and fins.

7

Fig. 2   *Hall I*
Detail of the Great Frieze, Pergamon Altar; figure of Nyx, goddess of the night
164–156 B.C.
Marble; ht. (of the frieze) 2.30 m.

The identification of this splendid figure of a goddess in the north frieze is still disputed. She is about to hurl a vase with a serpent coiled around it as a missile. The delicately modelled face with the hair drawn up on top of the head seems almost

girl-like. Her elaborate sandals are visible below the hem of her sleeveless garment, and a cloak which flutters up at her side and behind her head is fastened diagonally across her chest.

tion of this space, which was modelled on the Pantheon in Rome, as a place for thoughtful reflection has been realized again, making the rotunda one of the grandest museum interiors. From the rotunda, the visitor entered two galleries where statues depicting gods and heroes were displayed. In two further galleries there followed Roman statues of emperors and portraits, as well as Roman objects with relief decoration, many of them funerary, including sarcophagi and ossuaries. In keeping with the aim of presenting a comprehensive exhibition of sculpture, medieval and later works followed on the sculpture of Imperial Rome. But the large number of acquisitions made in the 19th century soon led to the separation of post-Classical sculpture from works of earlier periods.

As the Classical collection grew larger, it became necessary to depart from the original plan and to install the «Antiquarium» (the collection of ancient minor arts) in the lower level of Schinkel's building. Here were displays of ancient vases, terracottas, bronzes, gems, and metalwork in gold and silver. But because of additional extensive acquisitions, these holdings, too, soon exceeded the space allotted them.

A committee headed by Wilhelm von Humboldt, the founder of the University of Berlin, was instrumental in planning the original installation in the museum. The Berlin sculptor Christian F. Tieck wrote the first guide through the «sculpture gallery.»

The first archaeologist to be employed at the museum, Eduard Gerhard (1833–1855), had a decisive role in shaping the character of the Berlin Classical collection in its early years. More than almost any other museum of its time, it was conceived not simply as a place where a comprehensive collection representative of ancient culture was exhibited, but as an institution with additional responsibilities in research and in the dissemination of knowledge. This conception resulted in two innovations. First, a systematic collection of archaeological information was set up, comprising drawings of antiquities from Italy and Greece that soon numbered some 2500 items; this important source has yet to be exhausted. Second, the museum's peda-

gogical function provided the main focus for the installation and helped to define an acquisitions policy that was directed less toward securing masterpieces of Classical art than toward documenting the variety of artistic genres and cultures. Despite opposition, Gerhard purchased inexpensive casts, since he realized it would be impossible to achieve a complete conspectus of Classical art on the basis of the original works available for purchase. Thus, twelve years after the museum was founded, it obtained the collection of ancient plaster casts of the Berlin Academy of the Arts which had been acquired from 1796 on. In the following decades, the collection expanded quickly to become one of the largest of its kind. The combination of originals and casts henceforth determined the conception of the displays, which sought to reconstruct as completely as possible the history of Classical art.

Soon after its completion, the Museum am Lustgarten proved too small for its purpose, and so it was decided to erect another museum building adjoining it to the north. Between 1843 and 1855, the architect Friedrich August Stüler undertook the construction of the new building, which became known in Berlin museum history as the «Neues Museum» – the New Museum – in contrast to the Museum am Lustgarten, now termed the «Altes Museum» – the Old Museum. When the New Museum was finished, the numerous ancient Egyptian works of art that had been acquired found a home there, and were installed on the ground floor. On the museum's main floor, the casts acquired through Gerhard's ambitious policy were shown, integrated into an exhibition especially designed for them by Stüler, in which the wall paintings and décor of each gallery related directly to the culture or epoch shown in it.

But Stüler's installation based on the idea of a «complete work of art» could not be sustained. As a result of the continuing successful acquisition of ancient sculpture and minor arts, the collection of vases from the Antiquarium was moved in 1879 from the Old Museum into the New Museum. About two decades later, when the holdings were growing enorm-

ously by the excavations of the Berlin museums in Greece and Turkey, the old organization of the exhibition had to be abandoned entirely, and with it, the idea of a comprehensive cast museum. The collection of plaster casts was turned over to the University of Berlin as a teaching collection.

Excavations in association with the Berlin museums were first undertaken in 1875 at the site of Olympia in Greece. The continuing programme of this work resulted in the acquisition of excavated pieces, raising once again the question of exhibition space. The construction of an additional archaeological museum especially for Classical architecture had become inevitable. The structure, erected at Am Kupfergraben, was built by Ludwig Hoffmann to designs by the architect Alfred Messel; it was finally opened in 1930 on the occasion of the 100th anniversary of the inauguration of the first Berlin museum, the Museum am Lustgarten. The attraction of the new building for visitors to Museum Island was first and foremost its exhibition of architecture of the Graeco-Roman and Ancient Near Eastern world.

In three adjacent galleries provided with natural lighting from above, it was possible to exhibit reconstructions of ancient architecture on a one-to-one scale. This conception, which was undoubtedly novel for its time, was successfully defended against its critics in a bitterly fought controversy which became known as the «war of the Berlin museums.» This debate established the reputation of the Pergamon Museum, which has been ever since one of the most important architectural museums in the world. In the middle gallery, the west side of the Altar of Pergamon – probably the most important ancient Greek monumental altar (Front cover; pp. 2–3, Figures 1, 1a, 2) – was reconstructed. This marble structure, which was created between 164 and 156 B.C., continues to be one of the museum's principal attractions. The massive platform, erected above five steps, is divided into an undecorated socle and a frieze zone 2.30 m. tall, crowned by a projecting denticulate cornice. On the west side, an open staircase almost 20 m. wide cuts into the platform, which was approximately

9

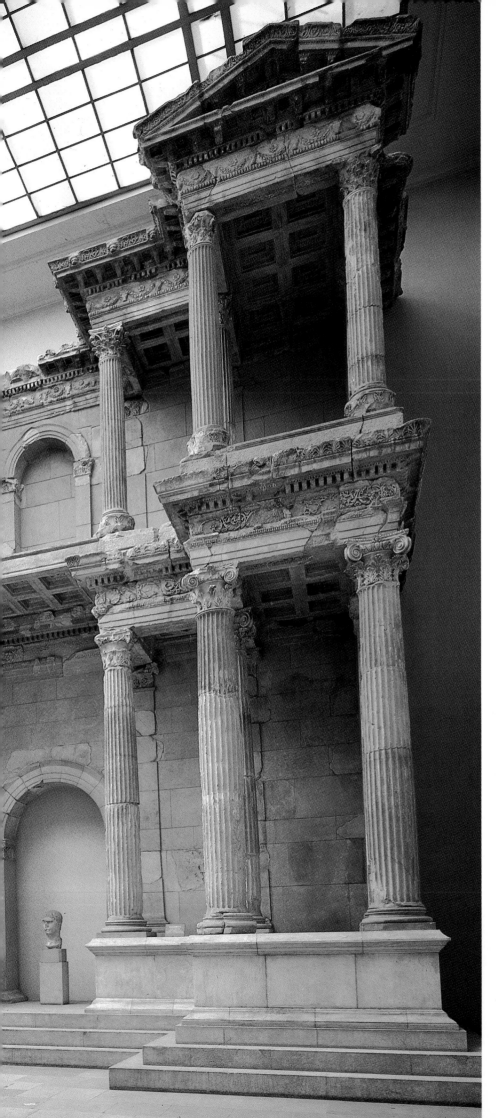

Fig. 3   *Hall III*
Market gateway from Miletus
Ca. A.D. 120
Marble; ht. 16.68 m.
The gateway found in the city of Miletus
is one of the most famous examples of
Roman façade architecture. It once gave
access to the city's south market; the
square in front of it was framed on two
other sides by the Hellenistic city hall and
the ornamental three-storey façade of
a nymphaeum. When Emperor Justinian
reduced the city's area and refortified it
in A.D. 538, the market gateway was incorporated into the city wall. At some
date before 1100, an earthquake
destroyed the wall. Between 1903 and
1905, German excavations under the
direction of Theodor Wiegand and
Hubert Knackfuß uncovered the main
parts of the monument, which was later
reconstructed in the Pergamon Museum
at its original size and using much of the
original material.

11

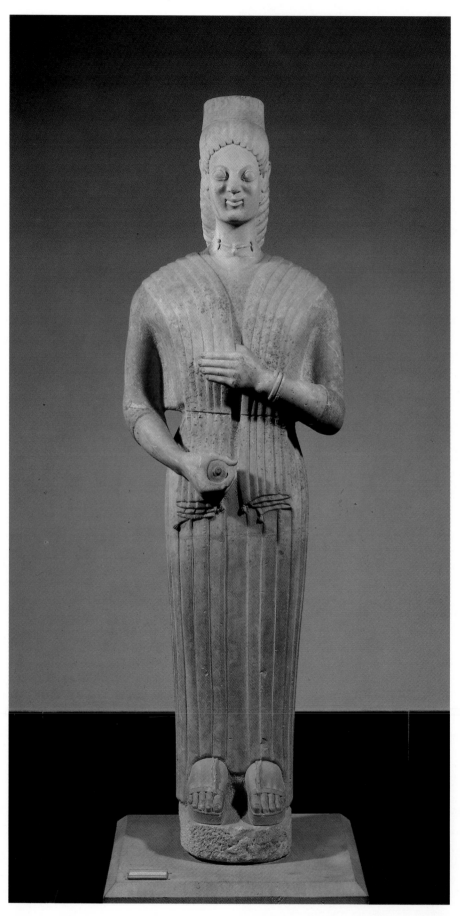

Fig. 4.   *Gallery 1*
The «Berlin Goddess»
580–560 B.C.
Marble; ht. 1.93 m.
Attic; acquired on the art market in 1924
Sk 1800
The statue owes its excellent state of preservation, including a certain amount of the original paint on the marble surface, to an ancient protective measure: in antiquity it was enveloped in a lead casing and buried at Keratea, in southern Attica, where it was discovered, still enveloped, early this century. The Archaic structure of the statue's body is rigid and the attitude clumsy. There is a curious contrast between sharply angled individual forms (for example, in the treatment of the mouth) and other organically rendered details such as the hands and toes. The more recent discovery of a comparable statue in Attica with an associated inscription has shown that the woman depicted is not a goddess but a mortal – in other words, the figure was a tomb statue.

Fig. 5   *Gallery 1*
Tomb relief from Chrysapha near Sparta (Laconia)
Ca. 550–530 B.C.
Marble; ht. 87 cm.
Acquired from the Sabouroff Collection
Sk 731
This marble relief from Laconia whose carving is remarkably crisp depicts two deceased figures sitting on a richly ornamented Egyptian throne with lion legs. The man holds a kantharos (a drinking cup) and the woman a pomegranate in one hand and a veil in the other. The serpent which rises up behind the throne is a symbol of the underworld. Miniature figures of worshippers – a man and a woman – approach the pair with offerings. According to the person who discovered the relief, it stood upright in the midst of a tumulus-like heap of earth and stones.

COLLECTION OF CLASSICAL ANTIQUITIES · PERGAMON MUSEUM

square in plan, to give access to a colonnade that entirely covers the upper surface. The delicate Ionic columns stand on moulded bases and carry cornices that originally bore numerous acroteria – figures of gods, griffins, centaurs and horses. The frieze, 120 m. in length and carved in high relief, surrounded the platform on all but the west side where it was interrupted by the open staircase (cf. page 2–3). With the exception of the frieze from the Temple of Athena Parthenos in Athens, it is the longest continuous band of relief preserved from the Greek world. Its theme is the battle of the gods and the giants, an episode in mythology that was used in the decoration of the altar to allude to the conflict of the Pergamene kings with the Galatians. More than 100 over-lifesized figures are shown engaged in dramatic scenes of mutual combat; both gods and giants are depicted in postures of great physical exertion. The defeated giants in particular show mental anguish and torment, and the experience of pain is expressed graphically (Figure 1–2).

Additional monuments from the Attalid residence of Pergamon that are found in the hall with Hellenistic Greek architecture include the propylon of the Temple of Athena, which has been completely reconstructed in the museum, and some andesite columns from the late 4th century B.C. Temple of Athena. The acme of Ionic architecture in Asia Minor is represented by two columns with entablatures from the Athena Temple at Priene, which was begun in the mid-4th century but not completed until two centuries later. In antiquity it was considered to be the prototypical Ionic temple and its design attributed to the architect Pytheos. In his tradition stood Hermogenes, who created the Temple of Artemis Leukophryene (end of the 3rd century to 129 B.C.) for the city of Magnesia on the River Maeander. Two reconstructed columns from the temple are displayed in the museum.

The hall devoted to Roman architecture is dominated by the gateway of a marketplace in Miletus (Figure 3) built under Emperor Hadrian (d. A.D. 138). It once formed the entrance to the southern agora of the city. Its two-storey marble façade is articulated by round arches and pilasters flanked by projecting antae. Between and beside the round arches stand paired columns with composite capitals. The upper storey rises above a jutting Ionic entablature with a sumptuous acanthus frieze. The columns of the upper storey bear Corinthian capitals and its entablature is decorated with a frieze of garlands and bucrania. The structure's design culminates in a cornice composed of three pediments. The central pediment has a «broken» form, supported on two pairs of columns, while the two at the sides are smaller, each projecting forward from a corner tabernacle. The position of the columns, the sumptuous floral architectural ornament, and the «broken» middle pediment create a fluctuating play of light and shade. The whole is testimony to the flourishing state of architecture in the Greek cities of Asia Minor under Roman rule. Other architectural elements, from Pergamon and Baalbek (ancient Heliopolis) in eastern Lebanon, provide additional impressions of Roman Imperial architecture.

The opening of the Pergamon Museum in 1930 brought to a conclusion the building programme of the Berlin museums for the collection of Classical antiquities. The damage to the buildings during World War II destroyed the circuit through the Classical world from the Old Museum by way of the New Museum to the Pergamon Museum. The building designed by Stüler remains a ruin; after the war the holdings of Classical antiquities were of necessity concentrated in the north wing of the Pergamon Museum. (In 1982, the museum was provided with a new entrance hall, whose foyer houses additional examples of Classical architecture, especially of Archaic Greece.) In any event, most of the objects from the New Museum were no longer available, because they had been stored during the war in what subsequently became the Federal Republic of Germany. These objects are now exhibited in the Antikenmuseum in Berlin-Charlottenburg, a part of the Staatliche Museen Preußischer Kulturbesitz.

After the war, the collection of Classical sculpture, which had been displayed in the Old Museum until 1939, was installed in the north wing of the Pergamon Museum. Almost 1000 years of the development of Classical art are presented on the main floor, with emphasis on the history of the creation and evolution of the representation of the human figure. The exhibition, which was remodelled in 1983–84, is presented as a stroll through the history of humankind and of the reproduction of the human form as reflected in the art of Greek and Roman times. The objects are arranged chronologically, beginning with examples of the Archaic Period from the end of the 7th century B.C. The spacious and well-lit galleries allow the plastic qualities of the sculptures to be appreciated to the full. The first gallery is dominated by *kouroi* – statues of youths – followed by marvellous examples of statuary of this early age depicting maidens and women. The «Berlin Goddess» (Figure 4) is prominent among them. Made in Attica and datable to the height of the Archaic Period, this statue has come down to us in a superb condition, preserving traces of the ancient painting. A masterpiece of the early Classical Period is the solemnly austere enthroned goddess from Taranto in southern Italy (Figure 7). In the next gallery follow examples of Classical Greek art of the 5th and 4th centuries B.C., the age of the flowering and of the crisis of the Greek *polis*. The collection includes excellent Greek originals – important works in marble that are presented thematically, with tomb and votive reliefs forming one grave, statues a second, and friezes a third. Many masterpieces of Greek art created by major artists are, however, preserved only in Roman copies. Some of these large-scale Roman interpretations of Greek sculptural works are shown in the gallery of «Athena Parthenos.» Such pieces are indispensable for the reconstruction of stylistic development in the 5th and 4th centuries B.C. Furthermore, they evoke for the visitor the pioneering achievements of the period which saw changes in Greek democracy and religion whose effects are discernible both in the private and public sphere.

Here and in the following rooms, the exhibition is arranged as a circuit documenting the transition from the late Classical to the Hellenistic Period running from the 3th to the 1st century B.C. Outstanding works of sculpture illustrate

Fig. 6   *Gallery 1*
Statue of a woman holding a partridge
Ca. 570–560 B.C.
Marble; ht. 1.43 m.
From Miletus
Sk 1791
In contrast to statues of the Archaic Period depicting nude youths (kouroi), contemporaneous figures of young women show them clothed. The costume of a finely pleated chiton with a broad belt and a draped cloak with a zig-zag hem was evidently highly prized. Whether such statues were intended for a tomb or were dedicated in a temple cannot be determined from their appearance. These statues of women and girls, with their graceful postures and the gifts they bear, like the partridge here, embody the aristocratic ideal of the 6th century B.C. The favour of the gods was sought not through the rendering of specific, individual likenesses but through the representation of a richly clad, perfect physical form.

Fig. 7   *Gallery 2*
Statue of an enthroned goddess
Ca. 460 B.C.
Marble; ht. 1.51 m.
From Taranto; purchased on the art
market in Paris, 1915
Sk 1761
Only a few cult statues of the Archaic
Period are known. This statue of a god-
dess from Taranto probably depicts
Persephone, the goddess of the nether-
world. Stylistically the figure is trans-
itional between the Archaic Period and
the «severe style» of the early Classical
Period. This outstanding work is char-
acterized by its formal severity of attitude
and a mildness of facial expression. In
spite of its seated posture, a restrained
rhythmical movement flows through the
body which embodies the ideal of con-
trapposto (the balance of tensed and
relaxed elements in the rendering of the
body) characteristic of the best works of
the Classical Period.

the new style and means of expression which evolved in response to the novel artistic commissions of Hellenistic rulers. Such themes as the depiction of the ruler and allegories centering on his person, genre sculpture and tomb reliefs characterize these works.

The circuit ends with Roman art. Its diversity – from official works created in the service of the state to private portraits and reliefs – is illustrated by selected examples from the museum's comprehensive sculpture collection. Because of the small amount of space available in the Pergamon Museum, only a very limited selection is currently on view; many important works can only be available to scholars in the storerooms.

This display, whose approach focuses on cultural history, is supplemented by Roman portraits shown on the floor above. As already mentioned, a large proportion of the objects once exhibited in the New Museum are now on view in the Antikenmuseum, Charlottenburg. But some of the comprehensive holdings of ancient terracottas, bronzes, and Greek vases have remained on Museum Island and a modest selection of them can be seen on the second floor of the Pergamon Museum. Among them are also important small-scale works in marble and bronze such as Archaic Greek sculpture from the Temple of Hera on Samos and Hellenistic finds from Pergamon. The collection of terracottas deserves special mention. The selection chosen for exhibition provides a many-sided overview of the development of figural works in clay, from the pieces of the early Archaic Period to the famous Tanagra figures and Hellenistic examples. Individual terracottas, such as the remarkably large «Heyl Aphrodite» (Figure on p. 5, described on p. 6), are virtually unmatched among the world's museum collections.

Acquisitions of Classical antiquities for the Berlin Museums

It took decades of strenuous effort on the part of many Berlin scholars and Enlightenment figures before the antiquities which had been used to furnish the park and palace of Sanssouci in Potsdam near

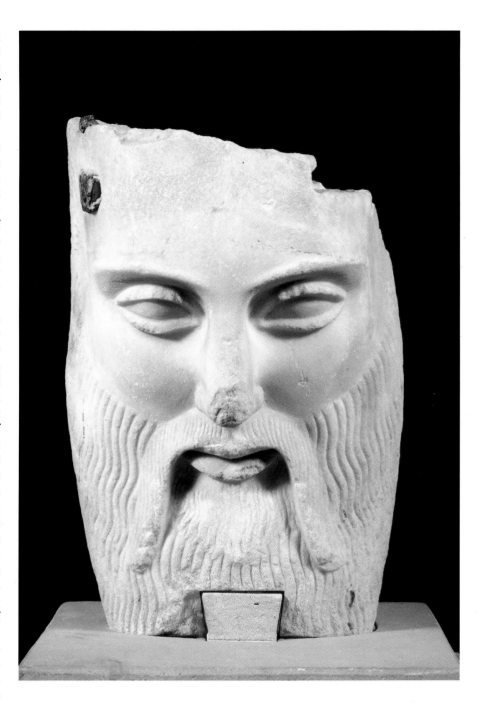

Fig. 8   *Gallery 3*
Mask of the river god Achelous
Ca. 470 B.C.
Marble; ht. 32 cm.
From Marathon; acquired in 1848
Sk 100
The «severe style» of the early Classical Period is particularly well represented by this face in which the «archaic smile» has been replaced by a new earnestness of expression and simplicity of form. Above the beard only a small area of the cheeks is shown, and the eyes are rimmed by heavy lids. Slots on the forehead show that the mask was completed with ears and horns of bronze. A votive relief from Megara exhibited in the same gallery shows that such masks were attached to a table. It is known that the river god Achelous, who was manifested in such bull masks, was worshipped in sanctuaries in the wild.

17

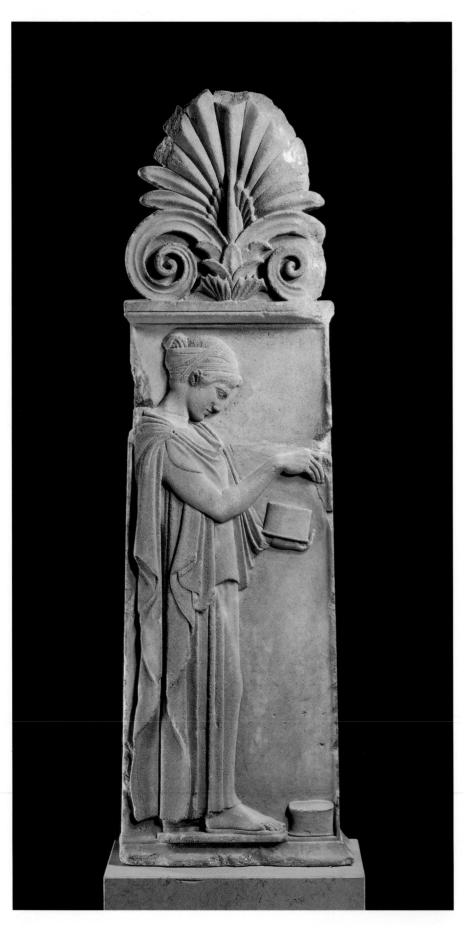

Fig. 9   *Gallery 2*
Stele of a girl
Ca. 460 B.C.
Marble; ht. 1.43 m.
So-called Giustiniani stele, after the name of a Venetian who once owned it; acquired in 1897
Sk 1482
The tall, tapering stela is crowned by a palmette. The figure depicts a young woman who gazes earnestly and fixedly at the small box from which she has just removed something, perhaps pellets of incense, originally rendered in paint and now lost. According to Greek literature and tomb epigrams, the deaths of maidens and youths who were no longer children but still unmarried were especially mourned. In funerary reliefs they were depicted in youthful beauty as the embodiment of blossoming life. The Classical attitude of the figure – the differentiation of the leg bearing the body's weight and the free leg, the slight turn of the torso, and the inclination of the head – exhibits clearly the «severe style» of Greek Classical art.

Fig. 10　　　　　　　　*Gallery 5*
Torso of a spear-bearer (doryphoros)
*Roman copy of a bronze statue of
ca. 440 B.C. created by the sculptor
Polycleitos of Argos; discovered in
1873 on the Palatine Hill, Rome
Marble; ht. 1.31 m.
From the collection of Count Pourtalès;
acquired in 1926
Sk 1789
With the aid of other replicas, the figure
can be restored as follows: the head was
turned slightly to the right, the left upper
arm bent backward with the lower arm
raised to shoulder a lance held in the
hand. The figure strode forward, with the
weight on the advanced leg while the toes
of the left only barely touched the ground.
This figure, the* doryphoros, *served as the
basis for Polycleitos's theoretical treatise
on the canon. Polycleitos sought to establish the natural and average proportions
of the human body by measurement and
to express his result in figures; by
this method he hoped to create an ideal
figure of the highest beauty.*

Fig. 11   *Gallery 5*
Statue of a wounded Amazon, attributed to the sculptor Cresilas or Polykeitos
Roman copy of a Greek original of 440–430 B.C.
Marble; ht. 1.83 m.
Acquired in 1869 in Rome
Sk 7
The Roman writer Pliny the Elder related the story of a competition held between four of the most famous Greek sculptors of the second half of the 5th century B.C. to create a statue of a wounded Amazon for the Temple of Artemis at Ephesus. Different versions of this theme are preserved in Roman copies. The Berlin piece is one of the very best replicas of the statue made by Cresilas. The exhausted Amazon, who wears a double-belted chiton, *raises her right arm above a bleeding wound in her armpit, and supports herself on a pillar. (The right arm, the lower left arm, both feet and the pillar are modern.)*

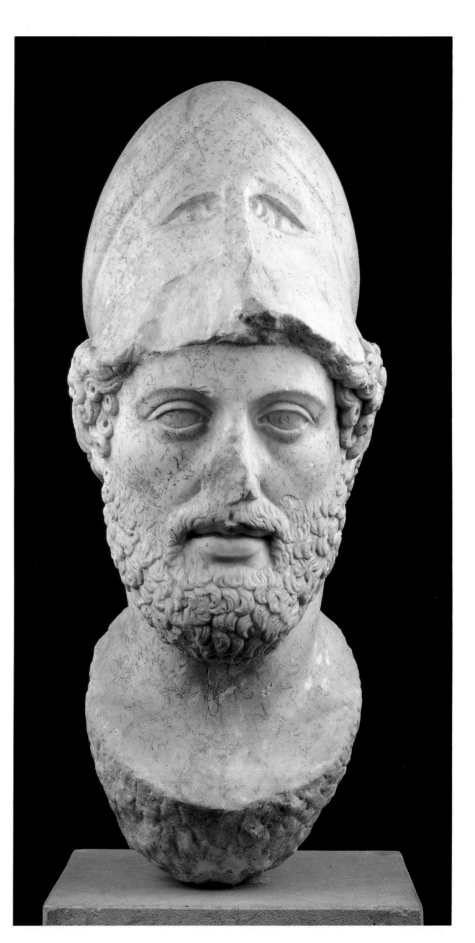

Fig. 12   *Gallery 5*
Portrait of Pericles wearing a Corin-thian helmet
Roman copy after a Greek original, presumably the statue made by Cresilas in 429 B.C. for the Athenian Acropolis Marble; ht. 54 cm.
Found on Lesbos; acquired on the art market in 1901
Sk 1530
The Athenian statesman under whose sway all Athens stood in the third quarter of the 5th century B.C. is not depicted with his own individual physiognomy here but as an idealized commander. The «portrait» of Pericles by Cresilas, who worked during the era of radical Athenian democracy, created a supra-personal image that was in keeping with a civic ideal founded upon the concept of equality. This portrait is remarkable for its quality and careful execution. The original stood on the Athenian Acropolis beside statues of Pericles's father Xanthippos and of the lyric poet Anacreon.

Fig. 13   Gallery 3
***Votive relief commemorating a victory in
a chariot race***
*Beginning of the 4th century B.C.
Marble; ht. (including the tangs) 81 cm.,
w. 98.7 cm.
Discovered in 1835 at Oropos; acquired
for Berlin in 1884 from the Sabouroff
Collection
Sk 725
Votive reliefs formed one category of the
gifts to gods deposited in their temples.
Most of them depict the deity in question
or refer to the myths in which he or she
played a role. The chariot race depicted
here was organized in honour of Am-
phiaraos, a god of healing at home at
Oropos, on the border between Attica
and Boeotia. A participant (who in the
course of the race had to jump from his*

*chariot and run on while carrying his
weapons) dedicated this relief to the god
after a victory in the competition. Details
like the reins and the wheels of the chariot
were not rendered in relief but in paint,
which is not preserved.*

Fig. 14   Gallery 2
Grave stele of Thraseas and Euandria
*Ca. 350–340 B.C.
Marble; ht. 1.6 m.
Discovered in Athens; acquired in 1884
from the Sabouroff Collection
Sk 738
Stelai like this one, which belonged to the*

*married couple named in the inscription,
once lined a street of tombs outside the
city of Athens. The deceased husband
Thraseas takes leave of his wife, who sits
on a stool. The figure in the background
is a female slave who turns away from her
master with a gesture of mourning. This
scene depicting the farewell to life evokes
the domestic image of the family and the
couple's strong mutual affection: they
gaze deeply into one another's eyes and
their handclasp emphasizes the message.
In the second half of the 4th century B.C.
figures were increasingly freed from
the relief ground, and they gained in
plasticity, breaking away from the
architectural framework indicated in
relief. Only a short time later the
architectural elements and the relief
came to be worked separately.*

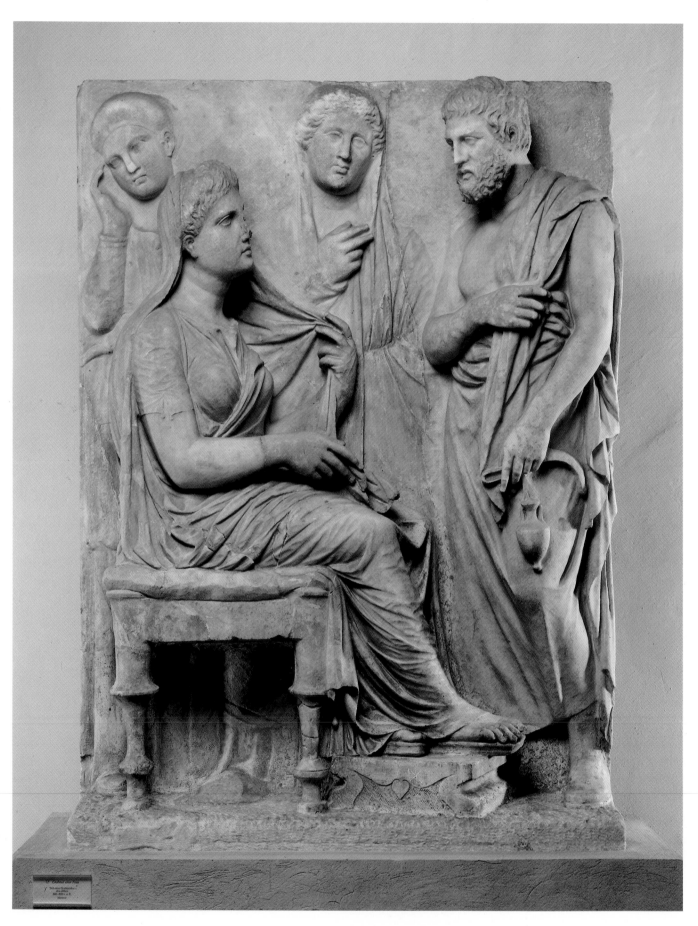

Fig. 15 *Gallery 4*
Grave stele relief of a married couple from Athens
Ca. 340–330 B.C.
Marble; ht. 1.25 m., w. 98 cm.
Sk 739
In the second half of the 4th century B.C. grave monuments in Athens became increasingly elaborate, prompting Demetrius of Phaleron to promulgate a sumptuary law against the practice in 317 B.C. This relief was only part of a particularly grand tomb that took the form of a small temple with two columns and a gabled roof. The separately worked architectural elements are not preserved.

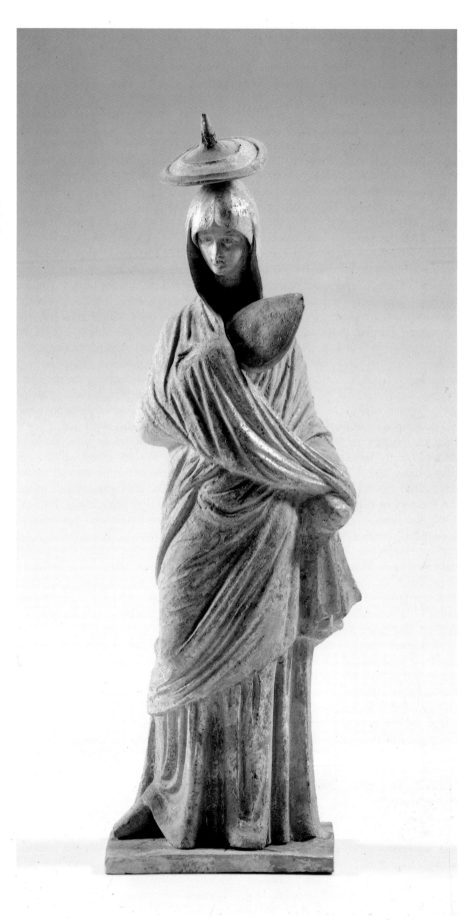

Fig. 16 *Gallery 4*
Woman with a sun hat and a fan
Ca. 320 B.C.
Terracotta; ht. 34 cm.
From Tanagra; acquired in 1880
TC 7674
Between 330 and 200 B.C. the so-called Tanagra style dominated the production of terracottas in Boeotia. Figures in the Tanagra style spread throughout the Hellenistic world. This early example still possesses much of its original painting in an excellent state of preservation: gold (on the border of the cloak and the fan), red and blue are in evidence.

Berlin and those few others in the palace in Berlin itself on what became Museum Island could be gathered together in a museum open to the public. The objects acquired under Friedrich II (1740–1786) and his successor Friedrich Wilhelm II (1786–1797) had been intended simply as decorative furnishings for their residences. At the end of the 18th century, the Prussian ruling house decided tentatively to amalgamate the holdings of antiquities in the city's palace. The development which followed – the establishment of a public museum – was doubtless encouraged by the «Musée Napoleon» in Paris which had been formed as a consequence of the Napoleonic wars, its holdings admittedly consisting simply of works of art stolen by Napoleon throughout Europe. After the return of antiquities from Paris to Berlin conditions were at last favourable for mounting a public exhibition in a purpose-built museum, as described in the preceding pages.

The sculpture and works of minor arts brought together in the Old Museum derived chiefly from older royal collections; these had a chequered history, determined by the interest and taste of the Electors of Brandenburg, who from 1701 had been Kings of Prussia. (An even older collection, whose composition can no longer be reconstructed, was destroyed in the Thirty Years' War.) The acquisitions of the Electors Friedrich Wilhelm (1640–1688) and Friedrich III (1688–1713) together formed a collection of European rank. For example, 12,000 coins came to Berlin from the estate of the Elector of the Palatinate and about 200 works of sculpture arrived from Rome from the collection of Giovanni Pietro Bellori (1613–1696), an Italian writer on art. Lorenz Beger, a librarian and antiquarian from the Palatinate, published these holdings in 1699 in the third volume of a monumental work of engravings, the «Thesaurus Brandenburgicus.»

But under King Friedrich Wilhelm I (1713–1740) this substantial collection was decimated. He gave August the Strong, Elector of Saxony, a substantial portion of the sculptures from the Bellori collection for the city of Dresden. Important new acquisitions were again

made under King Friedrich II. These, however, did not augment the «chamber of antiquities» in the ruler's residence in the city, but instead served to furnish the palace complex and the park of Sanssouci outside Berlin at Potsdam. Noteworthy acquisitions at Sanssouci are the many sculptures from the collection and excavations of Cardinal Melchior de Polignac, the antiquities from the collection of the Margravine Wilhelmine of Bayreuth (a sister of Friedrich II), who purchased them on a journey through Italy in 1754–55, and the bronze statue of a youth which stood until the king's death on the terrace at Sanssouci where it could been seen from the library. Known as the «Praying Boy,» it is still one of the gems of the collection (Figure 17). In 1764, Friedrich II was able to acquire the collection of ancient gems belonging to Baron Philipp von Stosch of Florence; at that time this was certainly the most important collection of such objects, and it remains to this day one of the major components of the Berlin collection.

Numerous acquisitions were made in the 1820's – to some extent with an eye to the founding of the museum. Prussian diplomats, like the representative to the Vatican Christian Karl Josias Bunsen, and artists from Berlin who spent time in Italy (expecially in Rome) like Carl Friedrich Schinkel, Christian Daniel Rauch, and Emil Wolff, were active in arranging purchases of large-scale statuary suitable for exhibition in the rotunda of the Old Museum. Most significant, however, was the acquisition of important private collections of minor arts that augmented greatly the holdings in that area: in 1823, the collection of the general Baron Heinrich Carl Menu Minutoli, which also included a comprehensive collection of Egyptian antiquities, came to Berlin, followed in 1827 by the collection of Count Ingelheim and a year later by that of Baron Franz von Koller. Finally, in 1831 the collection of the Prussian Councillor Dorow – who hoped to secure a position in the museum on account of it – came to Berlin.

In the following decades the acquisitions policy for Classical antiquities was determined by the influence of Eduard Gerhard, who was associated with the museum from 1833. His numerous so-

Fig. 17   *Gallery 3*
The «Praying Boy»
End of the 4th century B.C.
Bronze; ht. 1.28 m.
Acquired for the palace of Sanssouci, Potsdam, in 1747
Sk 2
This is one of the few lifesized statues in bronze that have survived from antiquity. The youth's right leg is bent at the knee and his head is tilted back slightly, so that his glance is directed upwards. The arms, although modern, probably approximate closely the movement of the original. The identification of the statue is uncertain. At first, scholars suggested that it depicted Ganymede, but it is more likely to be a votive statue of a worshipper from the Temple of Helios on Rhodes. From that island, the statue came to Venice, where its presence is documented as early as the 16th century. From Venice it passed through various European private collections until Friedrich II acquired it to furnish his palace of Sanssouci.

Fig. 18   Gallery 7
Corner block of a frieze of metopes and triglyphs depicting Helios
After 300 B.C.
Marble; ht. 85.8 cm., w. 2.012 m. (w. of the metope 86.3 cm.)
From the Temple of Athena at Troy; discovered by Heinrich Schliemann
Acc. no. 9582
This relief metope depicting Helios is the best preserved of all the metopes from the Temple of Athena at Troy. The sun god's team of four horses is shown tempestuously charging out from the sea. A diadem-like rayed halo surrounds the god's head. The sweeping surge of the team is emphasized by the deep, fluttering folds of Helios's garments and the diagonal, echeloned arrangement of the horses.

Fig. 19   Gallery 7
Portrait of Attalos I (?), King of Pergamon
Beginning of the 2nd century B.C.
Marble; ht. 39.5 cm.
Discovered in the Byzantine wall on the acropolis of Pergamon
P 130

This portrait, which has been identified as a depiction of King Attalos I (241–197 B.C.), derives from an over-lifesized statue that stood on the acropolis of Pergamon. It is one of the most impressive late Greek portraits that suggest the individual physiognomy of the person depicted while designating him a ruler by means of iconographic devices indicating mood – the wide-open eyes that seem to gaze into the distance, the energetically troubled forehead, and the tensed chin region. The locks of hair across the forehead are rendered in a markedly plastic manner, a feature which probably alludes to the ruler's posthumous divinization.

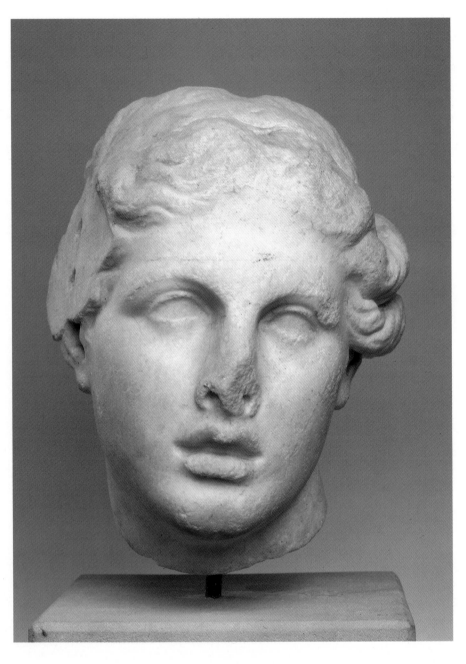

journs in Italy, his vast knowledge of the monuments and his familiarity with the Italian art market benefited the Berlin collection. In particular, the collection of Greek vases profited from his expertise, even if the committee responsible for purchases often denied his requests for funds. Gerhard's connoisseurship enabled him to expand the Berlin collection significantly through the acquisition of Etruscan works of art. Interest in the Etruscans had been aroused throughout Europe by the discovery of wall paintings at Tarquinia and the finds of vast numbers of vases in Etruscan tombs at Vulci. These drew attention for the first time to numerous original Etruscan works which had remained almost unknown outside Italy. With the Etruscan vases, bronzes and gold jewellery from the collections of Dorow and Koller, Berlin possessed a good core of Etruscan material, which Gerhard was able to augment significantly. By the beginning of this century, the acquisition of important groups of finds – such as terracotta acroteria from Caere and complete assemblies of objects from tombs in Tarquinia (such as the «Tomba del Guerriero»), Malacena and Poggio Buco – had made the Berlin collection one of the most important outside Italy.

Like Eduard Gerhard, Ernst Curtius, the director of the Antiquarium from 1872 until 1886, pursued an acquisitions policy which went beyond a narrow definition of Classical art and culture. It was Curtius who enriched the Berlin collection with works of art from ancient Cyprus, which had preserved its individuality over a long period from the 3rd millennium on despite alternating influences from Egypt, the Near East and Greece.

The purchases of plaster casts limited the funds available for acquisitions of original objects, but it was nonetheless possible to make significant purchases down to 1871 when, with the establishment of a united German state, Berlin assumed the role of cultural capital of the nation. In 1841–42, Gustav Friedrich Waagen arranged purchases for the sculpture collection from the old Venetian collections of Tiepolo, Grimani and Nani. In 1858, a second lifesized bronze statue came to Berlin (Figure 23); this had been

Fig. 20   *Gallery 7*
The «Beautiful Head» from Pergamon
Mid-2nd century B.C.
Marble; ht. 30 cm.
P 90
The head was discovered in a well on the *terrace where the Pergamon Altar stood. Although it does not belong to the altar's Great Frieze, its sculptural quality is comparable. The surface appears somewhat abraded, imparting a peculiar softness to the likeness.*

discovered in the River Rhine at Xanten, near the Dutch border. And in 1869 an excellent Roman copy of the statue of a wounded Amazon by the Greek sculptor Cresilas (or Polykleitos?) (Figure 11) was acquired. In the same year, the arrival in the museum of fifty-one silver vessels and utensils, presumably the table service of a Roman officer, caused a sensation. This find had been made at Hildesheim.

The cultural aspirations of the new capital led to a reorganization of the museum administration and to the availability of additional funds for acquisitions and for the excavations which were now undertaken.

Further important Greek works of sculpture came to Berlin with the acquisition of the collection assembled by Count Sabouroff, the Russian ambassador in Athens. Some Greek sculpture had arrived in Berlin in 1821 with the collection of Count Sack. (Both Sabouroff and Sack had purchased antiquities in Greece and had excavated there.) From that time onward original sculptures of quality characterized the Berlin collection, and they continue to be a major element in the display; the Greek grave and votive reliefs in Berlin are among the best works of Classical art to be seen anywhere.

Even during World War I the purchase of a splendid work of Greek sculpture was possible: in 1916, the enthroned goddess from Taranto (Figure 7) was acquired. 1925 saw the acquisition of another highly significant piece, the Archaic tomb relief of a woman with a pomegranate (Figure 5).

Many more acquisitions of this century could be cited. Among them one should mention the collection of ancient helmets belonging to Baron von Lipperheide, the Gans Collection comprising valuable ancient gold jewellery and glass, and thirty-five mummy portraits from the Fayyum in Egypt acquired in 1929 from the Viennese businessman Theodor Graf.

Many of the works of minor arts just mentioned are now displayed in the Antikenmuseum in Charlottenburg. The locations – east or west – of the different places where objects from the Berlin museums were taken for safekeeping during the war led to the division of the holdings in its aftermath. Objects which

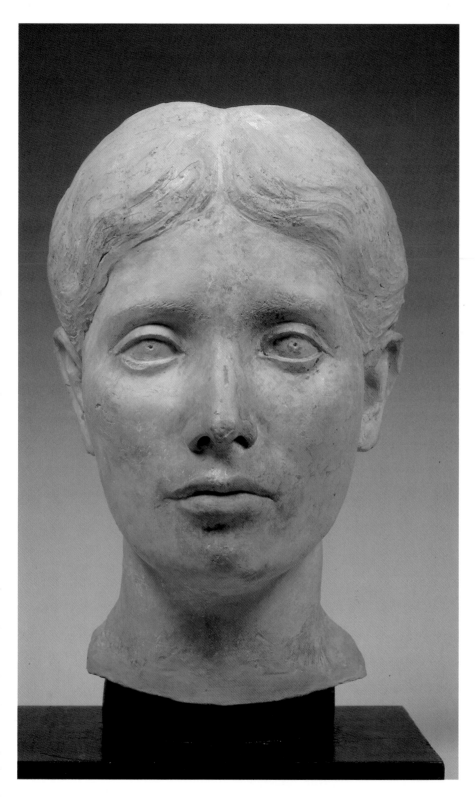

Fig. 21   *Gallery 8*
Head of a young Roman woman
Early Imperial Period
Terracotta; ht. 25.5 cm.
TC 551
This terracotta head of a young woman mobilizes the impressive skills of physio- *gnomic characterization typical of Roman art to capture the beauty of the person represented. The smooth hair is indicated only by a few waves, while the rendering of the eyes and mouth gives the likeness an intelligent and determined expression. The portrait was made in southern Italy.*

31

Fig. 22   1st floor, Gallery 8
Bust of Julius Caesar
1st century A.D.
Green schist; ht. 41 cm.
Provenance not kown
Sk 342
The style developed for private por-
traiture of the later Republican Period,
which strove for a high degree of re-
semblance to the subject, influenced
this likeness of the general and dictator
C. Julius Caesar. However, the form of
the bust with its indication of the tunic
and the toga suggests that the sculpture
was created in the 1st century A.D.,
many years after Caesar's assassination
in 44 B.C.

32

Fig. 23   *Gallery 8*
Statue of a youth wearing a wreath
Mid-1st century A.D.
Bronze; ht. 1.54 m.
Discovered in the River Rhine near Xanten in 1858
Sk 4
The statue very probably stood in a Roman villa where it served the function of a «dumb waiter,» its extended hands supporting a tray. The Romans apparently liked to display their good taste and erudition by using figures of youths, often replicas or reinterpretations of Classical statues of athletes, for such purposes in their villas.

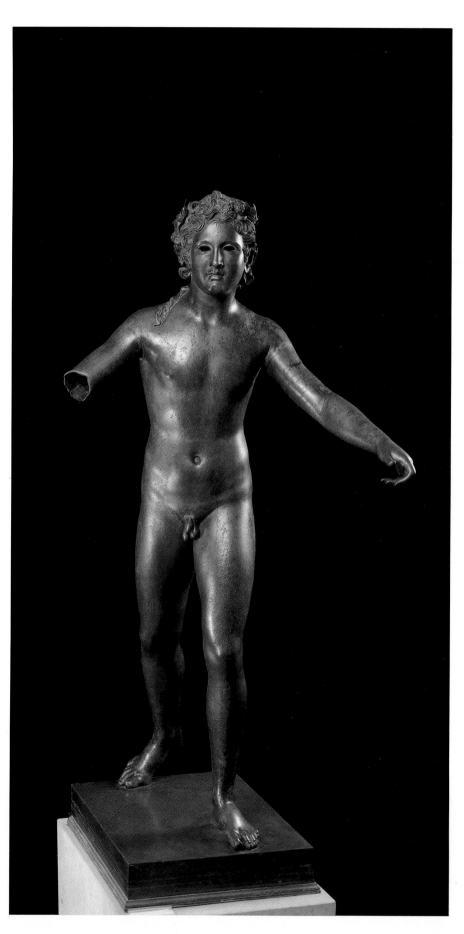

Fig. 24 (overleaf)   *1st floor*
Mosaic with a centaur from Hadrian's Villa at Tivoli
Between A.D. 118 and 128
Natural stones; ht. 58.5 cm., w. 92 cm.
Acc. Mos. 1
This mosaic, created for the residence of Emperor Hadrian at Tivoli, is one of the masterpieces of Roman mosaic art. All the mosaics in the room from which this example came showed separate scenes of similar content. The scene here depicts a battle between a centaur and the wild animals which have slain his mate. The well-balanced composition, the use of perspective, the landscape elements, and the unusually broad range of colour suggest that the composition derives from a Hellenistic prototype.

33

in 1945 had been in the later West Germany came under the jurisdiction of the Stiftung Preußischer Kulturbesitz and eventually were exhibited in Berlin-Charlottenburg. A large number of Greek vases and bronzes, most of the helmets, glass and gold jewellery from the Gans Collection and the Hildesheim silver treasure are now finely displayed in Charlottenburg. But the war caused lamentable losses. Almost all the objects stored in a bunker in Berlin-Friedrichshain – glass, countless vases, terracottas, bronzes and unstudied finds from excavations – were destroyed by fire.

The excavations of the Berlin museums

In 1878, three years after the first excavations of the Berlin museums at Olympia, there began a trial excavation on the acropolis of Pergamon which led to the systematic investigation of the site over the next eight years. The city, which is located near the west coast of Asia Minor, was discovered by Carl Humann (1839–1896). In collaboration with the director of the Berlin sculpture collection Alexander Conze (1831–1914), Humann retrieved in quick succession many elements of the great marble altar with its relief frieze (Figures 1–2). One of the most magnificent altars of the Hellenistic age, the Pergamon Altar was counted among the wonders of the world by the Roman writer Lucius Ampelius.

In the course of three campaigns between 1878 and 1886, Humann and Conze were able to recover the essential parts of the Pergamon Altar from a Byzantine fortification wall, to locate its foundations, and to excavate additional fragments of the frieze, as well as sculpture associated with the altar on the terrace where it had stood. Soon their excavations covered the entire acropolis which was built on several terraces. The Temple of Athena, the Roman Temple of Trajan, the royal palaces, and the theatre with the Temple of Dionysos were cleared and investigated, and other architecture as well. Important studies were also made of a remarkable system that provided the acropolis with water from a spring across the valley on another mountain range opposite. During these three campaigns,

the excavations won a complete picture of the Hellenistic city, which had been the residence of the Attalid kings and one of the most important political and cultural centres of the Hellenistic world. Thanks to the favourable terms of the licence granted to the excavators and to the contract negotiated with the Turkish authorities, the frieze, sculptures and architectural elements from the altar came to Berlin along with other finds. Thus one of the best-preserved monuments of Greek art was acquired for the museum. At a stroke, the splendid high reliefs of the frieze, with its depiction of the gigantomachy (battle of the gods and giants), presented a vision of the art of the Hellenistic Period, which had until then been almost unknown (Figures 1–2). Together with the earlier acquisitions and the finds subsequently excavated from other ancient cities and temples, they put the Berlin Classical collection on a par with the great collections in London and Paris.

The archaeologists and officials of the museum understood well how to turn Berlin's pretensions as the capital of Wilhelmine Germany to the advantage of the excavations and the acquisitions policy. Heinrich Schliemann's excavations at Troy, which began in 1871, had soon received enormous publicity, making the significance of archaeological fieldwork obvious. Schliemann, who had acquired a fortune as a businessman and entrepreneur, was able to finance his excavations at Troy, Mycenae and elsewhere with his own considerable private wealth, but Humann, who had been bankrupted as a building contractor, was dependent on patronage for the work at Pergamon. After many years he finally succeeded in winning the support of the Berlin museums for his excavations at Pergamon, whereas negotiations for a joint expedition of Schliemann and the museums failed. Yet Schliemann's Trojan antiquities did eventually enter the collection of the Berlin museums. They first came to the city's Völkerkundemuseum (Museum of Ethnology) as a gift to the German state; subsequently, in 1921, they passed to the former Museum für Ur- und Frühgeschichte (Museum for Prehistory and Early History). The famous Helios metope from the Hellen-

istic Temple of Athena at Troy (Figure 18) as well as some other finds from the Greek and Roman levels at the site are now in the Collection of Classical Antiquities.

As the laws of the countries where the museum participated in excavations came to restrict more and more the export of antiquities, the study of archaeological and historical problems began to assume priority over the search for acquisitions. Techniques for excavating urban centres developed in response to interest in the cultural and everyday life of a city.

The first excavations of the Berlin museums had been undertaken at Olympia, a site that Johann Joachim Winckelmann had dreamed of excavating in the 18th century. A wish of many generations of archaeologists was realized by Ernst Curtius, when in 1874 the contract for the excavation was agreed. The following year work was begun in the sacred grove of Olympia. Until 1881 archaeologists and architects such as Friedrich Adler, Wilhelm Dörpfeld, and Adolf Furtwängler worked at the site on behalf of the Berlin museums. Within the sacred precinct (the «Altis»), a temple dedicated to Hera, some of the treasuries, and the famous Temple of Zeus were entirely or partially investigated. It was possible to recover the sculptural decoration of the Temple of Zeus which had been created between 470 and 456 B.C. Famous works of sculpture were discovered, such as the Nike of Paionios and Praxiteles's Hermes. The Greek antiquities law permitted the export only of a limited number of duplicates, especially small finds. From the beginning of the excavations, therefore, their purpose was not the acquisition of objects for the collection but rather the investigation of this renowned pan-Hellenic sacred site.

Thus it was no coincidence that subsequent excavations of the Berlin museums were concentrated on the western coast of Asia Minor in Turkey, where licences for excavations were considerably more favourable than in Greece, and substantial acquisitions could be made at the division of finds. On the island of Samos, then under Turkish rule, at Myus, Cape Monodendri, Didyma and Miletus, the archaeologists discovered architecture, sculpture and minor arts of the Archaic

Fig. 25   *Gallery 7*
Statue of a girl playing knucklebones
Replica from the end of the 2nd century
A.D., after a Hellenistic original
Marble; ht. 70 cm.
Acquired from the Polignac Collection
Sk 494

Roman art readily took up Greek and Hellenistic genre motifs and adapted them to its own purpose. The seated girl playing knucklebones was one such motif that has come down to us only in numerous Roman replicas. A sculptor of the Antonine period transformed the head into a portrait of a girl with an up-to-date «melon» coiffure. The statue, which was discovered in Rome in 1730, subsequently served as a model for many artists.

Period for the first time, while at Pergamon, Magnesia, and Priene, Hellenistic monuments came to light.

The first excavations on Turkish soil – at Pergamon, Magnesia and Priene – were directed by Humann and Conze. After the death of Humann in 1896, Theodor Wiegand took over the excavations for the Berlin museums. (In 1899 he became director of the museums in Constantinople.) Humann had begun preparations for the excavations at Priene, at the foot of the Mykale Mountains in the valley of the River Maeander, and had planned the course of the work: it was to begin not at the Temple of Athena but at the city wall, and the site was to be investigated according to a systematic plan. During 1896–99 it was possible to clear a large part of this small Hellenistic city, and thus a relatively complete picture of the site was won.

Fig. 26   *Gallery 8*
The Emperor Caracalla
Between A.D. 212 and 217
Marble; ht. 58 cm.
Acquired in Rome in 1875
Sk 384
The Berlin bust of Caracalla is one of the most impressive portraits of an emperor from the middle Imperial Period. Roman portraiture of that era combined a powerful interpretation of individual physiognomy with a fully corporeal rendering of the body. The sword strap and cloak allude to Caracalla's military rank.

Theodor Wiegand's extraordinary diplomatic skill and his talent for organizing scholarly undertakings enabled him time and again to find new sources of funding for excavations and acquisitions and to maintain the Crown's interest in these projects. The extensive excavations in Miletus (1899–1913), at Didyma (1905–1913) and on Samos (1910–1914) are associated with his name. From the early Archaic Period, Miletus had shown a talent for colonization that led to the foundation of over eighty dependencies on the Black Sea and Mediterranean coasts. The archaeologists uncovered parts of both Hellenistic and Roman Miletus. Vases of the Mycenean era and important finds of Archaic sculpture (Figure 6) document the long history of the occupation of the site. (Current excavations at Miletus have finally located the levels of the Archaic city.) The excavated architectural remains of a gateway that gave access to a Roman marketplace at Miletus could be brought to Berlin – the last large-scale acquisition from excavations for the collection. The reconstruction of the gateway in the Roman architecture gallery of the Pergamon Museum continues to impress visitors with its monumentality and the richness of its architectural forms (Figure 3).

A sacred way led from Miletus to the famous oracle of Apollo in Didyma. Recently, important finds have been made along this route. At the site itself, the temple with its double colonnade *(dipteros)*, which was built about 540 B.C., could be investigated under the auspices of the museums between 1905 and 1913, in continuation of earlier work undertaken at the site by the Englishman Charles Thomas Newton in 1857–58.

Berlin archaeologists investigated another famous Greek temple before World War I, between 1910 and 1914. On the island of Samos, off the coast of Asia Minor, the Greeks founded a sanctuary in honor of Hera which, as the finds demonstrate, served as a cult centre for sailors and merchants from Greece, the Near East, Egypt and the western Mediterranean. In the 6th century B.C., under the tyrant Polycrates of Samos, a new temple for Hera was erected which was one of the largest Greek temples

ever built anywhere (the stylobate measured 55.15 x 108.68 m.). As in Didyma, the temple had a dipteral hall. Some architectural elements from the temple itself and a few others from the precinct, as well as Archaic and Hellenistic sculpture found there, came from Samos to Berlin and can be seen in the exhibition.

Finally, the excavations of the Berlin museums at Baalbek (ancient Heliopolis) in the Beqaa Valley of eastern Lebanon should be mentioned. The ruins of the Roman Temple of Jupiter there had been admired by travellers for centuries. Between 1899 and 1905, excavations and architectural recording were undertaken in the precincts of the temples of Jupiter and Bacchus. A small number of very conspicuous architectural elements came to Berlin; these are now displayed in the Roman architecture gallery of the Pergamon Museum, providing an impression of Roman temple architecture.

The excavations of the Berlin museums opened a new chapter in the study of the Greek and Roman world. These programmes came at the beginning of a tradition of German excavation which has continued down to the present at all the sites named except for Baalbek. After the cessation of fieldwork by the Berlin museums at the beginning of World War I, Theodor Wiegand saw to it that archaeological work could be continued by the Deutsches Archäologisches Institut (German Archaeological Institute). Today archaeologists of that institution and from German universities excavate on Samos, at Olympia, Pergamon, Miletus and Didyma, in continuation of the work begun by Humann, Conze and Wiegand.

39

Liane Jakob-Rost
Evelyn Klengel-Brandt
Joachim Marzahn
Ralf-B. Wartke

Museum of Western Asiatic Antiquity

History of the museum and its excavations

With the opening of «Museum am Lustgarten» (later called the Old Museum) in Berlin in 1830, Ancient Near Eastern antiquities were incorporated into the Department of Ancient Sculpture. Subsequently, in 1885, they were transferred to the Egyptian Department, and finally in 1899 a Near Eastern section was established as an independent department of the Königliche Museen zu Berlin, as the state museums were then known.

After the foundation of an Ancient Near Eastern department, the staff offices were located in the basement of the Kaiser Friedrich Museum (now the Bode Museum). Only part of the collection was accessible to the public in a temporary display. It was not possible to improve

Gallery 8

◁ *Reconstruction of Babylon's Processional Way*
Glazed bricks, coloured; l. 30.00 m., w. 8.00 m., ht. 12.50 m.
VA Bab 1379-1409
The reconstruction of the Processional Way (Gallery 8) presents to the visitor one of the most famous architectural achievements of antiquity which can be seen in the context of a museum. During the enlargement and reorganization of the palace precinct on the northern edge of the city under the first two kings of the Neo-Babylonian empire, Nabopolassar (625–605 B.C.) and Nebuchadnezzar II (604–562 B.C.), two roughly parallel walls up to seven meters thick were erected to define an avenue of approach to the Ishtar Gate. In the process, the street formed between them, which varied in width from 20 to 24 m., became for about 250 m. of its length a passageway ending in the square situated directly in front of the gate.

upon this unsatisfactory situation until 1926, when the south wing of the first floor of the Pergamon Museum was set aside for the Ancient Near Eastern antiquities. Work then began on the planning of a suitable and aesthetically pleasing installation of the monuments which had been acquired by purchase, as gifts, and, most importantly, through the division of finds which had followed extensive excavations at Babylon and Assur.

Walter Andrae, a professional architect and architectural historian who was director of the department from 1928 to 1951, assumed responsibility for the conception of the exhibition, whose basic structure has been retained down to the present. After years of excavation at Babylon and Assur, Andrae dedicated himself especially to the reconstruction of Ancient Near Eastern architecture.

In 1930 the middle section of the south wing was completed, with reconstructions of the Processional Way leading up to the Ishtar Gate and the façades of a Neo-Babylonian throne room and of a Parthian palace. Work on the installation of the remaining galleries occupied some years. Finally, in 1936 the collection could be presented to the public in its entirety.

With the outbreak of World War II only a few years later, the museum was closed. The most valuable movable objects were accommodated in the basement of the Pergamon Museum, while the architectural elements that had been incorporated into the monumental reconstructions were protected as well as they could be by brick walls built in front of them.

The inventory taken at the end of the war showed that all the holdings had survived, but the building had suffered such severe damage that it could not protect the antiquities properly. Immediately after the war the Soviet army secured objects which were endangered by exposure to the elements and the threat of theft.

After the Pergamon Museum had been repaired, the Ancient Near Eastern collection, under the direction of Gerhard Rudolf Meyer, was reopened in 1951 – with only four galleries at first.

Two years later the entire department, renamed the Museum of Western Asiatic Antiquity, reoccupied the space it had

filled before the war. In 1958, all the art treasures that had been in the keeping of Soviet museums were returned to Berlin. After reincorporation of these works of art into the collection and completion of a general renovation, the Ancient Near Eastern antiquities could be presented once again in their former extent.

The importance of the Berlin Museum of Western Asiatic Antiquity lies both in the range and quality of its holdings and in its superbly executed reconstructions of selected examples of Ancient Near Eastern monumental architecture. As a collection of Ancient Near Eastern antiquities it is unique in German-speaking countries. Except for the holdings in the Louvre and in the British Museum, there is no comparable collection in Europe.

The organization of the display in the Museum of Western Asiatic Antiquity, which includes objects spanning six millennia, follows both geographical and chronological principles of arrangement: the varied cultures of the different geographical areas are presented individually and the development of each is illustrated chronologically.

Prior to the beginnings of modern historical research, the cultures of the Ancient Near East had been forgotten. Our modern knowledge of them is owed to archaeological field work, which nowadays is effectively complemented by systematic scholarly research in libraries, with the cooperation of the natural sciences and information technology.

The earliest archaeological undertakings in the Near East date to the middle of the 19th century when Assyrian ruins were first explored by British and French scholars. German activity in the field began when Robert Koldewey (who later excavated at Babylon) led an expedition to southern Iraq in 1887–88. Following Koldewey's lead, Felix von Luschan worked at Zinjirli (ancient Sam'al) in northern Syria between 1888 and 1902, while the site of Toprak Kale (the old Urartian capital Tushpa) near Van in eastern Anatolia was explored by Carl Friedrich Lehmann and Waldemar Belck in 1898–99.

A direct result of the interest generated by the success of these undertakings was the foundation of the Deutsche

Orient-Gesellschaft (German Oriental Society) in 1898, an event which marks a first high point in the development of Ancient Near Eastern archaeology, then still in its infancy. In the same year, the Society commissioned Koldewey to undertake a major excavation at Babylon, where work began in 1899, continuing without a break until 1917. Working from a base at Babylon, archaeologists set up several minor and two major excavations at sites which continued to be centres of German archaeological activity after World War I. The following sites were among those explored: Fara (ancient Shuruppak), Abu Habba (Sippar) and Birs Nimrud (Borsippa) as well as the ancient Assyrian capital city of Assur where excavations began in 1903, continuing under the direction of Walter Andrae until 1914.

In 1906, work was begun in Anatolia at Boğazköy (ancient Hattusha, the capital of the Hittite empire), while initial soundings were made at the southern Mesopotamian site of Warka (Uruk) in 1912–13. At about the same time, from 1911 to 1913, Max von Oppenheim was active at the site of Tell Halaf in northern Syria. Work at Babylon and Assur was not resumed after the interruption of World War I. From 1928, the ruins of Uruk became the focal point of interest; it was also possible to resume work at Boğazköy in 1931.

In the years after 1945, new laws governing the export of antiquities from many countries in the Near East prohibited acquisitions through fieldwork. But thanks to the earlier divisions of finds from excavations, the Near Eastern Museum offers a well-balanced documentation of the cultures of Sumer (material from Uruk), Babylon, and Assyria as well as those of northern Syria and Anatolia (Zinjirli, Tell Halaf, and Toprak Kale). The material spans all periods from prehistoric times down to the Graeco-Roman Period.

The prehistoric period

The Near East is one of the regions where favourable environmental conditions encouraged settlement. The early cultivation of cereals and the domestication of

animals have been traced through excavation in the hilly flanks of northern Mesopotamia and in Anatolia. Numerous settlements arose where particular specialized crafts were developed. The appearance of the earliest pottery in the 8th millennium is particularly noteworthy. From a simple utilitarian product, pottery developed into a technically and artistically prestigious commodity whose distribution provides evidence for the cultural interrelationships between various populations and geographical areas. Because of pottery's importance for tracing such contacts, it has become customary in Ancient Near Eastern archaeology to designate prehistoric periods by the name of the initial findspot of a characteristic pottery type.

At Tell Halaf in northern Mesopotamia there was first excavated a high quality, polychrome pottery which spread during the 6th and 5th millennia from northern Mesopotamia through Anatolia and as far afield as Syria-Palestine (Gallery 2, case 6). (For clay figurines of the same period from Tell Halaf, see Figure 1.) A second, approximately contemporaneous ware first came to light in Samarra on the middle Tigris (Figure 2; Gallery 4, case 7). These products, too, were in use over a wide area of northern Mesopotamia.

Fig. 1   *Gallery 2*
Female figurines
Tell Halaf
6th–5th millennium B.C.
Painted clay; ht. 5.8 and 6.0 cm.
VA 12517, 12518
These statuettes depict seated women whose swelling bodily forms emphasize the female's life-giving and life-sustaining role. They document religious conceptions of the early inhabitants of Tell Halaf. The patterns painted on contemporaneous pottery point to the worship of the male principle in the form of a bull. The repertory of painting motifs for pottery included abstract renderings of bulls' skulls and numerous geometric forms. The potter's skill is demonstrated by the sophisticated firing, which must have been carried out at high but variable temperatures.

43

Sumer

About 3000 B.C., the first urban centres came into being in southern Mesopotamia as the result of continually increasing concentrations of population and agrarian exploitation of the region. The irrigation agriculture, which was necessitated by the climate, led to high yields in both plant and animal production as well as giving rise to rapid social differentiation. Technological advances were put to good use, the concept of private ownership developed, and before the middle of the 3rd millennium the impetus toward a monarchical political structure made itself felt.

Until about 2350 B.C. the political landscape was characterized by rival small states that had evolved along the paths of local irrigation systems. We know them by the names of the urban centres around which they developed: Uruk, Ur, Shuruppak, Kish, Umma, Nippur, Lagash/Girsu and Adab.

The most important component of the population was the Sumerians, named after their language, but contemporaneous peoples speaking a Semitic language can also be traced in the same area. About 2350 B.C. the Semitic element under the leadership of Sargon I overcame the tendency to territorial fragmentation which had prohibited further political development to create the first large-scale Mesopotamian state, the Kingdom of Akkad.

Internal contradictions and external enemies (like the highland Guti people) led to the disintegration of the Akkadian kingdom about 2200 B.C. Some of the smaller Sumerian states in the south reasserted their independence. For example, during the period following on the expulsion of the Guti, the state of Lagash developed again on its own under its ruler Gudea (ca. 2144–2124 B.C.), before Urnammu, the ruler of Ur (2112–2095 B.C.), succeeded in creating another territorial state based at Ur. This latter kingdom, known as the «Third Dynasty of Ur,» existed for about a century, but social tensions and particularism led to its downfall at the end of the 3rd millennium. The subsequent splintering of the area into several states (Isin, Larsa, Babylon) was eventually checked with Hammurapi's foundation of the state of Babylon in the 18th century B.C.

This historical sequence in Mesopotamia became known to scholars primarily through excavations at the sites named above and through the interpretation and analysis of original cuneiform documents discovered in the process.

Monuments of Sumerian culture from a number of sites are shown in two galleries (4 and 5) of the Museum of Western Asiatic Antiquity. The rapid socio-economic development of the «Early Dynastic Period» (before 2350 B.C.), which was made possible by a highly developed agriculture, is documented not only by objects of everyday use (handmade pottery, case 13; wares produced on the fast wheel and ceramic votive objects, case 8) but above all by luxury goods created for a wide variety of uses.

Stone-working was of particular significance. Some simple vases (case 8) were used for secular purposes, but most high-quality works of art in stone were manufactured for the cult. Ex votos for the temple were made in the form of plain or relief-decorated vessels (Figure 5; cases 9, 12, 13), and great mastery was achieved in the creation of small sculpture, of which many examples have been found among temple equipment (Figure 6; cases 9, 10, 12).

In addition to works in stone, metallurgy was of vital importance, providing the essential tools and implements for production (ploughshares, hoes, etc.) as well as weapons of war and hunting (case 8). Some outstanding works in metal were created for religious purposes (case 9). These smaller works in stone and metal are among the large body of evidence for Sumerian culture which has been recovered, much of it of notable quality. In comparison, the preserved evidence for the architectural complexes in which the finds were brought to light is sparse. In Mesopotamia the use of sun-dried (unfired) mud brick for most buildings has prevented visible architectural legacy.

While scholars have so far devoted relatively little attention to private dwellings, religious and royal architecture is better known, and there are impressive ruins of temple and palace buildings which compare favourably with anal-

Fig. 2   *Gallery 4*

Large painted bowl
Samarra
6th–5th millennium B.C.
Clay; ht. 9.0 cm., diameter
28.2 – 29.6 cm.
VA 13408
Prehistoric pottery was built up of coils of clay, shaped in a prepared form, or hand-turned on a slowly rotated wheel. The forms favoured by the potters of Samarra were large open bowls with everted rims and beakers with wide bodies. The painted decoration included various geometric patterns and representations of such hunter's quarry as ibexes, fishes and birds. Open bowls were also decorated with abstract renderings of human figures with flowing hair, arranged to suggest whirling movement.

Fig. 3   *Gallery 5*
Detail of a section of façade decorated with cone mosaic
Uruk, Eanna Temple, inner court
Ca. 3000 B.C.
Fired clay, some cones coloured; l. and diameter of the smaller cones ca. 12 and 2 cm., respectively
VA 10997
Mud brick temple walls, many of them articulated with niching, were decorated with clay cones stuck into mud plaster and arranged in patterns probably in imitation of textiles or wickerwork. Several types of cones were used. In addition to their decorative function, the hard-fired cone mosaics may have protected the brickwork against the elements. The technique demonstrates the artistic ambitions of the builders of these structures, which played an important role in the community. An immense amount of labour and an advanced firing technique were necessary to manufacture the countless cones for these mosaics.

Fig. 4   *Gallery 10*
Statue of a worshipper
Assur, from the cella of the Archaic Ishtar Temple
Ca. 2400 B.C.
Alabaster; ht. 46 cm.
VA 8142
The southern Mesopotamian practice of setting up in temples statues depicting members of the ruling family or priests was also followed in Assur. The bald-headed man wears a kilt whose form has been interpreted as representing a sheep's fleece. The eyes and eyebrows, like the nipples, were once provided with coloured inlays. Praying figures from Assur like this one are clearly related to the type found widely in southern Mesopotamia, but the fuller and more realistic form of the figures created in the north derives from a markedly different stylistic tradition.

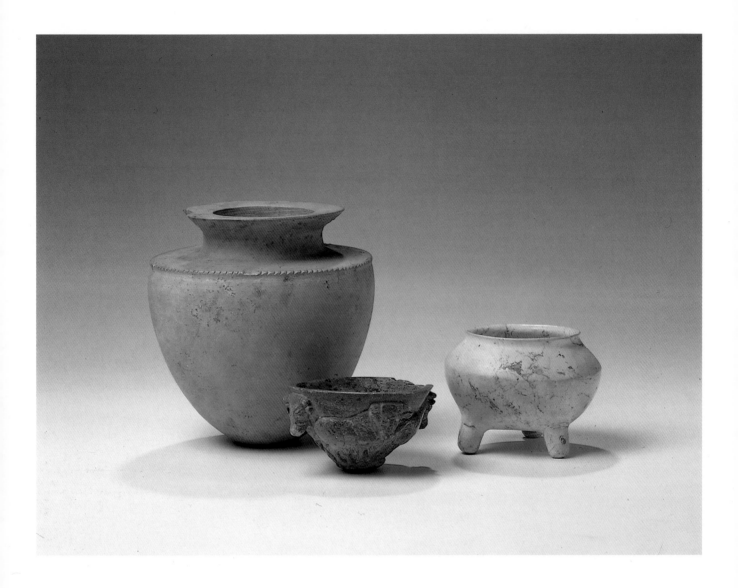

Fig. 5   *Gallery 5*
Three stone vases
Uruk
Ca. 2800–2500 B.C.
Limestone, steatite, marble;
max. ht. 13.4 cm.
VA 11064, 10113, 15215

Sumer was poor in raw materials; stone in particular was highly valued because it had to be imported from afar. Simple tools were used to form rough blocks into luxury articles. Vases of high artistic quality were produced with the aid of a primitive drill; those decorated with relief were especially prized. The vases document not only a high level of technological achievement but also the increasing specialization of the crafts at the beginning of the 3rd millennium B.C.

ogous structures produced by other cultures. Most significant among them are the excavated remains within the huge temple enclosure of Inanna at Uruk dating to about 3000 B.C. (Gallery 5, with a wall panel), whose precinct measured at least 450 x 250 m. The vast size of the temple complex, which comprised several buildings and enclosed courtyards, is indicative of its role as an economic and administrative centre, quite apart from its primary function as a place of worship (for the development of early administrative practice see the desk case 11). The rich architectural decoration in some parts is commensurate with the great importance of the Inanna complex (see the contents of case 12). The wall decoration of a courtyard in front of a three-bayed cult struc-

ture and the colonnaded terrace of the Eanna temple are particularly remarkable. The reconstructed façade of cone mosaics, which is displayed below the wall panel, formed part of the decoration of the courtyard (Figure 3). The niched front of its plinth and the preserved stump of a column with a diameter of 2.7 m. from the terrace, both decorated with cone mosaics, give some impression of the decoration of the complex and its monumentality.

Inseparably associated with this architecture – as well as documenting the antiquity of a practice that continues to this day – are foundation inscriptions which are found on sculptured figures, on bricks, on clay pegs and metal nails and on stone slabs (see Gallery 4, case 10; cf. Figure 24).

Babylon

The origins of Babylon can be traced back to the Kingdom of Akkad, but the city did not rise to political and cultural importance until the early 2nd millennium B.C. The most famous ruler of this «Old Babylonian Period» was Hammurapi (1792–1750 B.C.), who united a large part of Mesopotamia under his rule. Nearly 200 years after his death, this empire, which had weakened progressively in the interim, fell into the hands of the Hittites, who came from their homeland in Anatolia to plunder and destroy Babylon.

After the withdrawal of the Hittites, the land became prey to the Kassites who had been settled in the region for some time. Among the most important documents of

this period are the letters of the Kassite kings to Amenhotep III and IV/Akhenaten (first half of the 14th century B.C.). These formed part of the international correspondence between those Egyptian pharaohs and their Near Eastern contemporaries which was found in the archive at Tell el Amarna.

The rule of the Kassites in Babylon lasted about 400 years. The subsequent fortunes of the land were quite chequered. Babylon's northern neighbours, the Assyrians, as well as nomadic peoples from the steppes that bordered Mesopotamia to the west, conquered and destroyed Babylon repeatedly. But the existence and importance of the city itself was not threatened in the long run. Beginning with the reign of Tiglathpileser III, the Assyrian kings

Fig. 6   *Gallery 5*
Three small figures of recumbent animals
Uruk (Eanna precinct)
Ca. 2800/2700 B.C.
Marble, with lapis lazuli inlays, and green stone; max. l. 6 cm.
VA 11021, 7241, 14536
These figures of cattle and a ram, which bear witness to the high level of the lapidary's craft, were temple ex votos. In a manner characteristic of their time they combine the realistic depiction of the animal bodies with a stylization of attitude underscored by the use of inlays to render the markings of the hide. The figures demonstrate that everyday experience of the agrarian environment was incorporated into religious conceptions of the cosmos.

even called themselves «King of Babylon».

After the end of the Assyrian empire Babylon experienced a last great flowering. Nabopolassar (625–605 B.C.), and above all his son Nebuchadnezzar II (604–562 B.C.), undertook an immense programme of building in the city to which we owe some of the most impressive buildings of the Ancient Near East.

The entry of Cyrus, the Achaemenid king of Persia, into Babylon in 539 B.C. brought the splendid Neo-Babylonian Period to an end. The city escaped damage initially, but later it was brutally punished for attempting to revolt against Xerxes. The city wall was demolished and the famous ziggurat of the Marduk Temple (the Biblical «Tower of Babel») was destroyed. Although the once-powerful city's fate was sealed by these actions, Alexander the Great of Macedon chose it as the capital of his empire after he had conquered Mesopotamia. But following Alexander's premature death in 323 B.C., a new capital was constructed at Seleucia, while the Parthians (ca. 140 B.C.–A.D. 224), who succeeded the Seleucids as rulers over Mesopotamia, built their own capital at Ctesiphon. Thus Babylon came gradually to be forgotten.

We owe much of our knowledge of Babylon (Gallery 6) to seventeen years of excavations at the site. Few remains were found from the periods of the city's origin and of its growth during the Old Babylonian Period (first half of the 2nd millennium B.C.) because the ground water had risen to flood the early settlement levels. The most famous monument from this period is the stela inscribed with the laws of Hammurapi. Once set up either in Babylon or in Sippar, it was found in the Elamite capital of Susa, to which it had been carried off in the aftermath of a raid. The Museum of Western Asiatic Antiquity displays a plaster cast of the stela, which is in the collection of the Louvre in Paris.

The majority of the small finds from the excavations at Babylon comes from the much later Neo-Babylonian and Persian Periods. Inscribed objects are particularly numerous, especially clay tablets with cuneiform texts. Building inscriptions, economic documents, and the royal correspondence of the Kassite Period mentioned above («Amarna Letters») are representative of written materials of the 2nd and 1st millennium B.C. that came to the collection from the site of Babylon (case 15). Particularly noteworthy are the remarkably well-worked land grants and deeds of investiture which are inscribed on stone. The most important example of this kind dates toward the end of the 8th century B.C. and documents a grant of land from King Mardukaplaiddina II to a high dignitary.

Religious beliefs, ritual and magic played an important role in ancient Babylon. The gods received due worship in hymns, prayers, temple services and offerings, while every possible means was employed to break or to deflect away from oneself the power of inimical forces, which were mostly conceived of as demons. To this end apotropaic clay figures and amulets were manufactured and exorcisms performed with the help of omens and oracles. Priests were adept at the reading of the liver and entrails of sacrificial animals; they interpreted astronomical phenomena, the patterns made by oil poured on water in a cup, and the flight of birds. It was also believed that they could foretell the future. Apart from many cult objects, the lapis lazuli ceremonial seal of the god Adad (case 19) belonged to the equipment of a temple.

The most common objects used in everyday life were containers of various sizes, shapes and materials (case 20). Most of those displayed date to the Achaemenid, Seleucid and Parthian Periods; they are made of clay and glass and have elegant shapes as well as various forms of decoration, from a simple glaze to high-quality coloured enamel painting.

Articles in regular use included combs, hair pins and fibulae of bronze as well as little bottles and jars of glass (Figure 10), faience or semi-precious stones for oil, aromatics and cosmetics. Board and dice games doubtless occupied part of the leisure time of the Babylonians (case 22). The collection's unique objects include pieces of exquisite beauty, such as a sceptre of onyx (Figure 11) and a mace

Fig. 7   *Gallery 9*
The Ishtar Gate (reconstruction; partial view)
Babylon
6th century B.C.
Glazed clay bricks (originals and replicas); ht. 14.73 m., w. 15.70 m.
VA Bab 1408–1456
The gate in the northwest section of Babylon's city wall, here partially restored, bore the official name «Ishtar [is] the conqueror of her enemies.» This monumental construction «upon which humankind in its entirety will gaze with wonder» (in the words of Nebuchadnezzar II, the king who ordered it built), honoured one of the most important deities of the Babylonian pantheon. The goddess Ishtar was the embodiment of warlike and unrestrained female sexuality and was worshipped as the «Lady of Heaven» manifest in the planet Venus.
In spite of the association with the goddess expressed in the gate's name, Ishtar's sacred animal, the lion, is not found in its decoration but in that of the walls flanking the Processional Way which gave access to it and ended in front of it. Instead, Nebuchadnezzar II commanded that the walls of the gate carry representations of bulls (the symbolic animal of the weather god Adad) and dragons (the sacred animal of the god of state and city Marduk). The gateway was completed with bronze-plated doors of cedar and bronze statues of bulls and dragons. Nothing was recovered of these fittings, which were made of perishable and reusable materials, but we are informed about them by building inscriptions of Nebuchadnezzar II. One, carved in limestone, is now in the British Museum in London. The second was inscribed on glazed bricks and incorporated into the gate itself, and is preserved only in numerous fragments. On the basis of the complete text in the British Museum it has been partially reconstructed and the bricks inserted beside the lefthand tower of the gate. (The text's original location in the decoration of the gate is not known.)

Fig. 8 (overleaf)   *Gallery 9*
Model of the Processional Way and the Ishtar Gate of Babylon
Scale: 1:100
Execution: Hummel and Andrae
Painted gypsum; 2.20 x 1.17 m.
VAG 264
The model, which was made before 1930 by the Berlin firm of Hummel and painted by E. Andrae, illustrates clearly the relationship between the walled street and the bastions flanking the vestibule in front of the gate, as well as how they were connected with the gate itself. This layout was revealed by the excavations, but for reasons of space could not be reproduced in the full-scale reconstruction.
The model demonstrates to the visitor what an immense structure the double gate once was, how it was integrated architecturally into the double city wall, and, as shown by the section through the street, how the deposition of debris resulted in the elevation of the entire precinct in three phases.
A visitor who is interested in accuracy of detail will notice differences between the model and the full-scale reconstruction. At the time when the model was made, the

original appearance of the gate's superstructure was still a subject of discussion.

Fig. 9   *Gallery 6*
Fragmentary figurine of a mother and child
Babylon
6th/5th century B.C.
Terracotta; ht. 5.2 cm.
VA Bab 55
Numerous terracotta figurines were found at Babylon, as at most archaeological sites in the Near East. In addition to various types of male and female figurines, the Neo-Babylonian Period (7th–6th centuries B.C.) also produced animal statuettes, as well as depictions of furniture, boats and bells, most of which had a cultic significance.
Besides representations of nude women, which were popular as early as prehistoric times, statuettes depicting mother and child were especially common. Those found in private houses may have had a protective, magical purpose for the inhabitants, while others deriving from temples were probably votive gifts for the gods.

knob of the same material – both probably symbols of authority.

Selected products of the minor arts (case 21), several found in the ruins of private houses, give an impression of the forms and quality of Babylonian sculpture, which is otherwise scarcely preserved (cf. Figures 9 and 12).

One of the central building complexes of Nebuchadnezzar's Babylon was the Temple of Marduk. An architectural scale model of it in Gallery 6 shows the ground-level temple Esagila and the ziggurat (or temple tower) named Etemenanki.

The first two building phases of the Ishtar Gate of Babylon are illustrated in the wall panels of the same gallery; they provide information about the technical alterations that were made during its construction. The gate itself and the associated approaching avenue, the Processional Way, have been reconstructed on the main axis of the Museum of Western Asiatic Antiquity.

Babylon's Processional Way and Ishtar Gate

The reconstructions of the Processional Way (Gallery 8) and the Ishtar Gate (Figure 7; Gallery 9) present to the visitor two of the most famous architectural achievements of antiquity which can be seen in the context of a museum. But these splendid examples of Ancient Near Eastern architecture were only a small part of the monumental constructions that once graced the capital of the Babylonian empire. In comparison with the truly gigantic building complexes in Babylon, such as the principal temple of the city god Marduk or the royal palaces, the gate and the Processional Way were comparatively modest. Originally the gate was a secular structure. Named after the nearby temple of the goddess Ishtar of Akkad in the inner city, it was only one of at least seven gates in the double wall that surrounded Babylon.

Its special form, which even nowadays arouses the visitor's admiration, was related to several extensions of the royal palaces and defensive constructions on the northern edge of the city. These

Fig. 10   Gallery 6
Two spherical bottles
Babylon
8th/7th century B.C. (right)
6th/4th century B.C. (left)
Opaque coloured glass; ht. 8.7 and 6.7 cm.
VA 8452, 8449
These two bottles, which were deposited as funerary equipment, are interesting examples of the sand core technique used to produce hollow glass vessels. A core consisting of a mixture of clay and sand and corresponding to the form of a bottle's intended interior, was modelled on a rod. A thin layer of molten glass was applied around the core. After cooling, the sand core was removed with the rod from the inside of the bottle. This technology is attested from the mid-2nd millennium B.C.; only near the end of the 1st millennium B.C. was it superseded by the invention of the glass blower's pipe. The fused decoration of these vessels is very characteristic. Orange glass bands and white glass threads were melted into the black ground of the vase at the right, and white threads were applied to the neck in a feather pattern. Small perforated lug handles were fused to the body and a lip to the neck.

Fig. 11   Gallery 6
Sceptre
Babylon
Presumably 6th century B.C.
Onyx; l. 38.4 cm.
VA Bab 1625

Among many items from temple furnishings of Babylon's most brilliant age, a number of very characteristic elements from an object made of precious onyx were found in the house of a bead-maker. Their workmanship as well as the material set them apart. In the display, the pieces have been threaded onto a metal rod in an arbitrary order to form a sceptre. In the absence of comparable finds, it has not been possible to determine whether the sceptre was a piece of ceremonial regalia from a god's cult statue or whether it belonged to a king or an important dignitary.

Fig. 12   *Gallery 6*
Statuette of a nude woman
Provenance not known
Ca. 200 B.C.
Alabaster; ht. 19 cm.
VA 281
This small female figure is a delightful
example of Babylonian minor art. Its well-
rounded and carefully modelled body
shows Hellenistic influence. The bitumen
of the applied head-dress forms a delib-
erate contrast with the translucent stone
body. The eyes were once inlaid. The
separately worked arms were originally
attached to the body with wire or string.
(The right arm is modern.)

involved integrating the avenue of approach in front of the gate into a comprehensive architectural conception.

During the enlargement and reorganization of the palace precinct on the northern edge of the city under the first two kings of the Neo-Babylonian empire, Nabopolassar (625–605 B.C.) and Nebuchadnezzar II (604–562 B.C.), two roughly parallel walls up to seven meters thick were erected to define an avenue of approach to the gate. In the process, the street formed between them, which varied in width from 20 to 24 m., became for about 250 m. of its length a passageway ending in the square situated directly in front of the gate.

The figures of lions which decorate the walls of the Processional Way were mass-produced. Each is made of many bricks formed in special moulds; one stretcher side of each standard-sized brick (33 x 33 x 8 cm.) bore a small segment of a relief figure of a lion. First the bricks were composed into sections of eleven courses and these in turn then assembled to create each figure. Two complete sets of moulds were required, one for the lions walking to the right and another for the left-facing figures. The same technique was used to produce the relief figures of bulls and dragons that adorn the gate.

The polychrome effect, which is quite well preserved, was achieved by applying a range of coloured glazes to the bricks used to compose the figures, the variegated friezes and bands of rosettes. The decoration achieved a vividness which made this avenue of approach unique among those of comparable size in the city. The top of the walls was crowned by crenellations. The zone between them and the glazed sections at the bottom of the wall was composed of simple, unglazed crude brick with plastering.

In contrast to the walls flanking the street, the exterior of the gate was uniformly covered with glazed brick. In place of the lions, the gate shows alternating rows of bulls and dragon-like beings. The setting of the museum is much too small to convey the powerful spatial impression which the original complex must have made. Only 30 m. of the Processional Way could be reconstructed at only a third of its original breadth. And as far as the gate is concerned, only the smaller front part with its two flanking towers could be rebuilt; behind it the visitor must imagine the much larger main gate (cf. Figure 8, the model of the complex, in Gallery 9).

The double gate occupied an area 48 m. long and about 30 m. wide. (These measurements do not include the walls joining the city wall to the gate.) It had deep recesses to accommodate the leaves of the doors when they were opened wide, as well as rooms for guards and for access to a subterranean well to insure an independent water supply. A person walking through the gate had to pass through 48 m. of its structure before entering the city proper – an indication of the immense security arrangements that protected the capital.

The gate itself was remarkably tall. Immense quantities of debris deposited in connection with building projects at the site of the palace complex resulted in three consecutive phases of construction that differed from one another in decoration (illustrated by the wall panels and segments of reconstructed walls in Gallery 6). The lowest level revealed by excavations was decorated with depictions of dragons and bulls in relief composed of unglazed bricks. After a first change of plan, in the second phase the same motifs were executed in coloured glazed bricks but not in relief. At the height of about 15 m. above the original level, there was another change of plan, and the decoration was executed in glazed relief bricks, as reproduced in the reconstructed gate.

The excavators naturally did not uncover the gate in the state it is reproduced in the museum; they found instead only the foundations and countless fragments of glazed bricks, as well as some remains of the original colourful pavement of the street which consisted of white limestone paving stones flanked by red ones. But the remains were sufficient to enable them to identify the complex's form. Through painstaking restoration work it was possible to reassemble many original bricks to recreate a portion of the gateway as well as a part of the walls flanking the street, so far as the space in the museum permitted. The result pro-

Fig. 13   Gallery 12
Small round box with lid
Assur
14th/13th century B.C.
Ivory; ht. 8.4 cm.
VA Ass 1099
A brick crypt with several burials and rich tomb goods was found beneath a dwelling in the neighbourhood of the Temple of Ishtar at Assur. The dead and their mortuary equipment had not been interred at one time, but rather the burials had been deposited over a con-

siderable period. The finds included various objects made of ivory, pottery, and stone vessels, in addition to splendidly worked gold jewellery set with semiprecious stones.
This small ivory pyxis from the crypt may have been used for cosmetics. The incised decoration shows symmetrical groupings of two gazelles flanking a coniferous tree with roosters perched among the branches; the tableaus are separated by palms. In all likelihood, the motif possessed a religious meaning.

Fig. 14   *Gallery 12*
Bell with representations of demons
Assyrian; acquired by purchase
8th/7th century B.C.
Bronze; ht. 29 cm.
VA 2517
The search for protection against evil spirits, illness, accident, and magic played a prominent part in people's lives in the Ancient Near East. They endeavoured to protect themselves against these dangers by means of offerings and ritual. The bell, decorated with figures of lion-headed demons and protective deities, was used in magical rituals.

Fig. 15   *Gallery 12*
Relief with a camp scene (detail)
Nineveh, Palace of Assurbanipal
Ca. 650 B.C.
Alabaster; ht. 39 cm., w. 48 cm.
VA 965
The relief is part of a larger series in which the capture of the Elamite city Hamanu is depicted. In the background, a city wall is visible. Inside the two tents pitched in the foreground various activities are shown. In the tent at the right (only partially visible) a meal is being prepared; in the tent to the left, a servant receives a returning warrior. The other details depict similarly casual details: the animals (a sheep, a goat and two camels) have just been fed; and another servant at the upper left reaches into what seems to be a well or a container.

vides the visitor with an impression of the technical achievement of the Babylonians and at the same time tangibly demonstrates the results of archaeological research. All the animal reliefs and a large proportion of the other decorative elements have been reconstructed from ancient fragments; the modern glazed bricks used in the reconstruction are easily distinguished from the ancient ones reassembled from fragments. The reconstructed gate is 14.73 m. tall; the crenellated form of the upper termination is restored primarily on the basis of depictions of Babylonian architecture in Assyrian reliefs.

In antiquity, the significance of the complex, comprised of approach and gate, lay in its function in cult and religion. Every year the major festival of the land, the eleven-day new year's festival, began in Babylon. Statues of the gods from all the temples of the land were brought to the precinct of Marduk in the city. The festival concluded with a great procession of the gods as manifest in their statues, starting from the «new year festival house» outside the city wall and proceeding along the Processional Way through the Ishtar Gate. The structure's foundation inscriptions state that the festival provided the impetus for its splendid decoration, which set the Ishtar Gate and Processional Way apart from the other gates and avenues of approach in the city – and that it was executed in accordance with the wishes of the builder Nebuchadnezzar II.

The reconstructed sections of the two walls of the façade of a throne room decorated with colourful glazed bricks (on the short walls of Gallery 9) come from the southern citadel of Babylon. These, too, date to the reign of King Nebuchadnezzar II.

Assur

The site of the city of Assur was occupied as early as the 3rd millennium B.C., but its early history and the composition of its population in those times are inadequately known. For a time, the rulers of the Kingdom of Akkad (2340–2140 B.C.) and later of the Third Dynasty of Ur (2140–2000) in southern Mesopotamia extended their spheres of influence as far

59

Fig. 16   *Gallery 12*
Double vessel in the form of two piglets
Assur
8th/7th century B.C.
Clay; ht. 7.1 cm.
VA 5155
From the 3rd millennium B.C. on therio-morphic vessels (vessels in animal form) were very popular in the Near East. Made of stone, metal or clay, they were probably used on special occasions such as offering rites and at banquets. This double vessel from Assur may have served as a container for cosmetics or unguents. Its very unusual design was achieved most economically: the bases were pinched into the shape of piglets' heads while plastic details were added in clay or simply incised.

Fig. 17   *Gallery 12*
Fragment of a vessel
Assur
8th/7th century B.C.
Glazed pottery; ht. 19 cm.
VA Ass 2404
In the Late Assyrian Period glazing techniques were widely used in the ceramic industry; large-scale vessels with flat bases and straight sides, decorated with figural representations, are typical. Besides palmettes, rosettes and floral motifs, depictions of goats are among the commonest motifs.
The original decoration of the vessel from which this fragment derives can be easily reconstructed because completely preserved examples of the same type are well known. In a broad figural zone, crowned by crenellation, a pair of billy-goats jumped down from a mountain top. The rendering of the animals' bodies and legs imbues the scene with dynamic energy and displays a most careful observation of nature.
The other, lost side of the vase probably showed a symmetrical pair of goats standing on their hind legs and flanking a tree. The colours, now very faded, give only an imperfect impression of the luminous effect that the polychrome glazed painting produced when it was new.

as Assur. At the beginning of the 2nd millennium Assur achieved autonomy under some important rulers. For example, Shamshi-Adad I (1843–1781 B.C.) conquered extensive territory and embellished the city itself with numerous monumental buildings. The following centuries were marked by conflict with the empire of Babylon. Hammurapi (1792–1750 B.C.) in particular was able to dominate Assyria.

New coalitions came into being in the course of the second half of the 2nd millennium. The Kassite state consolidated its hold over southern and central Mesopotamia, while in the north the Hurritian state of Mitanni gained strength. In the 14th century Assur was able once again to build up an independent state. The Assyrian rulers pursued a policy of conquest directed toward the enlargement of their territory, acquisition of raw materials, and control over important trade routes and trading cities.

This development continued into the early 1st millennium, when Assyria became a military power feared throughout the Near East. At the royal residence of Nimrud (ancient Calah), Assurnasirpal II (883–859 B.C.) introduced the practice of decorating the inner rooms of the palace with large alabaster slabs of relief and colossal guardian figures flanking doorways (Gallery 10; Gallery 11 with the possible reconstruction of a room in an Assyrian palace). The reliefs, which are among the most impressive evidence of Assyrian culture, were recovered in the middle of the last century during the earliest systematic excavations. Many Assyrian kings erected new, splendidly appointed palaces, while maintaining the monuments in the traditional old city of Assur.

The rise of new tribal groupings and states in the territory bordering on Assyria, the opposition of subjected peoples, and internal weakness led to a decline of the Assyrian empire. A coalition of the Aramaic dynasty of Nabopolassar in Babylon with the Medes, who were becoming increasingly powerful in Iran, brought about the final collapse of Assyria. In 614 B.C. Assur was conquered and, like Niniveh which fell in 612 B.C., was completely destroyed.

After long stagnation the city of Assur experienced a revival during the last centuries B.C. when it became the residence of a Parthian governor. The Parthians, who came from northern Iran, conquered all of Mesopotamia and were frequently at war with the Romans.

The most important areas of Assur investigated by Walter Andrae during the excavations at the site from 1903 to 1914 included the city's extensive fortifications and the temples and palaces which lay in the northern part of the city, as well as a palace of the Parthian Period on its southern edge. As a result of the division of finds between the excavators and the Ottoman government, a large proportion of the finds from Assur came to the former Near Eastern section of the Staatliche Museen zu Berlin, and a representative exhibition was installed in its Galleries 10–12.

Remains from the early period at Assur were uncovered especially in the area of the «Archaic Ishtar Temple» that dates to the last quarter of the 3rd millennium B.C. The period is represented by statuettes of alabaster (Figure 4), pottery, stands for incense burners, and ex votos made of clay, all deriving from the furnishings of the temple where they were used in the cella (cases 29,30). In the succeeding periods, the goddess's sanctuary was rebuilt repeatedly. Tukulti-Ninurta I (1243–1207 B.C.) documented his work there by numerous building inscriptions incorporated into the foundation of the building. Some objects in the exhibition, like the massive stone blocks in the middle of Gallery 10 and the two lead tablets, each weighing 350 kilograms, which are located in front of the blocks, carry inscriptions of this king. In the temple itself several alabaster «altars» were discovered; on one of them are shown two figures of the king, one standing and the other kneeling in prayer in front of an «altar» of identical form (Gallery 10).

Many important works of art found in the excavations at Assur cannot easily be dated nor can their original positions be determined. One such piece is the large alabaster slab with the frontal depiction of a god of vegetation flanked by goats and small water goddesses. The relief probably dates to the first half of the 2nd

Fig. 18   *Gallery 2*
Orthostat relief with the depiction of King Barrekub
Sam'al (Zinjirli); northern hall
Ca. 730 B.C.
Basalt; ht. 113 cm., w. 115 cm.
VA 2817
The ruler who sits on a splendidly decorated throne with footstool holds a palmette-like object in one hand and raises the other in a gesture of greeting toward a scribe who stands before him. The latter is dressed much more simply than the king and clutches under his arm the tablets of wood or ivory on which the Aramaic alphabetic script was written. In his left hand the scribe holds his writing utensils in a case. The inscription across the top at either side of a crescent moon includes the ruler's name.

Fig. 19   *Gallery 13*
Statuette of a griffin
Toprak Kale
8th/7th century B.C.
Bronze; ht. 21.2 cm.
VA 775
This figure of a griffin, a composite being combining elements of a lion and of a bird of prey, once decorated a god's monumental throne. It comes from a temple at Toprak Kale, the site of the fortified residence of the later Urartian kings in their capital Tushpa (modern Van, in eastern Turkey). The statuette is hollow cast, with the lost tail made separately; eyes, brows and the small slots in the crown-like headdress once bore inlays. Minimal traces of gold foil on the surface show that the entire figure was originally gilded. The chased Urartian hieroglyph on the underside of the preserved front paw probably indicated the correct mounting of the figure. Other parts of the same or a similar piece of furniture are now in museums and private collections in several countries.

Fig. 20   *Gallery 7*
Bit with figural side pieces
From Luristan
8th/7th century B.C.
Bronze; max. ht. 11.5 cm., w. 19 cm.
VA 10119
The bit, acquired by purchase on the art market, must come from the equipment of a tomb found during an illicit excavation in Luristan, a province in western Iran. Revealing details of the figures, which depict winged ibexes, indicate that they were made by the lost-wax process. The frequency of representations of animals and the large number of pieces belonging to horse bridles among the «Luristan bronzes» testify to the nomadic origins of this culture, which has so far resisted historical and archaeological definition.

Fig. 21   *Gallery 7*
Spear-bearer of the bodyguard of Darius I (521–486 B.C.)
Susa
Glazed artificial stone relief; ht. 183 cm.
VA 14647
Depictions of warriors belonging to the bodyguard of the Persian king formed part of the wall decoration covering the vast exterior surfaces of the large audience hall in the palace of Susa. The splendidly dressed soldiers, their figures arranged to form a long, continuous frieze, carry only light spears. Their colourful garments are richly decorated with geometric ornament. The glazing technique documented in the reliefs from Susa is closely related to that used to produce the glazed moulded bricks in Nebuchadnezzar II's Babylon. The rich range of colours – black, white, brown, yellow, green, and blue – is comparable to that known from Babylon.

millennium B.C.; it was found shattered in a well in the temple of the god Assur (Gallery 10).

A large water basin reassembled in the middle of Gallery 12 comes from the same temple; its exterior is decorated with reliefs depicting water goddesses and priests clothed in fish skins. Like most of the small finds exhibited in the same gallery, the basin dates to the Late Assyrian Period of the 9th to 7th centuries B.C. The variety of the objects gives a good idea of the technical skill of the craftsmen, who not only made jewellery from precious metals and semi-precious stones (case 40) but who had also learned to manufacture glass as early as the second half of the 2nd millennium B.C. (case 37). Evidence for their mastery of glass-making is provided by small vases made with the sand core technique. They also made small sculpture and decorative rosettes of frit, a glass-like substance.

Religious and magical beliefs played a vital part in the peoples' lives in the Ancient Near East. Representations of the god Assur are found on an orthostat (large decorative relief block) made of clay and covered with coloured glaze (case 37) as well as on a stone orthostat relief in the middle window niche.

From the reign of Assurnasirpal II in the 9th century B.C., Assyrian rulers decorated the ceremonial inner rooms of their palaces with reliefs and the entrances with reliefs and monumental sculpture. The alabaster orthostats mounted on the walls of Galleries 10–12 give an impression of the themes represented in the reliefs and of the characteristically Assyrian artistic style (Figure 15). Lion hunts are shown in two particularly impressive reliefs. In Gallery 10, King Assurnasirpal is depicted standing in his chariot as he shoots the final arrow at a wounded lion, while in a small-scale relief, King Assurbanipal (668–627 B.C.) uses a lance to spear a lion with his own hand, later presenting a thank-offering to the gods. Several of the large-scale reliefs in Galleries 10 and 11 with representations of winged genies (often depicted with bird heads) were intended to protect the ruler and his palace from all the forces of evil.

Vaults were constructed beneath

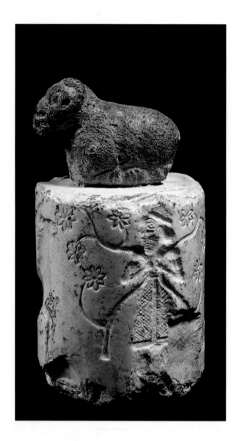

Fig. 22   *Gallery 6*
Cylinder seal with a «handle» in the form of a recumbent ram
Provenance not known; acquired not far off Warka
Ca. 2800/2700 B.C.
Marble, copper; ht. 5.4 cm., diameter 4.5 cm.
VA 10537
This large cylinder seal is one of the most beautiful examples of Sumerian glyptic art. The scene cut into the surface shows a man wearing a patterned kilt; his headgear designates him as an important personage, probably the ruler of a small city state. Goats nibble the rosettes on the branching vines that he holds in his hands. The motif has symbolic significance: the ruler as keeper of the herds is at the same time the guarantor of fertility and life.

houses and palaces in order to include the dead symbolically in the circle of the family. Replicas of two such house burials at Assur are included in the exhibition of the Museum of Western Asiatic Antiquity. The huge sarcophagus of King Assurnasirpal, which was reconstructed from original fragments found under the old palace at Assur, is exhibited together with the stone sarcophagus of another Assyrian king in the replica of a vault that is accessible down a stairway descending from Gallery 4.

The façade of a Parthian palace (1st century B.C.), which also comes from Assur, has been reconstructed opposite the Ishtar Gate. It reproduces one of the four entrance façades of the large halls which were grouped around an inner courtyard of the palace. This façade, which was influenced by Hellenistic and Roman architecture, is articulated by columns with decorated zones between them.

Syria and Anatolia

The geographical position of Syria favoured the role of a mediator between the cultures of Mesopotamia, Asia Minor and Egypt, while it also enriched the development in the Ancient Near East with many important achievements of its own. From prehistoric and early historic settlements, urban centres with far-flung trading contacts developed in the middle of the 3rd millennium B.C. The most important of these were Ebla and Byblos.

The cultural diversity of Syria, which resulted from the variety of its tribes and peoples – especially the Aramaeans and Hurrians – encouraged the development of a number of important centres, while hindering the formation of larger territorial states. In the 16th century the Hurrian state of Mitanni controlled great parts of Syrian territory; a little later the influence of the Hittites from Anatolia was increasingly felt. Like the Mitanni before them, the Hittites came into conflict with Egyptian interests in the Levant. Hostilities culminated in the historically significant battle between massed Egyptian and Hittite troops at Kadesh early in the 13th century B.C.

Like Anatolia, parts of Syria also suf-

fered at the hands of the so-called Sea Peoples who reached the borders of Egypt about 1200 B.C. One result of this «invasion» was the emergence of new political forces, among whom were the Phoenicians on the coast of Syria-Palestine and numerous smaller «Neo-Hittite» states in Syria proper and in northern Mesopotamia. The campaigns of the Assyrians and their intermittent annexation of large areas did not extinguish the continuing cultural and economic evolution of these small states.

The displays of the material culture of Syria in the Near Eastern Museum focus on objects from two important archaeological sites: Tell Halaf in northern Mesopotamia and the ruins of Sam'al/Zinjirli in northern Syria.

The excavations at Tell Halaf produced some prehistoric finds, but the most important levels revealed at the site documented the existence of a Neo-Hittite city, with a citadel in the centre. Many works of sculpture were discovered in the area of this «temple-palace,» the most impressive of them being the basalt sculpture of a bird (Gallery 2). Following a tradition that was native to both Syria and Anatolia, the exterior walls of the temple-palace of the 9th century B.C. were clad with basalt and limestone orthostats. A representative selection of these displayed in Gallery 2 gives some impression of the characteristic, highly imaginative works of art produced by the mixed Hurrian and Aramaean population of Tell Halaf. A selection of stone vessels, pottery, and small-scale basalt sculpture exemplifies the art forms that were used in everyday contexts (case 6).

The site of Sam'al, which was explored by German excavators, had an almost circular city wall surrounding a large citadel with several palaces and decorated gates. The gateway which gave access to the inner courtyard of the citadel has been rebuilt with original elements in Gallery 2. Incorporated into the jambs of the gateway are four large basalt lions which were intended not only as monumental decoration but also and more importantly as magical guardians against evil spirits. Both the walls adjoining the gate and the exterior walls of the palace were faced with basalt orthostats bearing representations of fabulous beings, gods, horsemen, warriors and officials of the palace. Members of the ruling Aramaean dynasty, which can be dated to the 9th and 8th centuries B.C., had themselves shown performing official actions (Figure 18) or proclaimed the superiority of their rule in inscriptions carved in stone. Some of the stone column bases that can be assigned to the entry halls of the royal palaces in Sam'al were decorated with floral motifs or supported by sphinxes.

The centre of attraction in Gallery 2 is a monumental statue of a weather god which was found near Sam'al. The inscription on the cylindrical body of the figure identifies the piece as a votive gift of a ruler named Panammuwa. The text is written in the Aramaic alphabetic script, a simpler form of writing than cuneiform, which came into general use in the Near East from the 8th century B.C. on.

Among the numerous small finds from Sam'al (cases 2 and 3) are finely worked ivory inlays, weapons, pottery, and terracottas; a small silver pendant with a scene of prayer is particularly noteworthy.

From its origins in Anatolia in the early 2nd millennium B.C. until its decline about 1200 B.C., the Hittite empire was a major power, encompassing at times not only much of Anatolia but also parts of Syria. Its capital Hattusha, which was discovered at Boğazköy in the early years of this century and is still being excavated today, comprised a mountain citadel with several palaces, storehouses, and a large number of temples, as well as the near-by open-air sanctuary of Yazilikaya, which was decorated in the 14th and 13th centuries B.C. with reliefs representing the «1000 gods of Hatti.» A number of the plaster casts of the reliefs at Yazilikaya made in 1882 by Carl Humann are important for scholars today because they show a better preservation than the originals. The casts are on exhibition in Gallery 1 of the Museum of Western Asiatic Antiquity.

The identification and proper study of the culture and religion of the Hittites was made possible by research on the Hittite language which was written in the cuneiform script and proved to belong to the Indo-European language family. A few of the thousands of Hittite documents

Fig. 23 Gallery 11
Obverse of Tablet A of the Middle Assyrian legal code
Assur
12th century B.C.
Clay (fired); 32 x 20.5 cm.
VAT 10000
The almost completely preserved tablet is one of a series inscribed with codification of the law of the Assyrian state, written in carefully arranged columns and sections for ease of reference. The reverse shows the same organization. This tablet occupies a special place in the history of law, because its fifty-nine sections are primarily concerned with cases involving women – laws governing theft, receipt of stolen goods, beatings and injury, sexual misconduct, and other marital and criminal matters.

67

Fig. 24   *Gallery 4*
Foundation figure (a kneeling god holding an inscribed peg)
Provenance not known
Time of Gudea, ruler of Lagash
(ca. 2144–2124 B.C.)
Bronze; ht. 17.4 cm.
Acquired by purchase
VA 3023
Metallur gy (especially the manufacture and working of bronze) was essential to the Sumerian economy for the production of tools and implements, but trading surpluses resulting from the export of grain and textiles also encouraged the use of metal for artistic purposes. Temples were customarily provided with foundation deposits that included figures like this one or other inscribed objects that furnish modern scholars with important dating information. The cuneiform text inscribed on the peg held by this bronze statuette names Gudea, ruler of the state of Lagash, who rebuilt the temple of the city god of its capital Girsu.

found at Boğazköy are shown in Gallery 2 beside examples of Hittite arts and crafts (cases 4 and 5).

Iran, Urartu and other holdings of the collection

In comparison with the civilizations of Mesopotamia, some bordering regions constitute peripheral areas which were profoundly influenced in their autonomous development by the cultural achievements of Mesopotamia. Within the overall plan of the Museum of Western Asiatic Antiquity, the sequence of rooms with Sumerian-Babylonian culture is followed by Iranian monuments in Gallery 7, while the material from the Kingdom of Urartu is shown in Gallery 13, as a continuation of the displays of Assyrian art and culture.

Because of its many and varied contacts with Mesopotamia, the cultural landscape of western Iran deserves particular attention. Apart from the development of southwestern Iran associated with the formation of the state of Elam with its capital Susa, our knowledge of the course of history in this region is very incomplete. The movements of nomadic tribes must have played a vital part in Iranian history, but the lack of written records renders them obscure, being discernible at best in typological changes in pottery forms, decorative motifs and other aspects of material culture. The social development of Iran first becomes comprehensible – and capable of integration into the known course of historical events – with the advent of the Medes and Persians, the establishment of the Median state, and the foundation of the Achaemenid dynasty.

Tepe Giyan, a site in the hill country of Luristan, has provided a sequence of pottery types that can be traced through different settlement levels on the ancient mound. On the basis of pottery forms with characteristic painting styles, five levels can be assigned to successive levels of the vast timespan from the 5th/4th millennium B.C. down to the early 1st millennium B.C. (cases 24 and 25).

The finds known as «Luristan bronzes» (Figure 20; case 26) derive from tombs that also included other funerary equipment such as jewellery and pottery. The objects do not derive from a homogenous culture; rather there are unmistakable stylistic and typological differences among them which are indicative of a variety of dates and cultures. Through careful analysis of excavated tomb groups, it has proved possible to assign the earliest phases of «Luristan bronze» production with certainty to the middle of the 3rd millennium B.C. and the latest phase to late 8th/early 7th century B.C.

Achaemenid art of Persia (6th–4th century B.C.), which was the expression of one of the latest independent cultures of the Ancient Near East, was throughout a creation of the ruling house and closely associated with the king. In addition to examples of the minor arts (case 27), there are outstanding relief fragments from the immense palace complex at Persepolis. Coloured glazed bricks with representations of the members of the royal bodyguard from a palace complex at Susa (Figure 21) demonstrate Achaemenid dependence on the glazed brick tradition of Babylon.

The history of the state of Urartu is brief. Established in the Armenian highlands in the mid-9th century B.C., Urartu was a serious political and military rival of Assyria intermittently until the second half of the 7th century B.C. Memory of this Ancient Near Eastern state seems to have been lost, but its name survived in the Old Testament. Only the consonants of the name Urartu were rendered in Hebrew, making ᶜrrt; after the original pronunciation was forgotten, the vowel *a* was supplied and Urartu became Ararat, today the name of the tallest mountain – and national symbol – of Armenia. In antiquity and for the authors of the Old Testament, the word signified the region and state of Urartu.

Apart from four stone inscriptions, all the pieces in Gallery 13 came from Toprak Kale, near Van in eastern Anatolia, which has been identified through excavations as the site of the late residential citadel of the Urartian metropolis Tushpa. The pieces on exhibition (cases 43–45) are objects of daily use, including utilitarian pottery and palace ware, and luxury articles of base and precious metal (Figure 19, metal fitting for a piece of furniture), weapons, tools, utensils, and votive objects.

A few additional holdings of the Museum of Western Asiatic Antiquity which could not be incorporated into the permanent exhibition are presented to the public in thematically oriented, special displays. The pieces were acquired either through excavations or by purchase. The most important groups of such objects are monuments from Palestine (Jericho/Tell es-Sultan and Megiddo/Tell el-Mutesselim), from ancient southern Arabia, and from the Syrian desert city of Palmyra.

The collections of seals and cuneiform documents

Cylinder and stamp seals are among the most familiar objects associated with the cultures of the Ancient Near East. The earliest stamps were made of stone and clay in the 6th/5th millennium B.C. The motifs cut into the surface of these objects ranged from simple geometric patterns and abstract representations of animals and humans to the depiction of complex scenes with several figures. At the end of the 4th millennium cylinder seals came to replace stamp seals in most regions of the Near East; stamp seals reappeared in significant numbers in the 9th and 8th centuries B.C., in connection with the spread of Aramaic alphabetic writing.

Cylinder seals, which were widespread especially in Mesopotamia, Elam and Syria, were made of stone, usually pierced, and bore incised designs, often of great complexity. An endlessly repeated impression in raised relief resulted when the cylinder was rolled over wet clay. At first cylinder seals were quite large, but in the course of their development they became relatively small. The materials used for their manufacture included limestone and semi-precious stones (especially haematite), but also clay, glass, metal and wood.

The motifs employed in the design of cylinder seals (also termed glyptic) are quite varied. Iconography and style vary regionally and according to period. The large number of seals known from throughout the Near East provide scholars with enough information to date them with some precision. Seals also furnish abundant data about the religions and the world views of the cultures which produced them and about the technical and artistic achievements of the glyptic artists who cut the designs.

The introduction of seals is closely associated with the development of personal ownership. Seal impressions facilitated control over property; doors to storerooms could be secured with a seal, as could pottery vessels or other containers. As laws developed in economic and other social contexts, written documentation was required for contracts and business transactions, and seals became an important means of authentication, the impression of a seal on a clay tablet certifying that its owner had been present. From the earliest times, too, representations on seals served a magical, protective function, so that the seals themselves acquired amuletic character for those who possessed them.

The spread of cylinder seals is closely related to cuneiform writing on clay. For this reason they progressively lost importance during the 1st millennium B.C. when alphabetic writing on parchment came to replace cuneiform scripts inscribed on clay tablets. Cylinder seals had all but ceased to be made by the 5th/4th century B.C.

In case 23, the visitor is provided with an overview of glyptic history – of the seal as an everyday object and as a work of art, of the evolution of motifs and style. The examples chosen are representative of the museum's comprehensive holdings numbering some 1700 examples of this category of minor art.

Only a small part of the collection of almost 25,000 objects inscribed in cuneiform is displayed. The examples have been selected to illustrate particular historical and cultural events and circumstances. The vast bulk of the collection provides the basis for international scholarly research into Ancient Near Eastern culture which progresses behind the scenes.

The script known today as cuneiform was devised in the Near East at the beginning of the 3rd millennium B.C. in response to the need to record economic and administrative transactions. The sign forms were pictorial at first, but by the middle of the 3rd millennium abstract linear shapes had evolved for the notation of syllables and words of the spoken language. The signs themselves were formed of little wedges impressed in wet clay. The Latin for wedge, *cuneus,* gave rise to the word cuneiform for the script. Although the main medium for recording cuneiform texts was the clay tablet, metal, stone, wood, leather and other media were also used.

The cuneiform script was first used to write Sumerian; later it was widely used to write not only Assyrian, Babylonian and Hittite – the principal languages of the Ancient Near East – but more than ten other languages as well. In the course of this development, which is comparable to the evolution of modern languages, a rich body of written literature was created, one of whose most valuable features is that many of the documents are contemporary with their composition.

Cuneiform texts document almost all areas of social life. Scholarly and philological texts, word and sign lists, syllabaries, mathematical, medical and astronomical texts, and even school exercises played an important role in the decipherment of Ancient Near Eastern languages which has been underway since 1802. Also preserved in quantity are historical texts (annals, chronicles, royal inscriptions), and economic and administrative texts, letters and legal documents.

This «everyday literature» was paralleled by a rich religious-cultic and poetic tradition to which belonged prayers, hymns, rituals, and oaths, as well as epics, myths, legends, laments and even anecdotes, satires and puzzles.

These documents, in combination with the whole range of archaeological, anthropological and enthnological data, have enabled scholars to form a relatively comprehensive picture of the development and functioning of Ancient Near Eastern society.

The central strength of the Museum of Western Asiatic Antiquity lies in its presentation of unique historically and culturally significant artifacts from Mesopotamia. The comprehensive geographical range of the collection can be demonstrated by naming the far-flung origins of the holdings. Ancient Kition (modern Larnaca, on Cyprus) is the westernmost site (the basalt stela of Sargon II [721–705 B.C.] in Gallery 3 was found there) while the limestone reliefs in Gallery 7 from the great palace terrace in Persepolis, Iran, come from the easternmost site. The north-south extent is marked by the finds from the Hittite capital Hattusha and those from the southern tip of the Arabian peninsula.

Fig. 25   *Gallery 6*
Cylinder seal and modern impression
with a scene from the Etana myth
Provenance not known
Ca. 2350–2150 B.C.
Serpentine; ht. 4 cm., diameter 2.6 cm.
Purchased
VA 3456

The cylinder seals of the Akkadian Period document admirably the development of Mesopotamian glyptic art. The variety of motifs in seal design is remarkable. During the Akkadian Period, a characteristic iconography was established for many deities that remained normative for many centuries. A theme which is documented by several seals and was evidently popular shows the shepherd Etana on the back of an eagle with whose help he ascended to heaven to fetch a plant that would insure his wife's fertility. Etana's companions, dogs, and the animals of the herd gaze with amazement as the shepherd ascends.

VERLAG PHILIPP VON ZABERN

Photographs: Jürgen Liepe

© 1992 Staatliche Museen zu Berlin – Preußischer Kulturbesitz
Photograph credits: Bildarchiv Preußischer Kulturbesitz
Verlag Philipp von Zabern, Mainz on the Rhine

ISBN 3-8053-1450-7 (Edition of Museum)
Type: Typo-Service Mainz
Lithography: SWS Repro, Wiesbaden
Paper: Papierfabrik Scheufelen, Lenningen
Manufactured by Zaberndruck, Mainz
Printed in Germany/Imprimé en Allemagne
Printed on fade resistant and archival quality paper (PH 7 neutral)

THE BORZOI PRACTICE BOOK FOR WRITERS

THE BORZOI PRACTICE BOOK FOR WRITERS

THIRD EDITION

MICHAEL HENNESSY
Southwest Texas State University

McGraw-Hill, Inc.

New York   St. Louis   San Francisco   Auckland
Bogotá   Caracas   Lisbon   London   Madrid
Mexico   Milan   Montreal   New Delhi   Paris
San Juan   Singapore   Sydney   Tokyo   Toronto

This book was developed by STEVEN PENSINGER, Inc.

THE BORZOI PRACTICE BOOK FOR WRITERS

2 3 4 5 6 7 DOC/DOC 9 9 8 7 6 5 4 3

ISBN 0-07-013648-3

This book was set in Times Roman by ComCom, Inc.
The editors were Steve Pensinger and James R. Belser;
the production supervisor was Richard A. Ausburn.
The cover was designed by Larry Didoni.
R. R. Donnelley & Sons Company was printer and binder.

About the Author

MICHAEL HENNESSY is Professor of English at Southwest Texas State University, where he directs the first-year writing program and teaches courses in beginning and advanced composition, modern literature, and the teaching of writing. He holds a Ph.D. in English literature from Marquette University and has taught at Memphis State University and John Carroll University. His publications include *The Borzoi Handbook for Writers* (with Frederick Crews and Sandra Schor) and *The Random House Practice Book*. He is also author of numerous articles and reviews on composition pedagogy and on the work of Shakespeare, W. H. Auden, and the contemporary British poet Charles Tomlinson. Professor Hennessy has served as chair of the Texas Association of Directors of Writing Programs and was recently awarded the Faculty Senate Award for Excellence in Teaching at Southwest Texas State University.

Contents

Preface

The Borzoi Practice Book for Writers, third edition, is a collection of some 240 exercises designed to accompany *The Borzoi Handbook for Writers,* third edition. While offering a full range of exercises for students who need individual instruction, the *Practice Book* also includes ample material for group work and class discussion. And since it comes free, shrink-wrapped with every new copy of the *Handbook,* instructors can draw on its many resources without adding cost for their students.

In this new edition, I have tried to preserve what worked well in the first two. Most importantly, the book retains its emphasis on editing practice rather than rote drill. Many exercises on usage, punctuation, and mechanics, for example, place error in context, asking students to edit sentences and paragraphs rather than filling in blanks. The *Practice Book* also continues to stress the entire process of composition, from exploring a topic to revising for rhetorical effectiveness.

Like its predecessors, this edition contains dozens of examples of colorful, informative writing from an array of published sources. Exercises incorporate material from speeches, popular magazines, historical documents, and classic essays. Students learn about mermaids, cucumbers, and elephants; about colonial women and Viking warriors; about Gothic architecture and the origins of American jazz. Exercises are meant to delight as well as to teach.

While retaining the best of its earlier features, the *Practice Book* incorporates a number of changes in this edition:

- *Additional exercises on every part of the writing process.* I have added, enlarged, or revised more than sixty exercises, some adapted from a related text, *The Random House Practice Book,* other designed specifically for this book. There is new material on clustering, developing a thesis, and peer editing; on organization, purpose, and tone; on using evidence and avoiding logical fallacies; on paragraph development, idioms, and figurative language; on fragments, agreement, verb tense, and punctuation.

- *A stronger emphasis on student writing.* The greatly expanded sixth chapter adds four complete student essays, illustrating the types of writing most often assigned in first-year composition courses. And the section on the research paper now includes two sample papers, one using MLA style, the other APA style. With a total of ten student drafts or essays, the book is an excellent resource for class discussion of rhetorical principles. Briefer excerpts of student prose also appear in nearly every chapter (indicated by an asterisk in the text).
- *More examples from published sources.* I have added new examples of published writing throughout the book, including excerpts from the work of Joan Didion, Annie Dillard, Paul Fussell, Martin Luther King, Richard Rodriguez, and Virginia Woolf.
- *A new emphasis on collaboration.* The fifth chapter teaches students to revise their own work and to become effective peer editors. Elsewhere in the book, many exercises invite students to work in pairs or small groups in developing ideas and making plans for revision.
- *An expanded treatment of the research paper.* Four chapters now give detailed attention to every aspect of writing a research paper, from arriving at a topic to documenting sources. Along with two finished research papers, the book includes samples of research in progress, allowing students to practice the skills they need for writing their own papers.

The organization of the *Practice Book* follows that of the *Handbook*. Each exercise is keyed to the particular *Handbook* section(s) that students should consult as they complete the exercise. This scheme makes it easy to use the two books in tandem and helps students learn the *Handbook*'s reference system. An Answer Key for the *Practice Book* is available on request from McGraw-Hill.

I owe special thanks to Frederick Crews for his continuing support of my work and to Steve Pensinger for his expert advice during the past ten years. At McGraw-Hill, James Belser, Anita Kann, and Rich Ausburn helped transform the manuscript into a finished book; they have my thanks. I am also grateful to colleagues at Southwest Texas State University who helped in various ways—especially Nancy Grayson, Dan Lochman, Carolyn Pate, Pat Pohl, and Miles Wilson—and to the reviewers named in the Preface to the *Borzoi Handbook,* Second Edition. Many students allowed me to reprint, and often adapt, their work in the exercises. Those who supplied full essays are credited in the text. Others whose writing is new to this edition include Shelby Cash, Chris Jenkins, Heidi Prather, Eva Reed, Andrew Straffon, and Lisa Valerian. Finally, I wish to thank my family—Susie, Nora, Kevin, Bridget, and Mary—for their many contributions to the book.

Michael Hennessy

I

COMPOSING ESSAYS

1
Arriving at a Topic

1.1 Reviewing Your Background as a Writer (*BHW* 1a)

In order to give yourself and your instructor an overview of your background as a writer, complete the following exercise.

1. Briefly describe the amount and type of writing you did in high school, especially in your English courses.
2. What type of writing have you done on your own, apart from formal course assignments?
3. List what you consider to be your strengths and weaknesses as a writer.
4. Briefly describe your expectations for this course. What do you hope to accomplish?
5. Drawing on your past experience and your expectations for the future, list the advantages of knowing how to write well.

1.2 Distinguishing between a Subject Area and a Topic (*BHW* 1b–c)

For each pair of items, indicate which is a subject area (SA) and which is a topic (T).

Example: The media   *SA*

            The *USA Today* editorial page   *T*

1. Personal computers   _____

   Writing on a Macintosh   _____

2. Technology and war in the 1990s   _____

   Long-range effects of war in the Persian Gulf   _____

3. Pets for apartment dwellers   _____

   Cats   _____

4. Eating a well-balanced diet   _____

   My Ultra Slim·Fast diet   _____

5. Living in a big city   _____

   Yuppie culture in Minneapolis   _____

6. Essay tests   _____

   How I passed Organic Chemistry   _____

7. News magazines   _____

   Newsweek's coverage of science   _____

8. Disney's *Beauty and the Beast*   _____

   Recent films   _____

9. *Huckleberry Finn*   _____

   Irony in "Christmas at the Dixie Motel"   _____

10. Women in the military   _____

    Should mothers be exempt from combat duty?   _____

1.3   Narrowing a Subject Area (*BHW* 1b–c)

Select five of the subject areas you identified in Exercise 1.2, and narrow each one to a topic.

Example: *the media → television → television news → television as a source of national news*

1. _____

   _____

2. _____

   _____

3. _____

   _____

4. _____

   _____

5. _____

   _____

1.4   Identifying the Features of Descriptive, Narrative, Analytic, and Argumentative Writing (*BHW* 1d)

Read the student essays listed below, and be prepared to explain how each one accomplishes its main purpose. Since a single type of writing rarely exists in isolation, you should also be prepared to discuss how the writers combine various purposes in developing their essays.

1. "Death of a Canyon," p. 77
   Main Purpose: To create visual images for the reader (description)
2. "Behind the Scenes," p. 81
   Main Purpose: To tell the reader what happened (narration)

3. "My Parents: Playing in Harmony," p. 86
   Main Purpose: To explain for the reader (analysis)
4. "Turning Citizens into Suckers," p. 90
   Main Purpose: To win the reader's agreement (argument)

1.5 Analyzing a Writer's Purpose (*BHW* 1d)

Both of the following paragraphs are directed at a general audience of educated readers. The first is an entry from a desk encyclopedia; the second is a paragraph from a popular astronomy book about the origin and development of the universe. Assume in each case that the source contains no other information about the planet Pluto. Keeping in mind the two sources, comment on the likely purpose of each passage. List specific features of the paragraphs to illustrate how the information and style of writing are matched to the writer's purpose.

1. Pluto, in astronomy, 9th and usually most distant planet from the sun, at a mean distance of 3.67 million mi (5.90 billion km). Because of the high eccentricity (0.250) of its elliptical orbit, Pluto occasionally (e.g., between 1979 and 1999) comes closer than the planet Neptune to the sun. Discovered in 1930 by Clyde Tombaugh, Pluto has an estimated diameter of 1,500 to 2,400 mi (2,400 to 3,800 km) and is thought to have a rocky, silicate core and a thin atmosphere containing methane. Its one known satellite, Charon, was discovered on June 22, 1978, by the American astronomer James Christy. It has a diameter estimated to be about a third that of Pluto.[1]

Purpose _____

_____

_____

Features _____

_____

_____

_____

_____

2. Pluto, found in 1930, was the ninth and last planet to be discovered in the solar system. Its orbit is farther from the sun than that of any other planet and probably marks the outer boundary of the solar system. Because Pluto is so far away, we have been able to learn very little about it, except that it appears to be a body similar in size and composition to the earth. It must be a frozen, silent world, far too cold to support any form of life. [2]

Purpose _____

_____

_____

Features _____

_____

_____

_____

_____

1.6 Reviewing Personal Experience and Keeping a Journal (*BHW* 1e–f)

In order to establish an inventory of potential essay topics, review your experience. Start by listing several topics for each of the broad categories given below. Then continue the process in a journal or notebook, recording ideas as they occur to you over a period of several weeks.

1. Early childhood memories _____

_____

_____

_____

2. Reading/books _____

_____

_____

_____

3. Sports/games/hobbies _____

_____

_____

_____

_____

4. Work/skills _____

_____

_____

_____

5. Education/school _____

_____

_____

_____

1.7 Reviewing Reading Assignments and Keeping a Journal (*BHW* 1e–f)

Review your reading assignments over several days, looking for ideas and opinions that arouse your curiosity or provoke a strong reaction. List five ideas that you might use as writing topics. Continue the process in a journal or notebook.

1. _____

_____

_____

2. _____

_____

_____

3. _____

_____

_____

4. _____

_____

_____

5. _____

_____

_____

1.8 Using Freewriting as a Source of Ideas (*BHW* 1g)

Read the following piece of freewriting. In the space provided, advise the student writer about potential paper topics that might grow out of the passage. What idea or image strikes you as interesting and worthy of further development?

My grandmother's dog died last week—twelve years old—which means my grandmother will be even more lonely. She relied on him for companionship and to give her something to do every day. Taking him for a walk, feeding him. On TV I saw a show about
5   pets being taken to nursing homes. It supposedly comforted the old people, improved their attitudes, to play with the pets. Pets are sometimes substitutes for people. People use them as outlets for emotions, even when they have family and friends. You can always talk to a dog without worrying that he might tell your secret
10 or be sarcastic or unsympathetic. And dogs are totally unrestrained in giving affection. Do they have "emotions" just as people do? That's why some people don't like them, I guess. Too willing to please—tails wagging, smiling, tilting their heads. Cats are different. They please no one, seem arrogant to me. People like them for
15 this quality. Cats are supposedly independent, sophisticated, and intelligent. But maybe they're just too dumb to recognize anyone but themselves. People admire personality traits in cats that they wouldn't admire in people. Cat and dog "personalities." They do seem to have personalities and character traits—Morris the cat or
20 Snoopy or a hundred other TV and cartoon dogs and cats. Maybe people project their personalities onto their pets. Or maybe pets reflect the personalities of their owners.*

_____

_____

_____

_____

_____

1.9 Developing a Topic with Freewriting (*BHW* 1g)

Freewrite for ten minutes on one of the following subjects or on a subject of your choice. Then follow the instructions in the preceding exercise as a means of discovering possible topics for a brief essay.

1. Charity
2. Fast food
3. Bumper stickers
4. Prejudice
5. Advertising

1.10 Using Brainstorming as a Source of Ideas (*BHW* 1g)

Look over the following notes from a brainstorming session. Find several groups of details in the material that suggest essay topics. In the space provided, list two or three of the most promising topics.

RESPONSIBILITY

Everyone has responsibilities
—maybe not young children
—old people?
—mentally retarded?
—others?

Parental responsibility
Responsibility of students
—to parents who pay for education
—to self
—to society—pay back benefits gained
Is "duty" same as "responsibility"—"duty to God and country"
Selective service law—responsibility/duty to register at eighteen
Why not women?
Is it more "responsible" not to register?
Obeying the law—duty/responsibility
Thoreau's essay "Civil Disobedience"—duty to follow conscience
    over the law
Does society have responsibilities?
Responsibility for poor, sick, disabled?
—protection/support
—welfare/medicare
Socialism—responsibility taken over by government?
Relationship of responsibility to freedom
Responsibility/duty to vote
Politics and responsibility
Personal responsibility
—relationship between men and women
—marriage
Financial responsibility
—not paying the rent
—credit cards
—living beyond your means
Taking care of pets
Responsibility in school
Crime and irresponsibility—irresponsible behavior punished?
What does the word "responsibility" mean—check dictionary for
    origin of word
Responsibility—other side of freedom?
Essay by Sartre in textbook—we are totally free but also totally
    responsible for what we do and are
What does religion say about responsibility?*

Possible topics _____

_____

_____

_____

_____

_____

1.11 Developing a Topic
with Brainstorming (*BHW* 1g)

Working by yourself or with a group, brainstorm for ten minutes on one of the following subjects or a subject of your choice. Then use the instructions provided in the preceding exercise to search for possible essay topics.

1. Work
2. Music
3. Happiness
4. Politics
5. Computers

1.12 Using Clustering as a Source of Ideas
(*BHW* 1g)

On the next page is part of a student writer's clustering on the word *holiday*. In the space provided, list two or three essay topics suggested by the student's work.

Possible topics _____

_____

_____

_____

_____

_____

_____

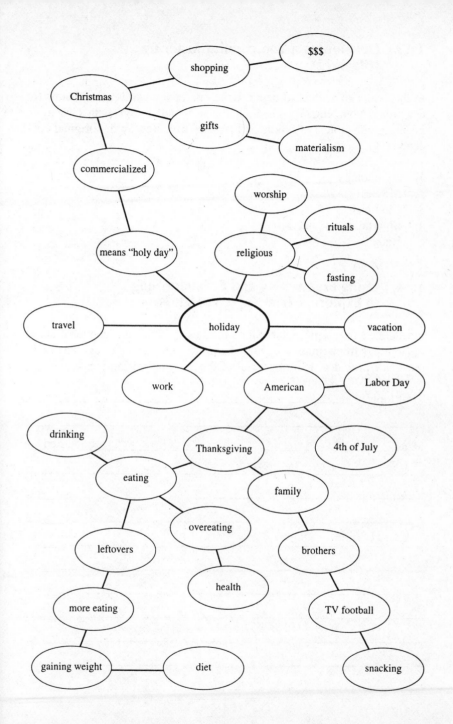

1.13 Developing a Topic with Clustering (*BHW* 1g)

In the center of a sheet of paper, write one of the words given below (or a word of your choice). Then fill the rest of the page with clustering, mapping out groups of words and phrases triggered by the original concept.

1. Technology
2. Movies
3. Clothing
4. Entertainment
5. Books

1.14 Using Freewriting and Brainstorming to Explore a Trial Topic (*BHW* 1h)

Formulate a trial topic suitable for a brief essay. Then develop ideas about the topic by freewriting or by brainstorming with a group of classmates. In the space provided, record several of the most promising ideas.

Trial topic _____

Ideas _____

_____

_____

_____

_____

_____

_____

_____

_____

_____

_____

_____

_____

_____

1.15 Asking Reporters' Questions
to Explore a Trial Topic (*BHW* 1h)

Use reporters' questions to explore the trial topic you developed in the preceding exercise (1.14). Write five questions beginning with the words in the following list. Use the questions to probe your topic, to develop further ideas and possibilities.

Example: Topic: The merits of television as a source of national news

Question: What, *if anything, does television news offer to compensate for its relative lack of depth (e.g., no editorial page, less coverage of "minor" stories)?*

1. Who _____

_____

_____

_____

2. What _____

_____

_____

_____

3. When _____

_____

_____

_____

_____

4. Where _____

_____

_____

_____

_____

5. How _____

_____

_____

_____

_____

6. Why _____

_____

_____

_____

_____

2

Developing
a Thesis

2.1 Evaluating Trial Theses (*BHW* 2a)

Evaluate the following trial theses, deciding whether each one contains a single idea that is adequately focused for a three- to four-page essay. In the space provided, briefly justify your answers. If the thesis is adequately focused, explain why; if it lacks focus, jot down suggestions for improving it. (*Reminder:* An adequate trial thesis may contain more than one point, but all points should be subordinate to the one main idea that the writer intends to develop.)

Example: Although television has several advantages as a source of news, a newspaper can offer things that a television program cannot.

Could be better focused—What kind of TV news? PBS? Networks? News specials? What kind of newspaper? What kind of

1. Most of the new skyscrapers in large cities have no character, and people prefer older styles of architecture that have more appeal because of tradition.

   _____

   _____

   _____

   _____

2. Knowing how to use a word processor is no longer a luxury but a fundamental skill that employers look for on a résumé, and graduates in most fields are well-advised to learn at least one of the major word processing programs.

   _____

   _____

   _____

   _____

3. The food in Commons cafeteria is bad, and something should be done to improve it.

   _____

   _____

   _____

   _____

4. I oppose a tax-supported recycling program in Wimberley because it will put a strain on an already tight city budget and unfairly penalize the many townspeople who currently participate in the successful volunteer program.

   _____

   _____

5. I believe that marriage and family development courses in high school should be designed to emphasize the financial situation of the couple, helping them learn to manage a household instead of teaching them about love, sex, and child rearing.

2.2 Revising Faulty Trial Theses
   (*BHW* 2a–d)

The following trial theses are overly broad or obvious, fail to take a definite stand, or merely announce a topic. In the space provided, indicate why each thesis lacks promise. Then draft a revised version.

Example: Making freshman English a pass/fail course has both advantages and disadvantages.

Problem *The thesis is wishy-washy. It doesn't take a definite stand.*

Revision *Making freshman English a pass/fail course would encourage students to concentrate less on grades and more on the gradual improvement of their writing skills.*

1. While some people favor the construction of a high-rise parking garage on campus, others oppose it.

Problem _____

_____

Revision _____

_____

_____

2. There are many ways to study for a test.

Problem _____

_____

Revision _____

_____

_____

3. In my essay, I will discuss the physical education requirement at this university.

Problem _____

_____

Revision _____

_____

_____

4. College should have fewer required courses.

Problem _____

_____

Revision _____

_____

_____

_____

_____

5. Walking is a popular way to stay fit.

    Problem _____

    _____

    Revision _____

    _____

    _____

    _____

2.3 Matching Thesis and Purpose—Analysis versus Argument (*BHW* 2b)

Learn about a specific academic policy on your campus. Then draft two theses about that policy, the first for an *analytic* essay explaining the purpose of the policy, the second for an *argumentative* essay in favor of the policy or urging its elimination.

1. Analytic thesis _____

    _____

    _____

    _____

    _____

2. Argumentative thesis _____

    _____

    _____

    _____

    _____

2.4 Developing a Trial Thesis (*BHW* 2a–d)

Using the trial topic and prewriting material you developed in Exercises 1.14 and 1.15, write a trial thesis for a three- to four-page essay. After seeking suggestions for revision from your instructor or a classmate, revise the trial thesis.

2.5 Analyzing Full Thesis Statements (*BHW* 2e)

For each of the following full thesis statements, underline the author's main point—the core of the thesis. Then put parentheses around the details or reasons that support the point. Finally, if the author indicates an objection to the main point, enclose it in square brackets.

Example: [Although nightly television news programs give a quick and clear summary of important world news and although they have the advantage of being able to use vivid film footage,] <u>a major daily newspaper is usually a better source of news</u> (because it gives a more comprehensive picture of world events, because it offers a kind of in-depth coverage rarely found on television, and because it can provide perspective and balance through its editorial page.)

1. Being able to plant a vegetable garden is one of the best reasons to rent a house with a back yard instead of living in an apartment because gardening is a relaxing hobby, because it gives the gardener a course in practical botany, because it provides good exercise, and because it costs nothing since it more than pays for itself with the food it supplies.

2. Showing a prize-winning, year-old heifer at a fair involves more than a city person might imagine, including selecting the right calf, feeding

and caring for it properly, training it to lead, learning to groom it for the show ring, learning to present it for judging, and caring for and presenting it at the fair itself.

3. While the practice of rotating the location of the Summer Olympic Games benefits the city and country that sponsor the games, the Olympics should be held at a permanent site in order to make the games less political and to place maximum emphasis on the skills of individual athletes.

2.6 Developing a Full Thesis Statement (*BHW* 2e)

Using the trial thesis you wrote for Exercise 2.4, develop a full thesis statement for a three- to four-page essay. The thesis should state your main point and indicate the major parts of your plan to support that point. Remember that a full thesis statement is a guide to help you gain an overall sense of direction, not a statement that will go verbatim into the essay itself. After you have formulated the full thesis statement, seek advice on its effectiveness from your instructor or from a group of classmates. Using the suggestions you gather, revise the thesis.

Full thesis _____

_____

_____

_____

_____

_____

Suggestions for revision _____

_____

_____

_____

Revised full thesis

3
Organizing

3.1 Using Your Full Thesis Statement as a Guide in Organizing (*BHW* 3b)

Use this exercise to analyze the full thesis statement you developed in Exercise 2.6. Your analysis should be helpful as you organize your essay.

1. In the space below, write the main idea contained in your full thesis statement.

_____

_____

_____

2. Consider possible ways to begin your essay that would draw the reader's interest toward this main point. Write one or two ideas below.

_____

_____

_____

_____

_____

3. If you are writing an argumentative essay and your full thesis statement indicates an objection you plan to address, write the objection below.

_____

_____

_____

4. Is this the only objection that the reader is likely to raise? List below any other objections you might wish to consider, however briefly, at some point in the essay.

_____

_____

_____

_____

_____

_____

5. List below the main points of support included in your full thesis statement. Jot down several details you could use to develop each point.

_____

_____

_____

_____

_____

_____

6. Will any of the points listed in item 5 help you meet the objections listed in items 3 and 4? Which points?

_____

_____

_____

3.2 Developing an Outline for Your Essay (*BHW* 3c–d)

Using the material you developed in Exercise 3.1, write a scratch outline or a formal outline for your essay.

3.3 Evaluating a Formal Outline (*BHW* 3c–d)

Evaluate the formal outline given below by answering the questions that follow it.

Thesis: A major daily newspaper has several advantages over television news programs as a source of national news.

I. Television news offers some advantages.

    A. Nightly television news programs give a clear, concise summary of the day's events.

    B. Television has the advantage of immediacy—a vivid, fast-paced presentation using words and film footage.

    C. Some people have little time for the news.

    D. News anchorpersons can be trusted.

II. Newspapers offer several advantages.

    A. Though not as concise, newspapers give a more comprehensive picture of national events.

        1. Newspaper coverage is more detailed.

III. Newspapers offer greater depth of coverage.

IV. Newspapers offer greater perspective and balance.

    A. The editorial/opinion page allows newspapers to provide a range of opinion on national news.

B. Major news is placed in the context of less significant news, giving the reader a better perspective.

1. Does the outline contain enough points for development in a three- to four-page essay? Too few? Too many? Explain.

_____

_____

_____

_____

2. Are the outline categories in logical relation to one another? Explain.

_____

_____

_____

_____

3. Do the points seem to be arranged in an effective order? Explain.

_____

_____

_____

_____

3.4 Revising a Formal Outline (*BHW* 3c–d)

Revise the outline in the preceding exercise (3.3), eliminating any weaknesses you identified.

3.5 Writing a Scratch Outline (*BHW* 3c)

Convert the formal outline you revised in the preceding exercise (3.4) into a scratch outline. Your outline should indicate the *main* points covered by the formal outline.

3.6 Outlining a Student Essay (*BHW* 3d)

Construct a formal outline of one of the following student essays:

1. "Death of a Canyon," p. 77
2. "Behind the Scenes," p. 81
3. "My Parents: Playing in Harmony," p. 86
4. "Turning Citizens into Suckers," p. 90

3.7 Outlining a Professional Essay (*BHW* 3d)

In a book, periodical, or the collection of readings used in your composition course, find an essay that you consider well organized. Design a formal outline of the essay, showing its main and subordinate points.

3.8 Constructing a Tree Diagram (*BHW* 3e)

Construct a tree diagram for one of the student essays listed in Exercise 3.6.

3.9 Using a Tree Diagram to Organize Your Essay (*BHW* 3e)

In lieu of the traditional outline recommended in Exercise 3.2, use a tree diagram to organize your essay. Start by writing your thesis statement at the top of the page. Then plan the main parts of your essay in several "branches." Develop each branch in enough detail to show key supporting points.

4
Drafting

ADDRESSING THE READER

4.1 Analyzing a Writer's Awareness of Audience (*BHW* 4b)

The following passages serve essentially the same purpose: each is the opening paragraph of a book describing CP/M, an operating system once used in many home computers. The first writer, however, makes different assumptions about his audience than does the second. Study the passages carefully, and be prepared to discuss the type of audience each writer seems to have in mind. Which passage contains more information about CP/M? What kind of information does each writer supply? How do the two passages differ in vocabulary, organization, and sentence structure? Note the features of each passage in the space provided.

1. The purpose of this chapter is to teach you how to perform basic operations on your computer system using CP/M. No prior knowledge of computers is required. You will first learn the vocabulary and the definitions related to the computer's operation. You will then learn how to turn the computer on, insert your *System Diskette,* and bring

CP/M up. You will learn about *files:* how to create them, give them names, and make copies of a file or a complete diskette. You will learn to use the keyboard as well as the screen and the printer to manipulate, display or print the contents of a file. By the end of this chapter, you will have learned how to use all of the most important CP/M commands.[3]

Audience _____

_____

_____

Features _____

_____

_____

_____

_____

2. CP/M is a monitor control program for microcomputer system development which uses IBM-compatible flexible disks for backup storage. Using a computer mainframe based upon Intel's 8080 microcomputer, CP/M provides a general environment for program construction, storage, and editing, along with assembly and program check-out facilities. An important feature of CP/M is that it can be easily altered to execute with any computer configuration which uses an Intel 8080 (or Zilog Z-80) Central Processing Unit, and has at least 16K bytes of main memory with up to four IBM-compatible disk drives. A detailed discussion of the modifications required for any particular hardware environment is given in the Digital Research document entitled "CP/M System Alteration Guide." Although the standard Digital Research version operates on a single-density Intel MDS 800, several different hardware manufacturers support their own input-output drivers for CP/M.[4]

Audience _____

_____

_____

Features _____

_____

_____

_____

_____

_____

4.2   Analyzing a Writer's Voice (*BHW* 4c)

A.   In the following paragraph, the writer's voice is personal. List several features that help establish this voice. [5]

Welcome to English 103, Writing for Business and Industry. My goal in this class is to help you become a better writer of letters, memos, and reports—the kinds of writing you will be doing on the job. Whether you plan to work in business, industry, government, or in another profession, you will probably be asked to write, and the better you can do so, the better your chances of getting the job done, avoiding problems, and advancing in your career.

_____

_____

_____

_____

B.   In this paragraph the voice is dry and impersonal. Again, list several features that help establish this voice.

English 103 is entitled Writing for Business and Industry. The primary objective of the course is to improve the student's ability to write correspondence, interoffice memoranda, and technical and professional reports. Obviously, professionals in business, industry, and government benefit if they have skill in written communication. The ability to write means greater productivity on the job and gives the individual greater opportunities for career advancement.

_____

_____

_____

_____

_____

_____

C. Describe a situation in which a writer might want to use each of the voices illustrated in the preceding passages. Which voice would be more effective for an actual course syllabus? Why?

_____

_____

_____

_____

_____

4.3 Using Personal and Impersonal Voice (*BHW* 4c)

Write two explanatory paragraphs on a topic you know well—anything from fishing to rock music. The first should be a dry, impersonal report. The second, which should include the same basic information as the first, should be written in a more personal voice, one that is appropriate for a college essay.

4.4 Analyzing a Writer's Stance (*BHW* 4d)

A. In the following passage, the writer adopts a forthright stance. Characterize that stance and list several features of the writing that help establish it.

As a body of doctors and health care professionals, we believe it is time to end hunger in America.

It is our judgment that hunger and related ill-health have no place in a democratic society, especially one with the resources of the United States.

• This nation has the resources and ability to end hunger. We have heard no one deny that this is true. America is not a poverty-stricken Third World nation caught between the pincers of a poor economy and inadequate food supply. To the contrary, we produce enough food to feed our people probably several times over. Our nation's warehouses bulge with food, so much food that each year thousands of tons are wasted or destroyed. Clearly, lack of food is not the cause of hunger in America.

Neither do we lack the financial resources to end hunger in this land. Ours is perhaps the strongest economy in the world. We cannot maintain that we lack the resources to end hunger when numerous other industrialized nations have done so. That is illogical. In fact, by increasing annual federal food programs just by the amount we spend on two CVN Nuclear Attack Carriers, we could probably eliminate hunger in the nation. No, lack of money is not the cause of hunger in America. [6]

_____

_____

_____

_____

_____

_____

B. In this passage, the writer adopts an ironic stance. Characterize that stance and list several features of the writing that help establish it.

Everyone knows that sports teams must have nicknames, but selecting an appropriate one is fraught with peril. Alabama, for instance, may be proud of the Crimson Tide, but it sounds like a bloodbath or a serious algae problem. Notre Dame's famous jocks are ossified as the Fighting Irish, though Hibernian-American athletes are about as rare in South Bend as they are on the Boston Celtics. Nothing exposed the nickname crisis more starkly than the 1982 NCAA basketball championship game played between the Georgetown Hoyas and the North Carolina Tar Heels. Even if you know what a hoya or a tarheel is, the only sensible strategy is to forget it. (For those overwhelmed by a need to know, hoya is short for *Hoya saxa!,* a garbled Greek and Latin cheer meaning "What rocks!," and tarheel originated during the Civil War as a disparaging term for folks from the Carolina pine forests.) Few knew what the Fort Wayne Zollner Pistons were when a pro basketball team played under that name. (They were players owned by Fred Zollner, who also happened to own a piston factory in Fort Wayne.) The early vogue of naming a team for a person seems to have come to an end with Paul Brown, the original coach of the Cleveland Browns. Fans who found the cult of personality distasteful at least were grateful that he wasn't named Stumblebrenner.

The Zollner Pistons eventually became the Detroit Pistons, showing that some names travel well. The Brooklyn Dodgers, named for the difficulty of evading trolley cars in the famous borough, are now the Los Angeles Dodgers, where evading mayhem on the freeways is equally hard. The name Los Angeles Lakers, however, makes no sense at all, though it did when the team was in Minnesota. Utah, with its Mormon tradition, could easily have accepted the New Orleans football team (the Saints, as in Latter-Day Saints and saints who go marching in). Instead it got the New Orleans basketball team, now known as the Utah Jazz, which makes about as much sense as the New Orleans Tabernacle Choir. [7]

_____

_____

_____

_____

_____

_____

C. Passage A is from a Physician Task Force report on hunger; passage B is from an essay in a popular news magazine. Why, in each case, is the stance appropriate? Describe other occasions and subject matters where the two stances might be used effectively.

_____

_____

_____

_____

_____

_____

_____

4.5 Using a Straightforward and an Ironic Stance (*BHW* 4d)

Write two paragraphs on some aspect of life on your campus—academic policies, registration, social life, dorm life. Adopt a straightforward stance in the first, an ironic stance in the second. Though your topic will be the same in both cases, the effect should be radically different: the first paragraph should be sincere and serious, the second biting, cynical, wry, flippant, or outrageous.

4.6 Recognizing a Writer's Tone (*BHW* 4e)

Read the editorial pages from two newspapers (your campus paper and a local daily will do). Look for a piece of writing with a notably measured tone and for one marked by uncontrolled emotion. Editorials and letters to the editor are both likely candidates. Bring the editorial pages to class and be prepared to discuss (or to write about) your findings.

4.7 Analyzing a Writer's Tone (*BHW* 4e)

A. In this passage, a student writer discusses her attitudes toward her parents and her emotionally disturbed sister. Although the subject is highly emotional, the writer manages to achieve restraint and under-statement. List several features of the writing that help establish a measured tone. How does the writer convey strong emotion without losing control of her tone?

Seemingly bereft of the patience and compassion my parents had cultivated, I could feel nothing but distaste for my sister and for the way my parents allowed her to control their lives. In a very real sense, she dictated how they lived. Even though I was contemptuous of my sister and of my parents for allowing themselves, as I perceived it, to be kept prisoners, I was also ashamed of this fault in my own character—and ashamed that my feelings were so ill-concealed. My parents never hid my sister away or made excuses for her. They expected everyone to accept her just as they did; they either disregarded or disdained the curiosity and fear of outsiders. Try as I might to disguise how I felt, I knew that my inability or unwillingness to share their feelings was always an unspoken source of disappointment.*

B. This passage is notably less restrained than the preceding one. List several features that contribute to the emotionalism of the passage. What effect do you suppose the author hoped to have on her original audience in 1886? How does the passage affect you? Why?

Like a swarm of bees about a very sweet flower, the affectionate lads surrounded their pretty playmate, and kissed her till she looked like a little rose, not roughly, but so enthusiastically that nothing but the crown of her hat was visible for a moment. Then her father rescued her, and she drove away still smiling and waving her hands, while the boys sat on the fence screaming like a flock of guinea-fowls, "Come back! come back!" till she was out of sight.

They all missed her, and each dimly felt that he was better for having known a creature so lovely, delicate, and sweet; for little Bess appealed to the chivalrous instinct in them as something to love, admire, and protect with a tender sort of reverence. Many a man remembers some pretty child who has made a place in his heart and kept her memory alive by the simple magic of her innocence; these little men were just learning to feel this power, and to love it for its gentle influence, not ashamed to let the small hand lead them, nor to own their loyalty to womankind, even in the bud. [8]

4.8 Analyzing an Essay—Audience, Voice, Stance, and Tone (*BHW* 4b–e)

Study the essay "Teachers' Tests," which follows, and be prepared to discuss these questions:

1. First published in *Harper's* magazine, the essay is aimed at a general rather than specialized audience. What features of the writing indicate that the author has kept this audience in mind?
2. Describe the author's voice. Is it personal or impersonal? Does the voice seem appropriate for the author's intended audience and purpose?
3. Characterize the writer's stance. Does he strike you as straightforward and trustworthy? Or is he aiming in part for an ironic effect? How does he signal his stance?
4. The author achieves a carefully measured tone. What features of the writing signal this tone?

Teachers' Tests
Pierre Szamek

Doris Green, a seventh-grade teacher in Akron, Ohio, is twenty-nine. She has taught for six years. She is proud of her work and serves it conscientiously. "I'm a good teacher, I think," she says. "Anyway, I like the kids, and that's what it's all about, isn't it?"

In her home state of New Jersey, Doris Green was moved casually through the full program of state teacher-training requirements at Newark State College (now Kean College). Taking the complete battery of prescribed courses, she received all of the required grades: an A in Educational Psychology, course number 3501 ("This course considers cognition, motivation, tests and measurements. . . ."); an A in Educational Psychology, 4501 ("Group Dynamics . . ., Group Function, Group Structure, Communication, Means of Observing, Group Information. . . ."); an A in Creative Techniques; an A in Health Education, 4333 ("Alcohol and Narcotics Education"); and wound up with a

B plus in Language Arts. With these suitably accomplished, she topped the list with eight of the ten courses offered in Reading Education.

Among these, the course she enjoyed most was Reading Education 4103. "We worked on the relation of intonation to meaning," she explains, "which is something I had never thought of before. I guess this is what makes education so exciting; it opens up so many new worlds."

Doris Green graduated from her teacher-training program with a near A average. After a one-semester practice-teaching period, she received her $13,000-a-year position within three months of graduation.

Armand Forestier, the thirty-three-year-old schoolmaster of a three-room school in Arcy-sur-Aube, a French town ninety miles west of Paris, followed a somewhat different road.

After graduating from the lycée, M. Forestier entered university, immersing himself in a six-year program of French history, French literature, and Romance philology, two years of philosophy, and a well-balanced science program combining six years of physics and chemistry.

Upon satisfactory qualification in these subjects, he was given the final written and oral tests that, when sustained, allowed him to apply for a teaching position at the primary level. So difficult is this examination that in a recent test given to 4,781 candidates, only 681 passed. Of those who failed, most were stopped by the meticulous demands of an avalanche of required compositions on abstruse historical and philosophical problems, some of which required as long as seven hours to complete. Even so, the French Ministry of Education remains cavalier. It refuses to lower its standards. There is no need to do so. French academic morale remains vigorous; Forestier's students regard him with a mixture of politeness, distance, respect, and admiration. Each year the ministry has more teaching applicants than it can consider. It solves the problem with frugal Gallic reasoning. It simply chooses the best.[9]

SUPPORTING A THESIS

4.9 Exploring Methods for Supporting a Thesis—Types of Evidence (*BHW* 4f–j)

In the following passages, writers use various types of evidence to support assertions. In the space after each passage, briefly summarize the writer's point. Then indicate the type(s) of evidence used to support that point: examples (4f), facts and figures (4g), quotation (4h), citation of authority (4i), reasoning (4j). Be prepared to discuss your findings in class.

Example: But even as the importance of college education increases, American families are finding it harder to foot the bill. Tuition at public and private colleges rose during the 1980s by an average of 26 percent, adjusted for inflation. During the same interval, a majority of American families watched their incomes decline. [10]

Main point *American families are finding it difficult to pay college costs.*

Type(s) of evidence *Facts and figures*

1. A number of colleges and universities emphasize the importance of teaching by bringing faculty members together to talk about their courses. Those faculty teaching in the Contemporary Civilization sequence at Columbia University meet weekly to discuss course readings, examinations, paper topics, and strategies for teaching. Faculty members implementing the new humanities program at the University of Denver have been meeting regularly for the last three years to discuss texts, syllabi, and teaching methods. At Brooklyn College of the City University of New York, faculty members come together in summer seminars not only to discuss the college's curriculum, but also to practice teaching parts of it—in front of colleagues. [11]

Main point _____

_____

_____

Type(s) of evidence _____

_____

_____

_____

2. The hunter-gatherer tribes that today live like our prehistoric human ancestors consume primarily a vegetable diet supplemented with animal foods. An analysis of 58 societies of modern hunter-gatherers, including the !Kung of southern Africa, revealed that one-half emphasize gathering plant foods, one-third concentrate on fishing, and only one-sixth are primarily hunters. Overall, two-thirds or more of the hunter-gatherer's calories come from plants. Detailed studies of the !Kung by A. S. Truswell, food scientist at the University of London,

showed that gathering is a more productive source of food than is hunting. An hour of hunting yields on average about 100 edible calories, whereas an hour of gathering produces 240. Plant foods provide 60 percent to 80 percent of the !Kung diet, and no one goes hungry when the hunt fails. Interestingly, if they escape fatal infections or accidents, these contemporary aborigines live to old ages despite the absence of medical care. They experience no obesity, no middle-aged spread, little dental decay, no high blood pressure, no coronary heart disease, and their blood cholesterol levels are very low (about half that of the average American adult). While no one is suggesting that we return to an aboriginal life style, we certainly could use their eating habits as a model for a healthier diet. [12]

Main point _____

_____

_____

Type(s) of evidence _____

_____

_____

3. The assigning of traditional grades (*A* through *F*) in a freshman writing course often works against the purpose of the course—to help students learn to write better. One problem with such grades is that they discourage rather than encourage progress and improvement.

At the beginning of a writing course, many students earn low grades because they are inexperienced writers. They simply don't know how to write an effective essay, and in the process of learning to do so, they make mistakes—and low grades. Such grades affect the students' confidence and morale, making writing an unpleasant task associated with anxiety and failure. As a result, students are discouraged; instead of working seriously on their writing, they spend time worrying about the easiest way to earn a better grade on the next paper—usually by writing "safe" papers that are simple and correct but lacking in thought.*

Main point _____

_____

_____

Type(s) of evidence _____

_____

_____

_____

4. [In this passage, civil rights leader Martin Luther King, Jr., responds to seven clergymen who criticized his use of civil disobedience.]

You express a great deal of anxiety over our willingness to break laws. This is certainly a legitimate concern. Since we so diligently urge people to obey the Supreme Court's decision of 1954 outlawing segregation in the public schools, at first glance it may seem rather paradoxical for us consciously to break laws. One may well ask: "How can you advocate breaking some laws and obeying others?" The answer lies in the fact that there are two types of laws: just and unjust. I would be the first to advocate obeying just laws. Conversely, one has a moral responsibility to disobey unjust laws. I would agree with St. Augustine that "An unjust law is no law at all."

Now, what is the difference between the two? How does one determine whether a law is just or unjust? A just law is a manmade code that squares with the moral law or the law of God. An unjust law is a code that is out of harmony with the moral law. To put it in the terms of St. Thomas Aquinas: An unjust law is a human law that is not rooted in eternal law and natural law. Any law that uplifts human personality is just. Any law that degrades human personality is unjust. All segregation statutes are unjust because segregation distorts the soul and damages the personality. It gives the segregator a false sense of superiority and the segregated a false sense of inferiority. Segregation, to use the terminology of the Jewish philosopher Martin Buber, substitutes an "I-it" relationship for an "I-thou" relationship and ends up relegating persons to the status of things. Hence, segregation is not only politically, economically, and sociologically unsound, it is morally wrong and sinful. Paul Tillich has said that sin is separation. Is not segregation an existential expression of man's tragic separation, his awful estrangement, his terrible sinfulness? Thus it is that I can urge men to obey the 1954 decision of the Supreme Court, for it is morally right; and I can urge them to disobey segregation ordinances, for they are morally wrong.[13]

Main point _____

Type(s) of evidence _____

5. Eating disorders stem partly from society's image of ideal feminine
   beauty. Models gracing the cover of *Vogue,* stars in the latest movies,
   mannequins lining store windows—even Barbie dolls—send the message that thin is in. Struggling to match such images, anorectics and
   bulimics develop an obsession with thinness, adopting unrealistic and
   unhealthful eating habits that lead to serious psychological and physiological problems. Susie Orbach, an expert on eating disorders, argues
   that society encourages women "to see their bodies from the outside,
   as if they were commodities." Having already devalued their bodies
   to mere objects, women manipulate these "objects" into a desirable
   form to appear feminine and sexually attractive.*

Main point _____

Type(s) of evidence _____

4.10 Analyzing an Essay—Types of Evidence (*BHW* 4f–j)

In the essay "Death from the Sky," which follows, Sam Iker uses various
types of evidence to support his claim that a nuclear war would have
disastrous environmental consequences. Study the essay and be prepared
to discuss Iker's use of evidence.

Death from the Sky
Sam Iker

The ultimate environmental calamity which might result from nuclear war would be the destruction of the fragile stratospheric layer of ozone which shields the planet from the deadly effects of ultraviolet radiation.

A nuclear detonation of sufficient size (more than one megaton) can inject large amounts of oxides of nitrogen into the stratosphere. Through a complex set of chemical reactions, this can result in the destruction of ozone. Atmospheric scientists, using the most sophisticated computer models, calculate that a full-scale nuclear exchange would wipe out around 50 percent of the ozone layer. This could double or triple the intensity of the most hazardous portion of the ultraviolet spectrum reaching the Earth. Some analysts believe that the trend toward smaller, more precisely guided weapons lessens this threat. But others feel that the heavier yield warheads remaining in the Soviet arsenal make the danger very real.

If the pessimists are right, the potential impacts would be cataclysmic. Scientists agree that the existence of the ozone layer enabled life to develop on the planet. Without its shielding effect (even for the two or three years it would take for the layer to partially regenerate), most living organisms would be threatened.

Human beings are especially vulnerable. Even at present levels, ultraviolet radiation causes great numbers of cases of skin cancer among those exposed excessively to the sun. If the radiation were increased by 200 or 300 percent, people couldn't remain outdoors for more than a few minutes at a time without risking life-threatening sunburn (unless they were completely protected).

Most animals and birds would be shielded by their feathers or fur. But their eyes would be vulnerable to the intense ultraviolet rays. According to University of Houston professor Donald Pitts, an authority on such effects, the exposures would cause "permanent damage to the cornea." Says Pitts, "Animals such as cattle, sheep, hogs, deer and so on would be rendered blind." Even birds and insects would lose their sight. The ecological implications are staggering.

Aquatic life would be equally vulnerable. Eggs, larvae and juveniles, which generally are found near the water's surface, have no way of detecting intensified ultraviolet rays (nor do they have effective natural defenses). Increased radiation, researchers find, is often lethal to such organisms. Many species of phytoplankton are also killed by powerful ultraviolet light. With mass die-offs of phytoplankton and zooplankton, says NOAA marine biologist David Damkaer, "the food chain is derailed. It's a domino effect."

Some crops are fairly resistant to ultraviolet radiation. But others, such as corn, sugar beets, tomatoes, beans and peas are highly sensitive. The rays affect the DNA of such plants and also retard the photosynthesis process. Most research (which is ongoing) has been done on commercial crops. Scientists still lack a detailed understanding of what the intensified radiation would do to other vegetation.

Even the global climate could be temporarily disrupted by the depletion of the ozone layer. More sunlight would reach the Earth and thus raise world temperatures. At the same time, however, less heat would be radiated back to the Earth by the thinned-out ozone layer. Given the immense complexities involved, the climatic impacts are uncertain. But even relatively minor changes in world weather patterns could disrupt or even devastate global ecosystems. [14]

4.11 Using Examples to Support a Point (*BHW* 4f)

Write a paragraph using examples to support an assertion about the pressures facing college students in the 1990s. Draw your examples from personal experience.

4.12 Using Facts and Figures to Support a Point (*BHW* 4g)

Write a paragraph in which you support an assertion by using selected "facts and figures" from the following list. Possible general topics: Cleveland as a place to locate a new business, Cleveland as a place to shop or live.

FACTS ABOUT CLEVELAND, OHIO

- 250,000 people come in and out of downtown Cleveland each workday.
- 150,000 people work in downtown Cleveland.
- Downtown Cleveland is headquarters for eleven of *Fortune* magazine's top 500 industrial corporations.
- Downtown Cleveland office workers occupy 15 million square feet of space.
- Downtown Cleveland has over 400 retail outlets, including two full-service department stores.
- Cleveland's Regional Transit System converges downtown and connects to local and suburban buses.

- Cleveland Hopkins International Airport is twenty minutes from downtown by rapid transit.
- Eleven airlines serve the city.
- Greyhound and Continental Trailways bus terminals are located downtown.
- More than ten colleges and universities are located in Cleveland and nearby suburbs.
- Three major highways (I-90, I-71, I-77) and three railroads serve downtown Cleveland.
- Over 55 percent of the people in the United States live within a 600-mile radius of Cleveland.
- A 424,000-square-foot convention center is located in a seventeen-acre mall in downtown Cleveland.
- The Cleveland area has a 17,000-acre metropolitan park system.
- Cleveland has a symphony orchestra and an art museum.
- Cleveland has professional baseball, basketball, and football teams. [15]

4.13 Using Authority and Quotation to Support a Point (*BHW* 4h–i)

Expand the paragraph you wrote for Exercise 4.11 (or write a new one) by citing and quoting at least one authority. You may quote from a printed source (check your campus newspaper or do some reading in the library). Or quote a student or an instructor who can speak with the "authority" of firsthand experience.

4.14 Using Reasoning to Support a Point (*BHW* 4j)

Write a paragraph based on the two premises given below. The paragraph should develop each premise and then end with a logical conclusion. After trying your hand with the sample premises, state two of your own and use them as the basis for another paragraph.

Premise: Foods heavy in fat, salt, and sugar are unhealthy.
Premise: A particular restaurant or cafeteria serves such food.
Conclusion: ?

4.15   Identifying Logical Fallacies (*BHW* 4k)

Each of the following passages illustrates a logical fallacy discussed in *The Borzoi Handbook for Writers*. Identify each fallacy by name, and be prepared to explain why the reasoning is faulty.

1. My aunt's secret recipe of molasses and herbs is a wonderful cure for a chest cold. My cold ended two days after I started taking the mixture.
2. Math teachers are poorly organized. The three I've had at this university knew their subject well but taught in a very disorganized manner.
3. This state must either reintroduce the use of capital punishment or face a massive increase in the number of murders each year.
4. Since Mayor Colson is from a wealthy family, we cannot trust him to represent the interests of ordinary citizens.
5. We should support Sarah Cohen's campaign for the Student Senate. After all, she has the backing of nearly everyone on campus.
6. Many students don't get enough exercise; therefore, the university should build a new recreational sports complex.
7. We could solve this country's economic problems if we simply balanced the federal budget.
8. We must either impose a heavy tax on all imported cars or witness the collapse of our nation's automotive industry.
9. Since marijuana is totally harmless, its use should be legalized.
10. The Edwards Aquifer supplies water for over one million people; therefore, we should limit its use as a source of irrigation water.

4.16   Analyzing Faulty Reasoning
(*BHW* 4e, 4k)

The following excerpts, many from published sources, contain examples of faulty reasoning. In some cases, the writer commits a specific logical fallacy; in others, the problem is inflammatory language or an exaggerated appeal to the reader's emotions. Study the passages, and be prepared to discuss their logical shortcomings.

1. [A letter arguing that liberal college professors stifle campus debate while promoting their own political views]

   Liberals lay many snares for those in search of the true path, and one has to be ever on guard! [16]

2. [A paper arguing in favor of phasing out the Social Security system]

Social Security does great harm to the economy. American productivity has been declining, and the economy is experiencing much slower growth than it did in the past. Who knows how much higher our standard of living would be today if American workers were allowed to keep the money they are forced to pour into the system.

3. [A paper arguing in favor of national health insurance]

If insurance costs continue to rise, employers will have to drop all group health insurance. This will leave most working people without health care. Either the government must insure all citizens or we will very quickly live in a country where only the rich can afford to be sick.

4. [A newspaper piece about the efforts to raise the drinking age to twenty-one]

The proposals for increasing the legal drinking age have been brought about due to the increase in [traffic] fatalities in the last decade. Over 250,000 people have died in alcohol-related crashes since the drinking age was lowered. [17]

5. [A letter to an editor]

Militant feminism is destroying America as the scourge of decency and civility. We have seen an explosion of broken homes, abused children and pornography in the last two decades. Any women who wear pants show their support for our spiritual demise. [18]

6. [An argument against using tobacco addressed to young men; published in 1875]

There is, probably, no tobacco-chewer in the world who would advise a young man to commence this habit. I have never seen a slave of tobacco who did not regret his bondage; yet, against all advice, against nausea and disgust, health and comfort, thousands every year bow the neck to this drug, and consent to wear its repulsive yoke. [19]

7. [An argument against smoking addressed to young women; published in 1898]

Girls sometimes have the idea that a little wildness in a young man is rather to be admired. On one occasion a young woman left a church where she had heard a lecture on the evils of using tobacco, saying, as she went out, "I would not marry a young man if he did not smoke. I think it looks manly, and I don't want a husband who is not a man among men."

Years later, when her three babies died, one after the other, with infantile paralysis, because their father was an inveterate smoker, the habit did not seem to her altogether so admirable.[20]

8. [A letter to an editor]

How long are we going to tolerate the bunch of flimflam artists who hide in their ivory towers in city hall?[21]

9. [A paper arguing in favor of changing first-year English to a pass/fail course]

If the pressure to earn high grades were removed, students would concentrate more on improving their writing skills.

10. [An argument claiming that popular music is subversive]

In a leading national sex-crazed magazine [*Playboy*], the Beatles, in an exclusive interview, volunteered additional information about their religious convictions, or better, their agnostic-atheistic convictions.[22]

4.17 Analyzing an Unreasonable Argument (*BHW* 4e, 4k)

The following paragraphs deliberately illustrate a host of unfair, unreasonable, and ill-conceived techniques for supporting a thesis. Study the passage, and be prepared to point out as many fallacies as you can. You might want to try your hand at writing a similar masterpiece of illogic.

Inspired by the rabid environmentalists and liberal news media, a few vocal people in the state are agitating against the construction of a nuclear reactor at Larkin's Point. This small contingent of

bleeding hearts has swallowed the muddle-headed notion that
5   nuclear reactors are unsafe. Nothing could be further from the
truth! There has never been a significant nuclear accident in this
country, and federal regulations guarantee that there never will be.
Our government isn't about to let anyone construct an unsafe
reactor. Those who think otherwise are playing into the hands of
10   soft-headed, left-leaning types who fear progress and mistrust our
elected leaders.
As I see it, there is no alternative to the new reactor. If it isn't
built, economic disaster will surely follow. Unless we can guarantee an adequate supply of electricity for industries in the area, the
15   economy will collapse and countless jobs will be lost to other,
more progressive parts of the country. Furthermore, the construction of the reactor will ensure lower electric rates in the future.
Those who foresee an increase in rates are ignoring the facts. Sure,
there might be a short-term increase to help pay for construction,
20   but think of the long-term savings once we are all enjoying that
clean, safe, inexpensive electricity generated by the new reactor!
On the other hand, if we continue to rely on existing sources of
electricity, the cost of coal and other fuels will soon make it
impossible for us to light our homes and operate our industries!
25   So, the choice is yours: a bright, prosperous future with ample
energy and a booming economy or a dismal future without
growth, sweetness, or light. Think about it!

4.18   Identifying Points for Concession
and Refutation (*BHW* 4l)

Reprinted below is a portion of an article from *The Chronicle of Higher
Education,* a publication read mainly by college professors and administra-
tors. The author, an English professor, argues in favor of required class
attendance. Read the passage carefully. Then, working alone or with a
group of classmates, make a list of Brown's main points in favor of
required attendance. If you were asked to write an essay arguing against
such a policy, which of the points on the list would you handle by concession and which by refutation? Make notes to indicate the arguments you
might develop in refuting Brown's main points. Be prepared to discuss
your ideas in class.

Why I Don't Let Students Cut My Classes
William R. Brown

Last year I announced to my classes my new policy on absences: None would be allowed, except for illness or personal emergency. Even though this violated the statement on cuts in the student handbook, which allows freshmen cuts each term up to twice the number of class meetings per week and imposes no limit for upperclassmen, my students didn't fuss. They didn't fuss even after they discovered, when I telephoned or sent warning notices through the mail to students who had missed classes, that I mean business.

Part of their acceptance of the policy may have resulted from the career orientation of our college, but I don't think that was the main reason. After I explained the policy, most seemed to recognize that it promoted their own academic interests. It was also a requirement that virtually all of them would be obliged to observe—and would expect others to observe—throughout their working lives. It had to be Woody Allen who said that a major part of making it in life is simply showing up.

I told my classes about recent research, by Howard Schuman and others, indicating that academic success is more closely tied to class attendance than to the amount of time spent studying. I shared my sense of disappointment and personal affront when I carefully prepare for a class and a substantial number of students do not attend. I think they got the message that the policy is not arbitrary—that I care about their learning and expect them to care about my professional effort.

I don't claim to have controlled all the variables, but after I instituted the no-cut rule, student performance in my classes improved markedly, not so much in the top rank as at the bottom. In fact, the bottom rank almost disappeared, moving up and swelling the middle range to such an extent that I have reassessed my evaluation methods to differentiate among levels of performance in that range. The implications of so dramatic an improvement are surely worth pondering.

Additional benefits of the policy have been those one would expect to result from a full classroom. Student morale is noticeably higher, as is mine. Discussions are livelier, assignments are generally turned in on time, and very few students miss quizzes.

The mechanics of maintaining the policy kept me a little busier than usual, especially at first, but the results would have justified a lot more effort. I called or mailed notes to several students about their cuts, some more than once. I eventually advised a few with invincibly poor attendance to drop my course, when it seemed that an unhappy outcome was likely. They did.

No doubt this kind of shepherding is easier in a small college. But it can work almost anyplace where a teacher cares enough about the educational stakes to make it work. The crucial element is caring. . . .

Why do students cut so frequently? I can cite the immediate causes, but I first want to note the enabling circumstance: They cut because they are allowed to. They cut because of the climate of acceptance that comes from our belief that responsibility can be developed only when one is free, free even to act against personal best interests. That that is a misapplied belief in this case can be easily demonstrated. When substantial numbers of students do not attend, classroom learning is depreciated, student and teacher morale suffer, and academic standards are compromised. Students who miss classes unnecessarily are hurting more than themselves. With our complicity, they are undermining what colleges and universities are all about.

Students cut for two general reasons. They have things to do that appear more important than the class, or they wish to avoid what they fear will be painful consequences if they attend. In regard to the first, nursing an illness or attending family weddings or funerals are good excuses for missing a class. But other excuses—the demands of outside jobs, social engagements (including recovering from the night before), completing assignments for other courses—are, at best, questionable.

The other general reason is more disturbing and perhaps less well recognized. A few years ago, I asked several classes what they most disliked about the way courses were taught, and the answer was plain—anything that produced sustained tension or anxiety. I believe cutting is often a result of that aversion. The response of students to feelings of personal inadequacy, fear of humiliation, or a threatening professorial personality or teaching style is often simply to avoid class. This response feeds on itself, as frequent absences make attending even more threatening.

But what accounts for frequent cutting where the teacher tries to make the material interesting, knows the students by name, and approaches them with respect, help, and affability? I accept that question as unanswerable. I simply tell my students: Attend my class regularly or drop the course. That's the rule. [23]

4.19 Using Refutation in an Argument (*BHW* 4l)

A. Write a paragraph or two refuting one of the points you identified in the preceding exercise (4.18). First give a fair and objective statement of the point. Then write a reasonable refutation using the notes you developed.

B. Write an essay supporting or opposing required class attendance on your campus. The author of the article printed in Exercise 4.18 writes as a college professor addressing his colleagues. In your essay, write as a student addressing your classmates. You may wish to concede minor points that count against your argument, but you should meet head-on the strongest objections to your case, handling them through refutation. Take care to state objections fairly before you refute them.

5

Collaborating and Revising

5.1 Using a Peer Editing Worksheet (*BHW* 5a–c)

Read the following draft, which Mark Hemingson wrote in his first-semester composition class. Hemingson and his classmates were asked to write a 500-word essay discussing the way in which some recent invention or technological innovation has affected the way people live (for good or ill). Assuming that you are Hemingson's classmate, complete the peer editing sheet that follows his draft.

```
Mark Hemingson

English 111

FIRST DRAFT

          The Pager: A Modern Convenience

     As the elevator doors close, an alarming

''beep-beep-beep'' sound is heard. All five people

in the elevator reach for their pockets. A man in
```

the back calls out ''It's mine.'' This common sound and sight result from the electronic pager. This is one of the most popular forms of communication technology used today. The pager has brought inexpensive, instant communication to many people.

Doctors and business people often carry pagers. These electronic devices help them stay in contact with their offices. Pagers are small boxes. The user can easily clip them onto a belt. They can also be kept in a purse. Most people who have pagers rent them. The fees range from three to thirty dollars per month. This is a small price for doctors and business people to pay for instant communication with their offices.

There are three types of pagers. The beeping pager only emits a beeping noise when you call it. The digital pager displays the phone number that a caller enters from a touch tone phone. The voice pager that receives a voice message from the person who is calling. Each pager is designed for a different need.

The beeping pager is preferable for someone who wants to stay in touch with only a select caller. This type is often called the ''baby beeper.'' Many fathers-to-be, like myself, have used this type of pager. I wore this type of pager when my wife and I were expecting a baby. She was able to contact me when she went into labor. I worked on construction at the time and could not be near a phone. The pager allowed me to work without the worry of missing the birth of my daughter.

I also used a digital pager the night my daughter was born. Digital pagers are important to people who do not stay by a telephone during the day (such as my supervisor at work). His digital pager enables people to stay in contact with him while he is on the road away from a phone. These pagers can store up to six telephone numbers. Which helps when a person cannot get to the phone right away. They can also be left on at night while a person is sleeping. This is how I used the digital pager when my daughter was born. I had agreed to let my supervisor at work know of the birth and notify him that I would not be at work the next day. When I got home from the hospital after the delivery, I called my supervisor's digital pager and spelled out B-A-B-Y by using the numbers on the telephone. The next morning when he checked his pager for messages, the numbers 2-2-2-9 displayed on his pager told him that I would not be at work that day.

The voice pager works like a digital pager. Except that the person calling can leave a voice

message instead of leaving only a number. Large
companies use voice pagers to keep in constant
communication with employees.

Pagers help keep people in contact with family,
friends, and co-workers.

Peer Editing Worksheet

Writer _____

Title of Paper _____

Peer Editor _____

1. After an initial reading, what is your main impression of the draft?
    What strikes you as its strongest and weakest features?

2. Is the thesis (a) clearly and prominently stated, (b) adequately lim-
    ited, and (c) interesting enough to merit development? Suggest im-
    provements.

3. Is the essay well organized? What could the writer do to improve the arrangement of ideas and examples?

4. Are the writer's points adequately developed? Where would you like to see more evidence or explanation?

5. Is the tone consistently appropriate to the writer's purpose? If not, explain.

6. Does the essay begin effectively by engaging your interest and setting a clear direction for the paper? Is the title appropriate? Suggest improvements.

7. Is each paragraph in the body of the essay well organized, unified, and coherent? Suggest improvements.

8. Does the essay end effectively by giving an appropriate sense of completion? Suggest improvements.

9. Check the style of the writing. Are the sentences clear and varied? Are there adequate transitions within and between paragraphs? Are words chosen effectively? Mark suggested improvements on the draft.

10. Do you notice errors in usage, punctuation, mechanics, or spelling? Mark examples on the draft.

5.2 Peer Editing: Developing a Plan for Revision (*BHW* 5a–f)

Working alone or with a group of classmates, develop a plan for revising the following student draft. For the first four items, summarize your advice on a sheet of paper.

1. What are the strengths of the essay? Be specific.
2. Is the writer's main idea clear and adequately developed? What improvements could he make?

3. Is the essay organized effectively? How could the organization be improved?
4. Has the writer considered the audience for which the paper was written (his instructor and his classmates)? Should he clarify or delete any material in order to meet their expectations?
5. In the margins of the draft, note problems with paragraph unity, continuity, and development.
6. In the margins of the draft, note any editorial revisions that would improve the paper. Consider the following:

   - Sentence structure
   - Word choice
   - Errors in usage
   - Errors in punctuation
   - Errors in spelling

I have always thought that organized sports bring out the best in a person. Sports demand a great deal of determination, which strengthens ones character and

5   developes a high standard of moral and social deportment. I learned a lot about this during my years as a competitive bicycle motocross racer. Although I wasn't a poor sportsman in public, but I often

10   revealed to myself signs of being a poor loser. My only real competition at National events was my arch rival Bob Doran. He lived a couple of miles from me, and was the absolute best racer in the thirteen year old

15   expert class in the United States.

He was sponsored by the Raleigh factory

team, and had countless co-sponsorships from other manufacturers. He traveled in a huge van with elaborate custom painting,

20 tauntingly listing his accomplishments on the rear doors. He was a hero to some, but to me he was very lucky.

At this time I was national number 6, had co-sponsorships from a few companies,

25 and traveled in my dads nineteen seventy five chevy suburban with custome rust. I loathed Bob Doran, not as a person or as a racer, but because of the way he overshadowed me. I had beaten him a few

30 times at local races, but they were of such little consequence, that no one really noticed. Whenever I lost to Bob I would make excuses, saying to myself, ''If I had all the latest state of the art equipment, I

35 would win to.'' I even told some people that he trained in Europe during the off season and that his house is filled with the most sophisticated training equipment from the Germans. But the simple truth is that he had

40 more natural ability than me, he would probably always be upstaging me.

Nevertheless, I began training harder than ever for the world championships which

were three months away. I tried different
45 gearing ratios, and different methods of
gatestarts. I even had my dad videotape a
few of my races, to try and analize my
mistakes; but none of this made me
significantly faster. Bob recognized my
50 extra efforts, he noticed that I was staying
closer to him than ever before. And one
night, while we were both practicing under
the lights at the local supercross, Bob
offered to help me develope a new technique
55 for speed jumping, which he guaranteed would
take three seconds off my sprint time. At
first I was hesitant, because this guy was
my rival and I couldn't believe that he
would help me, and possibly put himself in
60 jeopardy. But after working with Bob for
about an hour I realized that he actually
was trying to help, and it really did take
three seconds off my time. I then realized
that I had terribly misjudged Bob. When I
65 asked him why he had helped me, he replied,
''I need some competition and your the only
one who is fast enough.'' This proved to me
that winning isn't everything. Bob and I
became the best of friends and remained
70 competitive, and although he still won the

majority of our races, I never felt bad
after a loss.

5.3 Peer Editing: Seeking Advice about Your Draft (*BHW* 5a–f)

Exchange drafts with a classmate, and use one of the following as a guide for peer editing:

1. The peer editing worksheet on page 58, Exercise 5.1
2. The revision guide on page 61, Exercise 5.2
3. The Checklist for Revision on the inside front cover of *The Borzoi Handbook for Writers*

5.4 Analyzing a Student's Revisions (*BHW* 5a–f)

Working alone or with a group of classmates, study the following drafts, written by Keith Lincoln in his first-year composition class. The one on the left is Lincoln's first draft; the one on the right is his revision. Compare the two versions section by section, making notes at the bottom of each page. Be prepared to discuss your findings in class.

1. List any conceptual and organizational revisions made by Lincoln, paying close attention to the thesis, the organization, and the development of ideas.
2. List changes in the way Lincoln begins and ends the essay.
3. List any changes that alter the tone of the essay.
4. List key editorial revisions made by Lincoln: changes in paragraph development; in sentence structure; in word choice; and in grammar, usage, punctuation, and other conventions.
5. List the major strengths of the revised version of the essay.
6. List any remaining flaws in the revised version of the essay, paying attention to minor details that might be changed in order to make the essay more effective.

DRAFT	REVISION
Public schools should be the target of some hard core criticism. After going to public schools for 12 yrs., and entering college, my confidence was blown after discovering that my knowledge of math and English was weak. High school fails in its purpose of preparing a student for college. Students are not prepared for college because they are too busy learning how to do important things. Rather than taking classes such as trigonometry and writing, students are learning how to run option plays, play the tuba, and fix dents in their car. Emphasis on the football team, band, and vocational programs illustrate how high schools' priorities are all wrong. Most of my high school's attention was focused on football uniforms, a new band hall, and an elaborate vocational program.	High schools often fail in their purpose of preparing students for college because students are too busy learning how to do more important things. In many high schools, the emphasis has shifted from teaching math, English, and the sciences to a much more valuable set of skills. The new breed of high school student is learning to catch a football, play the tuba, or fix a dent in his car. This effort to change the high school curriculum is clearly illustrated at my alma mater, Garfield High School.

NOTES

DRAFT	REVISION
This was a wise investment, considering that all the football players learned how to run, throw, and catch, but didn't know what a book looked like. My sophomore geometry class, which contained the quarterback, offensive line, and a few students was taught by coach Ed Alexander. The Football players learned how to loaf in the halls, flirt with the cheerleaders, and ask the coach who he thought was "gonna win the superbowl." Coach never complained if they brought him doughnuts instead of their homework. However, he did buckle down during tests and forced the players to wait until they finished their tests, before they could go to Dunkin' Donut. His peers praised him for how well the players were doing in his class. Students tried to do their work with the help of other students. They were motivated with a 20 point curve. Coaches knowledge of Geometry was limited, so was ours after the year. Coaches class was crowded, so he never really minded if the players left.	During my sophomore year at Garfield I quickly learned that the school's priorities rested on its football team, not on academics. It seems that the faculty and administration were too righteous to allow football players to slack off academically, so they simply made some classes easier for everyone. My geometry class, taught by Coach Ed Alexander and stocked with the quarterback and the offensive line, was one of those classes. If a student didn't have his homework ready for class, he could simply stop by the nearby Dunkin' Donut and pick up a jelly roll to turn in instead. Coach never complained because the process worked smoothly; other teachers praised him for his students' high grades. Coach was a great guy, but his knowledge of geometry was limited, and so was ours at the end of the year.

NOTES

DRAFT	REVISION
Classes were crowded because money allotted for expansion was used to build a new band hall. The building was a giant, 3 story modern building which made the rest of the campus look like the projects. The rooms needed paint and new desks. Lockers were broken and inoperable, students had to keep their books in their cars to prevent them from being stolen. The cafeteria's long lines and tastey cuisine forced students with enough money and a car to resort to eating out. The parking lots were too small and not paved. Everytime it rained cars would be stuck (or I would have to park 3 blocks away and run to class.) High school doesn't have to be a vacation paradise, but it shouldn't be unbearable.	During my junior year, classes were not only easy, but also crowded because the money originally allotted for more classrooms was mysteriously spent on a new band hall. The school brought in second-hand portable buildings from the nearby Marine Military Academy to accommodate the increased number of students. Air conditioners broke down every two weeks, and left students to bake in the South Texas heat. I never felt bad as long as I knew our band was practicing in a cool, comfortable climate. With all the school's money being spent on the band hall, the rest of the campus became a pitiful sight. The rooms needed paint, trees needed trimming, and the potholes in the parking lot swallowed cars. The penetrating aroma of the school cafeteria was an unpleasant reminder of what laid in store for those brave enough to enter its forbidden doors. The school's environment, overall, was not conducive to education.

NOTES

DRAFT	REVISION
My senior year I found myself needing only two classes: English & Economics, and was hoping to get into a vocational program which would allow me to get an afternoon job. I assumed that the school would reward me for those hard years of work and let me get out of their way. But, it seems my grades had been too high, and I was not allowed to indulge. I would have been rewarded if I would have flunked out and couldn't read or write. So my senior year was spent productively; I took the two required classes and four useless electives, which made for a thrilling day.	In my senior year, after becoming accustomed to the classes and campus at Garfield High, I was once again dazed by the school's bureaucracy. During registration I discovered that I needed only two classes to graduate. With this in mind, I decided to sign up for the school's highly respected vocational program. Doing so would have allowed me to hold an afternoon job to earn money for the coming year's college expenses. But, upon inspection of my grades, the director of the vocational department refused to admit me: my grades were too high. The school's policy stipulated that only students with a C average or lower could be admitted to the program, since they needed to learn job skills. The policy was meant to help failing students find jobs after they finished high school but it backfired and instead motivated students to do poorly in their classes so that they could enroll in the vocational program.

NOTES

DRAFT	REVISION
Although these problems were very obvious at GHH, they are shared by other schools. There is no one to blame but the ignorant district taxpayer who allows his money to be spent on a school without any emphasis on education. Because I had lived elsewhere, I knew what a school was supposed to be like. Where would taxpayers hear any complaints? Certainly not from the Football players or the faculty members who valued their jobs. If high schools shifted their priorities to academics, a good education isn't going to hurt any one. Maybe some day students will be prepared for college and not feel bad if they are not on the football team or in the band. Who knows? They might even be able to get into a vocational program.	The problems at Garfield High were obvious, and they are evident to varying degrees at many other high schools. In Garfield's case, the problems are partly the fault of poorly informed and uninterested taxpayers who have allowed their money to be spent on a school that places little emphasis on academic education. Because classes were easy and students were passing, few people complained. Of course, football players and band members were happy; they were getting a big share of the money. Because I was a transfer student from Richland, Texas, and had attended a different type of school, I knew that there was something wrong at Garfield. If high schools would concentrate more on academics and use football, band, and vocational classes as rewards for good grades, maybe more students would leave high school ready for college, not for a job at McDonald's.

NOTES

5.5 Selecting a Title (*BHW* 5f)

Here are five possible titles for the essay given in Exercise 5.4. Which do you think is the most effective? Justify your choice in the space provided.

1. Why High Schools Are a Failure
2. The Crisis in Our Nation's Schools
3. The New, Improved High School
4. Garfield High
5. Preparing for College: Football or Academics

Your choice _____

_____

_____

5.6 Writing a Title (*BHW* 5f)

Reread the draft about motocross racing in Exercise 5.2. Suggest two possible titles for the essay, and be prepared to justify your choices.

5.7 Proofreading (*BHW* 5h)

Sharpen your proofreading skills by locating the minor errors in the following passage, the types of errors that often go undetected in final drafts: misspellings, missing letters, apostrophe errors, typographical errors, and punctuation errors. Make the necessary changes in the space above the lines, and circle any punctuation that is not needed. The first paragraph is done for you as an example.

                                   en
     Michael is a twenty-four-year-old'

student, majoring in petroleum engineering.

This spring he will complete the
     ir
requirements for his master's degree. He is

71

5   an attractive and articulate man who speaks
    with assur*a*nce about his chosen prof*s*ession.

    Before he began to think of himself as
    a engineer, Michael had imagine himself as a
    teacher of the handicaped. While in junier
10 high school, he became freinds, with a boy
    who had cerebral palsy. Although the boy was
    Michaels age, mentally and physicaly he was
    far behind. Moved by the boys handicap,
    Micheal develop an interest in helping those
15 with mental and physical disorders. He was
    sure that apecial education, was the ideal
    carere for him.

    But in high school he found new friends
    and beacme involved in atheletics and the
20 Natonal Honor Society. Gradualy he began to
    turn away from special education, and move
    toward enginering as a career choice. His
    friends could not beleive that, he actually
    want to teach ''retards.'' They informed him
25 that jobs like that were for woman. His
    teacher's encouraged him to seek a more
    ''challenging'' proffesion. They said that
    with his intellectaul ability, he could
    study medicine or science. His parent were
30 proud of his williness to help mentaly
    retarded people, but they were also

''practical.'' They wanted him to chose a proffesion that could offer financial securety.

35　　　Michael is an example of societys steriotyping of mens occupational roles. At this piont, he is well established in his field and has given up hope of becomeing a teacher of the menally retarded. Yet he

40　　still often wonders if he made the write chioce. And he may continue to wonder for a long time.*

6

Observing the Writing Process

6.1 Studying an Essay in Progress
(*BHW* Chapter 6)

For an essay you plan to write in the near future, save all your notes and drafts—everything from preliminary jottings to the final typed copy. (If you use a word processor, save enough printed text to show the essay in several stages of development.) After reviewing your notes and drafts, outline the steps you followed to produce the essay. The following questions may help guide your analysis.

1. How did you arrive at a topic? What procedures did you use to narrow the subject?
2. How did you develop ideas? Did you take notes? Freewrite? Brainstorm?
3. How and when did you formulate a thesis? Before you began to write a draft? After you had drafted several pages?
4. What use did you make of outlining? In drafting the essay, did you follow a detailed outline? Or was the outline merely a general guide?

5. How did you go about revising the essay? Did you write a complete first draft before revising? Or did you revise as you wrote the draft?
6. What sort of conceptual and organizational revisions did you make? When did you make them?
7. What sort of editorial revisions did you make? When did you make them?
8. Did you make last-minute changes as you prepared the final copy? If so, what were they?

6.2 Studying Methods of Composing (*BHW* Chapter 6)

Talk with two or three people about the methods they use in writing for school or work. Begin with your classmates, but also consider interviewing one of your instructors or a person who works in the field you plan to enter after graduation. The following questions may be useful. Be prepared to discuss your findings in class.

1. What type of writing does the person do? How much writing?
2. What relative importance does the person give to (a) formulating a topic and conceiving a main idea, (b) planning and outlining, (c) drafting, and (d) revising?
3. Which parts of the writing process are least difficult for the person? Which are most difficult?
4. If the person uses a word processor, how does it affect the way he or she writes?

6.3 Studying a Descriptive Essay

Read the student essay printed below, and be prepared to answer the questions that follow it.

Wanda L. Pritekel

English 1310

Ms. Pohl

Death of a Canyon

I first visited Big Thompson Canyon in 1969.
Five other twelve-year-olds and I were on our way to
a summer camp tucked into the woods just outside
Estes Park, Colorado. My fellow campers were better
traveled than I and had made this trip many times
with their families or on previous church camp
pilgrimages. Although I was a native Coloradan, I
had not seen much of my home state. I had been
raised on the table-flat farm land of northeastern
Colorado, and to me, the mountainous areas of the
state were only jagged purple cut-outs against the
sky.

While my friends occupied themselves with talk
of boys and rock groups, I found myself surrounded
by a world I had visited only through television and
movies. To my right, rising like massive tombstones,
were the sixty-foot granite walls of the canyon. On
my left was the Big Thompson River. Unlike the
churning, bubbling Arkansas River, which ran through
southern Colorado, this river was a placid
meandering strip of water that splashed noiselessly

over the small flat rocks that lay in its bed. The
granite walls and gently drifting stream mesmerized
me, and I found that the twenty-mile trip through
the abyss of the Big Thompson passed too quickly. I
was already looking forward to the trip home so that
I could take in more of the canyon.

During my weeks at camp, I talked of little
else but the beauty of the canyon; to my dismay,
most of my fellow campers saw the narrow pass as
nothing but a means to an end. For most travelers,
the Big Thompson Canyon Road was a way to get to
Estes Park, a tourist town nestled in a green velvet
valley at the threshold of the Rocky Mountain
National Park. For others it was a route to the park
itself or a means of getting to the aptly named
Grand Lake. While these sites all had charm, I found
them less appealing than the twenty-mile stretch of
two-lane highway snaking through the canyon itself.

Years later, after I was old enough to drive, I
contrived to take several excursions through the
canyon each year. With each new season, the face of
the canyon changed. Summer found Big Thompson full
of campers, their tents sprouting like miniature
mountain peaks on every available piece of flat
ground. Fly fishermen, cocooned in hip boots, waded
in the well-stocked river. Fall brought the changing

of the aspen, and as the sun hung suspended in the crisp, cloudless sky, brightly colored leaves ignited the canyon in flames of crimson, coral, and canary. Winter drained the color from the canyon, locked the river under sheaths of ice, and dusted the canyon walls with snow. Finally, in spring, my favorite season in the Big Thompson, wild flowers speckled the woods and filled the wrinkles in the face of the canyon walls. The river bounced and reveled through the canyon, engorged and icy from the melting snow.

When I visited the Big Thompson in May, 1976, I could not have known that in a few weeks, my splendid canyon would be irrevocably changed. On the evening of July 31, 1976, two storm systems veiled the early evening sky above the canyon in inky blackness. Daggers of lightning slashed a hole in the sky, deluging the area just above the canyon with fourteen inches of rain in five hours.

The water that surged through the narrow chasm changed everything in its path. Heavy highway bridges were wrenched from their foundations and tossed downstream. Cars, homes, and campers were strewn like toys down the valley. Large boulders were ripped from the canyon walls and deposited indiscriminately about the canyon floor. And the

fragile human occupants of the Big Thompson--
tourists and residents--were flung about like
discarded rag dolls, some clinging to tree limbs or
scaling the slippery rock walls. Those walls--once
a kaleidoscope of light, color, and shadow--were
now the walls of a watery tomb. No one knows for
sure how many people died in the canyon that night;
the official death toll stands at 134.

The material damage, estimated in the hundreds
of millions of dollars, is repaired now: highways
and bridges have been rebuilt. A few brave canyon
residents have put the pieces of their homes and
lives together. Many people think the canyon is
better now because of the new roads and the concrete
retaining walls that have supposedly made a
recurrence of the 1976 catastrophe impossible.

I've twice returned to the canyon since it was
reopened, and I quickly discovered that it had lost
its allure for me. I found myself searching for the
familiar images I cherished for years. My treasured
river is full of boulders dropped randomly by the
hand of nature, like pebbles in a puddle. I can no
longer hear the breath of the wind in the canyon. I
only hear the specters of the night--the water and
the unanswered cries of the lost.

STUDY QUESTIONS FOR "DEATH OF A CANYON"

1. Pritekel describes Big Thompson Canyon before and after the storm. Does she have a purpose beyond mere description? Does the title signal that purpose?
2. What is Pritekel's attitude toward her subject? How does that attitude change over the course of the essay?
3. Where and how does Pritekel use concrete, specific language to sharpen her descriptions? Cite several examples.
4. Identify the many examples of figurative language used in the essay. Do these enliven the description? Why?
5. Review the various methods for ordering a description. How is this essay organized? How are individual paragraphs organized? Is Pritekel more skillful in beginning the essay or in ending it? Why?
6. After reading this essay, one student wrote, ''Part of the writer 'dies' along with the canyon.'' Do you agree? Explain.

6.4 Studying a Narrative Essay

Read the student essay printed below, and be prepared to answer the questions that follow it.

Susan Butcher

English 3311

Mr. Hennessy

Behind the Scenes

As I read the alarm clock, I think of two things: I'm glad I remembered to wind it last night, and I wish I could get another three hours sleep. But it's already 5:20, so I crawl out of bed and start getting ready to make the move.

My trailer is well organized, so only a few items need to be set down on the floor: the television, a handful of pictures, and the plants. The plants are the most difficult thing to relocate for each move, and I often think of getting rid of them. But they add such a homey touch that I usually only grumble about them at 5:30 in the morning.

The drive today is seventy-five miles, a fairly typical move for the circus. But it will be difficult because the show is moving from Long Island to a small town on the other side of New York City. There was talk of making the move last night to avoid all the traffic, but some of the trucks didn't have working lights and might have been ticketed.

As I climb into my truck with a thermos of coffee, I see that nearly all the other vehicles are already gone; most of the show trucks left thirty minutes ago, their drivers refreshed with a strong cup of coffee and a couple of sweet rolls. Breakfast isn't served until we make it to the next lot, a rather obvious carrot tactic.

As I drive along the highway, I keep an eye out for the small red and white paper arrows that tell me where to turn or where the lot is going to be. The show is very lucky today; usually the highway patrol removes the arrows from the telephone poles or highway markers. We are given route slips to compensate for that eventuality, and today the slip proves very helpful even though most of the arrows are still up. All the traffic makes me nervous, and the exit for the Verranzano Bridge nearly slips by me. It has started to rain.

Finally, the seventy-five miles are behind me and my thermos is empty. I have arrived at the circus lot. The tent is already stretched out, and the elephant has started pulling up the side poles. I drive my truck and trailer into the backyard where the performers are supposed to park. I try to find a fairly level spot for my home on wheels and then make my way over to the cookhouse.

The flag is still up over the tent that covers the tables where breakfast is being served. I wait in line behind several other performers who are trying to stay dry by huddling under the wing of the cook truck. It is under this wing and through the window it protects that I occasionally see a hand passing out a plate of grits, eggs, toast, and bacon. The line moves along rather quickly considering that Doris the cook really does prepare the eggs the way we want them. As I sit alone in the tent eating my breakfast, I review the list of things that need my attention today. One thing about life in a circus, you quickly learn to do two things

at once; wasting time is a major offense. If you are
not doing two things, you are at least thinking
about doing something else.

The rain this morning is going to slow
everything down. I can usually set up my equipment
by ten-thirty. Today I probably won't get up the
tight wire and trapeze until noon.

[Draft paragraph deleted at this point. See Item 5 below.]

After breakfast I go back to my trailer and
start performing some of the rituals of the day.
I put the plants and TV back in place and survey
the trailer to see if there is any damage from
the drive. Fortunately everything has stayed in
place.

Because it is raining, I get out costumes
that won't be ruined by the weather; feathers are
out of the question. It begins to cross my mind
that much of the rest of the world is cozy and
dry on this rainy gray Tuesday. I start thinking
about a house on a foundation instead of a house
on wheels. I think of people working in a dry
safe building instead of working in a leaky
dangerous tent. I think about the security that a
''real'' job provides, and then I remember the
applause. I put on my galoshes and go out to set
up my props.

It takes me about an hour and a half to put my rigging together. The prop boss helps me drive the long iron stakes into the ground. Today the ground is soft and the work is easier; sometimes it feels as if I have to pound the stakes through concrete. Some of the other performers pay the prop hands to put up their rigging, especially on days like today. But my dad always said that one mistake in setting up the equipment could cost me my life, and that isn't something to put in someone else's hands.

As I finish the last of the dirty work I think about the fact that the audience sees me perform for ten minutes on the trapeze and for seven minutes on the tight wire. I wonder if they ever consider all the behind-the-scenes work that goes into that seventeen-minute performance. I realize that they probably don't.

STUDY QUESTIONS FOR "BEHIND THE SCENES"

1. Like most narrative essays, Butcher's is rich in descriptive detail. What does this detail contribute to her essay?
2. Butcher uses present tense. Is the choice a wise one? How would the narrative differ if she had used past tense?
3. How effective is the opening of the essay? What effect does Butcher gain by gradually letting us know what she does for a living rather than revealing the information at the beginning?
4. What unifies the narrative, gives it purpose? Does it have an implied point? Does it create a dominant mood? Explain.

5. In an early draft of the narrative, Butcher included the following paragraph at the point noted in the text:

> I come to the conclusion that I should do laundry, but it has started raining harder, and I realize that I will never be able to get my truck off the lot in all this mud. It always surprises me that the show can still find an empty field for the tent in this part of the country. When we drove in this morning the highway seemed to wind through a continuous stream of concrete buildings, making it difficult to tell one town from the next—a real concrete jungle. And yet the agent found another space for our little mobile village. I will be glad to get back to the part of the country where there are trees and mountains and clear running streams. But money dictates, and the money is here. The rain dripping off the top of the tent onto my head brings me back to reality and I get up and clear my plate.

Was Butcher wise to delete this paragraph in the final version of the essay? What is gained by the deletion? What is lost?

6. Is Butcher's closing paragraph effective? Why, or why not?

6.5 Studying an Analytic Essay

Read the student essay reprinted below, and be prepared to answer the questions that follow it.

Marykay Crouch

English 101

Mr. Wilson

My Parents: Playing in Harmony

They weren't exactly June and Ward Cleaver, and we weren't exactly the Brady Bunch, but my parents didn't have to be television-type parents to have a happy family. They were (and still are) two ordinary people who worked hard to raise four children, two girls and two boys. I think my parents' secret was their harmonious approach to parenting. Although they differed in at least one way, they shared a number of similarities as parents, and those similarities were an important asset for their children.

The main difference between my parents was the way they reacted to problems. Mom was in the trenches daily, and she handled minor skirmishes with the poise of a seasoned veteran. The messy bedrooms and sibling arguments didn't upset her much, but an unexpected ambush did. A poor report card could transform my usually calm, quiet mother into a screaming maniac. Dad, on the other hand, was not as accustomed to the daily chaos four children could create. He tended to overreact to the small problems, while facing the bigger ones calmly. Coming home fifteen minutes after curfew carried a potential one- to two-week grounding if Dad was in a bad mood, but my speeding ticket only warranted a meeting at the kitchen table to discuss the seriousness of my actions and a warning not to let it occur again.

Despite the difference in their initial reactions to misconduct, my parents shared the same basic ideas about discipline. Neither of them believed in physical punishment, so we were not spanked, but they did follow a fairly strict and consistent set of guidelines. We were not especially mischievous kids, but when we did get into trouble, we could almost predict our punishment before it was decided. No television was the usual sentence when we were young. As we grew older, no telephone became the standard, and in a drastic situation, we would have to surrender the keys to the car. Whether one parent or both determined the punishment, the final sentence was about the same. I can't remember my parents disagreeing about discipline.

Another characteristic that my parents shared was their high expectations for their children. Though they didn't spell out what they expected, we knew instinctively what the standards were. I had to do well in school. A's were expected, few B's were tolerated, and C's were forbidden. My parents knew that I was capable of doing well in school, so they demanded it. In other areas they expected me to give my best effort, though they always loved me even if I wasn't the best. I didn't have to become a brain surgeon, but I did have to go to college. I didn't have to win every race, but I did have to go to my swim workout every day with a positive attitude.

While they set high goals, Mom and Dad also gave all the support they could to help us reach those goals. They always encouraged us to take risks, to try something new. Without complaint, they drove carpool after carpool for the four of us. They sat through countless piano recitals, choir concerts, and school programs. They cheered loudly and proudly at hundreds of swim meets and soccer, volleyball, and basketball games. And they always gave words of congratulations or comfort, whichever was needed.

My parents' most fundamental similarity was the values they worked to instill in their children. They encouraged honesty, loyalty, patience, understanding, and forgiveness. And they usually did so by setting an example, not by giving a lecture. They took us to church on Sunday, they made sure we ate dinner as a family, and they treated us in the same way that they expected us to treat other people. I believe that their shared values were the foundation on which my parents' other similarities rested.

My parents will always strike me as distinct personalities, but their styles as parents were almost identical. Their similarity created a vital continuity and stability in our family. Judging them independently is difficult because they so often functioned as a team. They worked in unison, like two notes in a chord; they could be played separately, but together they made a complete

harmony. This harmony was a blessing in a world
where the music is often out of tune.

STUDY QUESTIONS FOR
"MY PARENTS: PLAYING IN HARMONY"

1. Underline Crouch's thesis. Is it adequately focused for a brief essay?
    Is it clear and significant enough to warrant development?
2. Write a scratch outline of the essay. What methods does Crouch use
    to organize her points?
3. What kinds of evidence does Crouch use to support her assertions?
    Does she use evidence effectively?
4. What is the function of Crouch's second paragraph? How is it related
    to what follows?
5. Evaluate Crouch's introduction. Does it engage your interest? How?
6. Crouch's instructor praised her concluding paragraph. What are its
    strengths?

6.6   Studying an Argumentative Essay

Read the student essay printed below, and be prepared to answer the
questions that follow it.

Becky Alexander

English 1A

Mr. Marks

            Turning Citizens into Suckers
      Since our state is among the majority that now
run an official lottery to supplement tax revenue,
your television screen is probably as saturated with
lottery come-ons as it is with ads for toothpaste,

beer, and deodorant. The lottery commercials, you may have noticed, dangle incredibly huge sums before your eyes and leave the impression that the only real fools are the people who won't try their luck at becoming richer than kings. No mention is made of the odds against winning. There is no way to tell that if (by a near miracle) you do choose all the right numbers, about half of your prize will be kept for taxes and that the rest will be doled out over many years, while the state continues to earn interest on the unpaid balance. And the ads never refer to the problem of compulsive gambling--an addiction that ranks just behind substance abuse as a social problem. On the contrary, the state seems determined to *create* a certain number of compulsive gamblers from among its poorest and least educated citizens.

A stranger from a non-lottery state, turning on a motel TV and seeing those upbeat commercials, might wonder at first why the government was allowing them to be shown. Only gradually would it dawn on her that the state itself is ''the house,'' enticing and fleecing its own people. Even then, she might not realize that up to three-fourths of the state's advertising budget is spent on promoting the lottery. Very little is left over, therefore, to warn citizens about the risks of AIDS, drunken driving, smoking, and pollution. The state focuses nearly all its publicity effort on merchandising a get-rich-quick fantasy--one that will come true for only a handful of people while encouraging millions of others to think of success as a product of luck, not honest work.

I admit, however, that I have been presenting only one side of a complex issue. There are, after all, perfectly sound arguments for allowing state lotteries to continue and spread. Americans are going to gamble anyway; for example, they now bet more than $1 billion yearly on football alone. Lotteries may actually reduce the incidence of illegal gambling, and they certainly do produce extra funds for transportation, education, care of the elderly, and so forth. Though it is too bad that Americans resist being openly taxed to cover all the social services they demand, the lottery is a relatively painless and even entertaining way of making up the deficit.

Even so, there is a fundamental difference between merely supervising a game and actively manipulating and deceiving the public. I think we should insist that tax dollars not be spent on the recruiting of players who will put lottery tickets ahead of groceries and shelter for their families. I recommend, therefore, that a law be passed requiring truth in lottery advertising--by which I mean full disclosure of the odds against winning, an explanation of the taxes and installment payouts that apply to the prizes, and warnings against compulsive gambling. If these reforms cause fewer dollars to flow into the state treasury, they should also help to keep some marginally solvent families self-sufficient--and thus off the welfare rolls. The point of state government, after all, is not to get and spend as much money as possible but to improve the quality of life. Refraining from turning citizens into suckers would be one small but welcome step toward that goal.

STUDY QUESTIONS FOR "TURNING CITIZENS INTO SUCKERS"

1. Alexander does not state her thesis until the last paragraph. What advantage does she gain, if any, by leading up to her central point rather than announcing it near the beginning?
2. Is the essay well organized? Write a scratch outline indicating the main stages in Alexander's argument.
3. Most effective arguments handle opposing viewpoints through concession or refutation (see *The Borzoi Handbook for Writers,* 41). What opposing points does Alexander acknowledge? How does she address them?
4. What types of evidence does Alexander use to support her argument?
5. Evaluate Alexander's introduction. Does it engage your interest? Why, or why not?
6. Reread Alexander's final sentence. Does it provide a satisfying conclusion for her argument? Why, or why not?

II
PARAGRAPHS

7

Paragraph Unity and Continuity

PARAGRAPH UNITY

7.1 Recognizing Paragraph Unity (*BHW* 7a–c)

Underline the main sentence in each of the following paragraphs—the sentence that states the central point developed in the rest of the paragraph. Then decide whether each paragraph is unified. If not, identify the problem by circling any material that is not clearly related to the central point. In the space provided, briefly explain the problem.

Example: I had always assumed that when I finished my degree in Computer Information Systems, I would get a job and do exactly what I had been trained to do—write programs. I discovered, however, that this was a false assumption. During my junior year I took a computer course in which the professor told the class that writing is often an essential part of a programmer's job. Programmers, he explained, must keep logs, fill out reports, and carefully document the programs they write. In fact, documentation is an essential part of the job because it enables an employer or co-worker to understand what the programmer has done. Most computer majors have little time for electives because their degree programs require so many courses in computer science. When they do take electives, technical fields usually win out over humanities.*

After two introductory sentences, the paragraph develops its main point: on-the-job writing for programmers. Then the paragraph shifts to a new point: electives taken by computer majors.

1. Many professional musicians complain that the violins, cellos, and other string instruments produced today cannot match those crafted at the close of the Renaissance by a group of Italians working in the city of Cremona. The sound from many modern instruments has an unpleasant edge when certain notes are played, similar to the effect of a hundred violins all playing the same note with one ever so slightly out of tune. In addition, most of today's instruments are not well balanced—some notes are richer and more resonant than others—and their sound does not carry as well as that from a Cremonese instrument. Violins are today made throughout the world; no single country or community has cornered the market on fine instrument making. [1]

_____

_____

_____

_____

2. For thousands of years human beings have communicated with one
    another first in the language of dress. Long before I am near enough
    to talk to you on the street, in a meeting, or at a party, you announce
    your sex, age and class to me through what you are wearing—and very
    possibly give me important information (or misinformation) as to your
    occupation, origin, personality, opinions, tastes, sexual desires and
    current mood. I may not be able to put what I observe into words, but
    I register the information unconsciously; and you simultaneously do
    the same for me. By the time we meet and converse we have already
    spoken to each other in an older and more universal tongue. [2]

_____

_____

_____

_____

3. The social weaver is a superlative bird architect, and flocks of birds
    build enormous "apartment house" nests in the flat-topped acacia
    trees of the South African veldt. The American Museum of Natural
    History has thousands of nests in its collections and vaults. Crafted out
    of coarse grass and twigs, weavers' nests are not woven but thatched
    like a haycock. The result is a large, hanging mass of straw whose
    underside is perforated by the entrances to individual nests. Every year
    the flock adds to the nest, and sometimes the weight of the nest will
    cause the supporting branches to collapse. Nests have been observed

in use over 100 years, and the very largest can reach almost 2,000 cubic feet in volume.[3]

_____

_____

_____

_____

4. Since I had been away at college for only a month, I expected everything to be the same when I made my first visit home. But to my surprise, a considerable amount of change had occurred. My sister had taken little time in moving into my room, which included not only a large bed but also my television. And because my parents had turned my sister's room into a study for their use, I had to stay in the guest room. I had expected this to happen, of course, but I was surprised at the quickness with which it was done. Although more happened than I had anticipated, the family atmosphere itself remained the same. When I first arrived, there were the usual "hellos" and questions about college life. And after a good meal and several hours of talk, everything settled back into a comfortable routine.*

_____

_____

_____

_____

5. More than three centuries after the Indians first showed Captain John Smith how to grow it, pumpkin is still regarded as an incredibly versatile ingredient. You can wake up to a plate of pumpkin pancakes or pumpkin muffins spread with tangy pumpkin preserves. Or follow a dinner of pork with pumpkin sauce with a slice of mouth-watering

pumpkin apricot brandy pound cake or pumpkin cheesecake. It's little wonder that in 1683 a Colonist rhymed: "We had pumpkins in the morning and pumpkins at noon. If it were not for pumpkins, we'd be undone soon."[4]

_____

_____

_____

_____

7.2   Supplying Main Sentences (*BHW* 7a–c)

The following paragraphs lack explicit main sentences. For each one, write a sentence that sums up the point developed in the paragraph. Is the paragraph more or less effective with its central point explicitly stated? Why?

1. At Halloween, children bob for apples and find them nestled in their "trick-or-treat" bags among the candy and popcorn balls. At Thanksgiving, grade schoolers make turkeys from apples rigged with pipe cleaners, paper cutouts, and marshmallows. During the summer months, every child looks forward to eating a sticky candied apple while walking down the carnival midway. And when fall rolls around, good boys and girls everywhere present their teachers with polished red apples, the traditional academic offering.*

    Main sentence _____

    _____

    _____

2. The roof of the house sagged in several places, the ceilings were badly stained where water had leaked in over the years, and the walls were bare in a dozen places where the paper had peeled away from the slatted wood. In the kitchen, nearly half the tile was off the wall behind the sink, and the countertops badly needed regrouting. Hardwood boards popped up everywhere, squeaking and groaning as we walked

101

over them. In one spot the floor was rotted away by years of moisture that had seeped in around an old chimney pipe that ran from the basement up through the roof.*

Main sentence _____

_____

_____

3. The familiar *slip joint pliers* are named for the two-position pivot that provides both normal and wide jaw openings. Broad-jawed *lineman's pliers* have side cutters which equip them for heavy-duty wire cutting and splicing. *Channel-type pliers* with multiposition pivots adjust for jaw openings up to 2 inches and will grip any shape. *Long-nosed pliers* are used to shape wire and thin metal, and often for cutting as well. *Diagonal-cutting pliers* have no gripping jaws and are used for cutting only. Also for cutting only are *end cutting nippers,* which can snip wire, small nails, and brads.[5]

Main sentence _____

_____

_____

7.3 Selecting Details for a Unified Paragraph (*BHW* 7a–c)

This exercise contains a list of factual statements about elephants. Use appropriate details from the list to write a paragraph on one of the suggested topics. Underline your main sentence. Some of the information may be relevant for either paragraph. Feel free to add details that are not in the list.[6]

Topic 1: The elephant as an endangered species

Topic 2: Humankind's use of the elephant

1. People have trained Asiatic elephants for thousands of years.
2. Because of their size and inefficient digestion, elephants require enormous amounts of food.

3. For more than a thousand years, hunters have killed African elephants for their ivory tusks.
4. Laws now forbid the killing of elephants for ivory.
5. There may now be fewer than 1,300,000 elephants in Africa and fewer than 25,000 in Asia.
6. Elephants are used today in southern Asia as work animals.
7. A dwindling food supply is an even greater threat to the elephant than are ivory hunters.
8. Before the invention of heavy machinery, elephants were the most powerful force available to humans for pushing and carrying objects.
9. Humans are taking over more and more of the land in Africa and Asia—land once used by elephants for feeding.
10. Today elephants are used to help clear forests and to do other heavy labor.
11. The price of ivory today is extraordinary; a single pair of tusks may sell for more than $20,000.
12. Elephants have been used in circuses for at least 2,000 years.
13. Some zoos regularly feature elephant rides.
14. Poachers continue to kill elephants for their tusks.
15. We may always be able to see elephants in zoos, but will they survive in the wild?

7.4 Writing a Practice Paragraph
(*BHW* 7a–c)

Write a unified paragraph, beginning either with one of the following main sentences or with a main sentence of your own.

1. A good tennis player (or any other athlete) must have a disciplined mind as well as a disciplined body.
2. Living in a dorm room (or an apartment) is much easier (or more difficult) than I thought it would be.
3. *Dances with Wolves* (or another movie) appealed to audiences mainly because . . .
4. If high schools want to prepare students for college, they should concentrate on . . .
5. When we went to clean up the next day, we found that the room had been devastated by the all-night party.

7.5 Paragraph Continuity: Responding to a Previous Sentence (*BHW* 7d)

Assume that each sentence given below is the first sentence in a paragraph. Write two sentences that could follow it—one a sentence of illustration, the other a sentence of limitation.

Example: Ludwig almost always prefers old-fashioned ballroom dancing.

Illustration *Last week he refused to go out unless we all agreed to foxtrot.*

Limitation *But on a rare occasion he kicks loose and does the Lambada.*

1. In the past year the local animal shelter picked up more than three hundred dogs and cats.

Illustration _____

_____

Limitation _____

_____

2. In the cafeteria last Thursday I ate one of the best meals I've ever had.

Illustration _____

_____

Limitation _____

_____

3. Most television programming today is designed to appeal to twelve-year-olds.

Illustration _____

_____

Limitation _____

_____

4. Smoking ought to be banned entirely in campus dormitories.

Illustration _____

_____

Limitation _____

_____

5. My brother told me that I was crazy to buy this old wreck of a car.

Illustration _____

_____

Limitation _____

_____

6. Puppies appeal to just about everybody—even cold-blooded cynics.

Illustration _____

_____

Limitation _____

_____

7. The 1991 war in the Persian Gulf prompted ardent displays of patriotism across the country.

Illustration _____

_____

Limitation _____

_____

8. A cluttered desk is the sign of a cluttered mind.

Illustration _____

_____

Limitation _____

_____

9. Many students have given up pen and paper in favor of the word processor.

   Illustration _____

   _____

   Limitation _____

   _____

10. To a world-class caffeine addict, there is no such thing as a "bad" cup of coffee.*

    Illustration _____

    _____

    Limitation _____

    _____

7.6 Recognizing Paragraph Continuity
(*BHW* 7d–h)

In the following paragraphs, circle the words and phrases that contribute to paragraph continuity. Then, in the space provided, explain briefly the main method(s) used by the writer to achieve continuity: (1) transitions, (2) pronouns, (3) repeated key words and phrases, (4) repeated sentence structure.

Example: (Fannie) was the worldiest old (woman) to be imagined. (She) could do whatever (her) hands were doing without having to stop talking; and (she) could speak in a wonderfully derogatory way with any number of pins stuck in (her) mouth. (Her) hands

106

steadied me like claws as (she) stumped on (her) knees around me, tacking me together. The gist of (her) tale would be lost on me, but (Fannie) didn't bother about the ear (she) was telling it to; (she) just liked telling. (She) was like an author. In fact, for a good deal of what (she) said, I daresay (she) *was* the author.[7]

The main device is the repeated use of pronouns to refer to Fannie.

1. Like the other degenerative diseases, heart disease is ordinarily present for a long time in the body before drastic symptoms appear. In fact, in our country, heart disease often begins in the early twenties, growing worse as the years pass until finally the inevitable heart attack strikes. For most people the first heart attack does not come until the fifties or sixties. But for thousands of people every year, the first heart attack comes in the twenties. Occasionally even a person in his teens may experience a fatal heart attack.[8]

2. When my dad comes through the door at the end of the day, he has only two things on his mind: a cold beer and a hot meal. His straw hat is the first thing to go before he washes his callused hands and heads for the kitchen. During supper he wears the same worn-out boots he's had for years. His cotton shirt is still new, but his blue jeans, patched on both knees, would make better rags than pants. His tanned skin is leathered from too much sun, his strong arms hardened from throwing calves and building fences. And his legs are bowed to fit the saddle he uses every day. Work and age have started to gray the tips of his hair.*

3. Jeans are the invention of Levi Strauss, a Bavarian immigrant who designed them as sturdy work clothes for California gold miners in the 1850s. Strauss's first jeans were brown, not blue, made from the rugged tent canvas he sold before becoming a clothing merchant. He soon switched to an even tougher fabric—now called denim—which he dyed deep blue. Within a decade of their creation, Strauss's jeans were standard wear for farmers, ranchers, and miners of the American West. And by the 1880s, he had given the trousers most of the features we associate with modern-day Levi's: orange stitching, rivets, and the classic two-horse leather patch sewn above the right-rear pocket. [9]

4. For years, Chinese Americans have been labeled a model minority. We read in the newspapers how diligently they have worked and saved. We see on television how quietly they obey the laws and how conscientiously they stay clear of crime. We learn in magazines how they climb the economic ladder and how much better than the Caucasian kids their children do in school. [10]

5. By the end of my day as a volunteer at the therapy clinic, I had been hit, cursed, praised, hugged, and thoroughly indoctrinated into the world of health care. This introduction to the field I hope someday to enter produced unexpected feelings. Primarily, it made me doubt whether I could endure life as a doctor. Most of the patients receiving

treatment were old, and I could accept their disabilities by arguing that they had already lived full lives. However, when the first young person came in—an eight-year-old girl who had lost her foot to a lawn mower—I could see no justice. The vision of that maimed child tormented me all day, making it difficult for me to work. From this, I concluded that doctors must be able to "turn off" their emotions. I also noticed, though, how gentle and caring the therapists were with their patients. I realized that a therapist would become ineffective if she built a shell around herself. Putting these two observations together, I understood that the secret lies in a delicate balance between compassion and the ability to forget. The therapist must learn to love and care for patients without being overcome by their suffering.*

_____

_____

_____

_____

7.7 Recognizing Paragraph Continuity in Your Own Writing (*BHW* 7d–h)

Photocopy several paragraphs from one of your own essays, and circle the words and phrases that contribute to continuity. Look for explicit transitions as well as pronouns or repeated words that help link sentences together in a coherent pattern.

7.8 Revising for Continuity (*BHW* 7d–h)

Revise the following paragraph to improve its continuity. Supply transitions where appropriate to strengthen connections between sentences. Underline the transitions you add.

Anyone can make strawberry shortcake. Take one of those spongy, little store-bought "cakes" (they come six to a package), fill the indentation with a spoonful of strawberries (thaw them first), and plop on a dab of Cool Whip. If you want to make the real thing, you have to do some work. Make the shortcake from scratch—not the spongy kind, but a good drop biscuit dough with plenty of sugar thrown in. Pour on the strawberries (don't be stingy)—fresh, ripe, sliced thin, sprinkled with sugar, and left to stand for at least three hours. Put a big scoop of natural vanilla ice cream on top. (Homemade is best; if it's not available, use only the finest commercial brand.) Crown the whole thing with a thick mound of freshly whipped cream. *That* is strawberry shortcake.*

7.9 Review Exercise: Peer Editing for Paragraph Unity and Continuity (*BHW* 7a–i)

Bring to class a rough draft of your current essay. Exchange papers with a classmate, and carefully check each other's work for paragraph unity and continuity. Use the following guidelines:

1. *Unity.* Underline any material that does not belong in a particular paragraph; then write a brief note explaining why you underlined the material.
2. *Continuity within Paragraphs.* Note in the margins any paragraph that lacks continuity; point specifically to places where transitional expressions or repeated words could improve the links between sentences.
3. *Links between Paragraphs.* Check the transitions between paragraphs. Note in the margins any places where one paragraph could be linked more effectively to another.

If your classmate points out any paragraphs in your essay that lack unity or continuity, revise them before submitting the final copy.

8

Paragraph Development

8.1 Recognizing Patterns of Paragraph Development (*BHW* 8a–c)

In the space provided, identify the method of development used in each paragraph—direct, pivoting, or suspended. Then underline the main (or topic) sentence, and indicate with a bracket which sentences, if any, limit the main point and which support it.

Example: [As a poet, W. H. Auden has always had his share of detractors, first in the 1930's with the negative response to his work in the influential journal *Scrutiny,* and later in two articles by Randall Jarrell criticizing various ideological changes in his poetry. Even today some argue that Auden's work is uneven or that it represents a serious decline from the brilliance he demonstrated in the 1930's. Despite all this, however, Auden is generally regarded today as one of the major poets of the twentieth century. Several of his poems are well established as

Limit

111

standard anthology pieces and his work as a whole is recognized for its impressive range of thought and its technical brilliance. [11]

Pivoting Paragraph

1. The fighting bull is to the domestic bull as the wolf is to the dog. A domestic bull may be evil tempered and vicious as a dog may be mean and dangerous, but he will never have the speed, the quality of muscle and sinew and the peculiar build of the fighting bull any more than the dog will have the sinews of the wolf, his cunning and his width of jaw. Bulls for the ring are wild animals. They are bred from a strain that comes down in direct descent from the wild bulls that ranged over the Peninsula and they are bred on ranches with thousands of acres of range where they live as free ranging animals. The contacts with men of the bulls that are to appear in the ring are held to the absolute minimum. [12]

2. I do not believe that the dorm visitation hours on school nights should be extended to midnight. It is true that college students are mature enough to regulate their own lives, and, indeed, there are several good reasons for extending the hours to midnight. But finally, the very nature of dorm life makes the earlier hours preferable. For one thing, some students do most of their studying late at night, and visitors on the floor inevitably disrupt their work. An occasional late visitor would be fine, but with dozens of people living together, a visitor is likely to be on the floor nearly every night. Security is another good reason for the 10:00 P.M. curfew. In the past month several prowlers have been reported in the dorm. One room was

cleaned out by thieves—at 11:00 P.M. on a Tuesday. Earlier visitation hours won't solve such problems, but they will make it easier to keep out unwanted visitors late at night after many dorm residents are asleep.*

---

3. In many ways, writing is the neglected half of literacy. It has received far less attention from researchers than reading, and we know less about the relationship between early experience and later success in school for writing than we do for reading. Most primary-grade teachers give more time and attention to teaching reading than to teaching writing, and writing instruction is often limited to worksheet exercises in handwriting and spelling. During the last several years, however, there has been increasing interest in the early development of writing, both in and out of school, and in new approaches to the teaching of writing in the primary grades. Both of these areas of inquiry stress the importance of looking at what children *do* with writing, and of considering writing as a process rather than as a collection of skills such as handwriting and spelling. [13]

---

4. In normal life the woodchuck's temperature, though fluctuant, averages about 97 degrees. Now, as he lies tight-curled in a ball with the winter sleep stealing over him, this body heat drops ten degrees, twenty degrees, thirty. Finally, by the time the snow is on the ground and the woodchuck's winter dormancy has become complete, his temperature is only 38 or 40. With the falling of the body heat there is a slowing of his heartbeat and his respiration. In normal life he breathes thirty or forty times each minute; when he is excited, as

113

many as a hundred times. Now he breathes slower and slower—ten times a minute, five times a minute, once a minute, and at last only ten or twelve times in an hour. His heartbeat is a twentieth of normal. He has entered fully into the oblivion of hibernation.[14]

---

5. Punctuation thus becomes the signature of cultures. The hot-blooded Spaniard seems to be revealed in the passion and urgency of his doubled exclamation points and question marks *("¡Caramba! ¿Quien sabe?"),* while the impassive Chinese traditionally added to his so-called inscrutability by omitting directions from his ideograms. The anarchy and commotion of the '60s were given voice in the exploding exclamation marks, riotous capital letters and Day-Glo italics of Tom Wolfe's spray-paint prose; and in Communist societies, where the State is absolute, the dignity—and divinity—of capital letters is reserved for Ministries, Sub-Committees and Secretariats.[15]

---

6. My job as a blood bank laboratory technician occasionally has its lighter moments. One day our shipping department decided to have some fun with us. Late that afternoon they brought a small, unusually labeled box into the laboratory. On the box were several stickers that read, "Caution!" "Handle with Care!" and "Biohazard!" After eyeballing the box from a distance for some time, I walked up and cautiously opened it. Inside, among shredded newspaper and foam rubber, was a single pint of green liquid. Quickly, I snatched up the invoice and read, "Enclosed: One pint of rare type O witches' blood." For the first time that day I realized the date—October 31.*

---

7. In countries where the intellectual functions of education are highly valued, like France and Germany and the Scandinavian countries, the teacher, especially the secondary-school teacher, is likely to be an important local figure representing a personal and vocational ideal worthy of emulation. There it seems worth becoming a teacher because what the teacher does is worth doing and is handsomely recognized. The intellectually alert and cultivated teacher may have a particular importance for intelligent children whose home environment is not highly cultivated; such children have no alternative course of mental stimulation. All too often, however, in the history of the United States, the schoolteacher has been in no position to serve as a model for an introduction to the intellectual life. Too often he has not only no claims to an intellectual life of his own, but not even an adequate workmanlike competence in the skills he is supposed to impart. Regardless of his own quality, his low pay and common lack of personal freedom have caused the teacher's role to be associated with exploitation and intimidation. [16]

---

8. Many Cajun terms refer to popular Louisiana foods. Perhaps the best-known is *gumbo,* the word for any kind of thick soup containing fresh seafood, okra, and onions. *Jambalaya,* another colorful local term, describes a highly seasoned dish made with rice and some kind of meat, such as ham, shrimp, crab, sausage, or chicken. Justin Wilson's famous book *How to Make a Roux* explains the technique for concocting a perfect brown sauce for every Cajun dish. As any native Louisianan knows, a key ingredient in any such sauce is *filé* (pro-

nounced fee-lay), a seasoning and thickening powder made from leaves of the sassafras tree.*

---

9. There are circumstances where the otherwise absolute obligation of the law is tempered by exceptions for individual conscience. As in the case of the conscientious objector to military service, the exception may be recognized by statute or, as in the case of the flag salute for school children, it may be required by the First Amendment. But in countless other situations the fact that conscience counsels violation of the law can be no defense. Those are the situations in which the citizen is placed in the dilemma of being forced to choose between violating the dictates of his conscience or violating the command of positive law.[17]

---

10. [This paragraph lacks an explicit main sentence. In the space provided, write one. Would the addition of your sentence improve the paragraph?]

On a cold, snowy evening Kevin and I left Seattle bound for home, a three-day, nonstop drive back to Texas through some of the most beautiful country I know. That night I started the first driving shift on slick, snow-covered roads. As I was driving up the mountains, just outside Seattle, my headlights shone on a figure in the road that appeared to be a horse. I started slowing down, trying to figure out just what it was. Just then Kevin said, "It's a big buck!" I stopped the truck about twenty feet in front of him—the biggest deer I'd ever seen. He just stood there, blinded by the headlights, breathing frosted clouds of air from his nose. He looked proud and beautiful standing with snow on his antlers and a look of fury in his eyes. We got out for a closer look, but as we did, he took off, hardly making a sound. I remembered looking into his eyes all the way home.*

8.2 Writing Practice Paragraphs: Patterns of Development (*BHW* 8a–c)

Write three paragraphs—one using *direct* development, one *pivoting,* and one *suspended.* Use your own topic or develop one out of the general suggestions given below.

1. The benefits or drawbacks of being an expert typist
2. The benefits or drawbacks of high school athletic programs
3. The benefits or drawbacks of a standardized test (such as the SAT)
4. The importance of reading skills for a first-year college student
5. The food in a particular restaurant

8.3 Revising Skimpy Paragraphs (*BHW* 8d)

The following paragraphs are skimpy—they provide too little information to support the writer's point. Working alone or with a group, flesh out the first two paragraphs, adding as much detail as necessary to achieve adequate development. For the third item—a series of skimpy paragraphs—you may either rearrange or delete some of the information in order to give the resulting paragraph an adequate focus.*

1. Most students today attend college in order to get jobs when they graduate. Because of this interest in careers, students major in fields that offer the best job opportunities. Fields of study that do not lead directly to jobs are not as popular as they once were.
2. Mr. Mahon's yard was the envy of the neighborhood. His grass was

always thick and neatly trimmed. In the front of his house was a beautiful garden of climbing roses.

3. Most people consider charity an obligation. They give a few dollars at church every week or they make donations elsewhere.

    People often seem to be more concerned about tax donations for charity than about the charity itself.

    Few people are willing to give up their own time for a charitable purpose. It is easier to write a check.

8.4   Revising a Rambling Paragraph (*BHW* 8d)

The following paragraph is poorly developed because it contains too much information without an adequate focus. Working alone or with a group, revise the paragraph, deleting irrelevant material and focusing the paragraph on a single idea. If you prefer, you may change the passage into a series of paragraphs, each one developing a point contained in the original rambling paragraph.

When I write a paper, I usually type out a complete first draft, triple-spaced. I then revise it by handwriting changes in the margins and between the lines. I often spend an hour or more making changes right on the typed draft. When my paper is a barely readable maze of cross-outs, arrows, inserts, and marginal notes,
5   I usually decide to quit revising. I then type a final copy from my marked-up draft, sometimes making additional minor changes as I type. I have always written this way, and I suppose I always will; the method has become a comfortable habit. I find it hard to
10 pinpoint my specific strengths and weaknesses as a writer, partly because I lack objectivity about my work. I think I have a good attitude toward writing, better than I used to have, but I do have a hard time writing for a specific audience. When I write a paper, I simply write; I rarely think about gearing my work for a specific
15 reader, and sometimes this leads to problems. Some would consider my procrastination a weakness, but I consider it a strength. Putting off a writing project until near the deadline helps me concentrate on my subject and focus my energy. My method of writing is also very efficient. Since I limit my drafting and revising
20 to a single copy of the paper, I spend much less time recopying

than most people do. Once my heavily edited first draft is finished, I go straight to the typewriter.*

8.5 Review Exercise: Peer Editing for Paragraph Development (*BHW* 8d)

Bring to class a rough draft of your current essay. Exchange papers with a classmate, and carefully check each other's work for adequate paragraph development. Use the following guidelines:

1. *Well-Developed Paragraphs.* Put a check in the margin next to any paragraph that you consider especially well developed.
2. *Skimpy Paragraphs.* Identify any paragraph that needs further development; make specific suggestions for revision, writing your advice in the margins or on a separate sheet of paper.
3. *Rambling Paragraphs.* Identify any paragraph that contains too much information without an adequate focus; make specific suggestions for revision, writing your advice in the margins or on a separate sheet of paper.

If your classmate points out any paragraphs in your essay that need improvement, revise them before submitting the final copy.

9

Paragraph Functions

9.1 Recognizing Paragraph Functions (*BHW* 9a–i)

This exercise illustrates the paragraph functions discussed in Chapter 9 of *The Borzoi Handbook for Writers*. Analyze each paragraph, considering its function as well as its unity, organization, and continuity. Use the following questions as a guide, and be prepared to discuss your answers in class.

1. What function does the paragraph serve? Does it

   a. Create a vivid description?
   b. Recount an event?
   c. Illustrate a point with details?
   d. Support a point with reasons?
   e. Draw a comparison or contrast?
   f. Analyze causes or effects?
   g. Clarify the meaning of a term or concept?
   h. Show the parts or steps that make up a whole?
   i. Develop an analogy?

Note: In some cases, paragraphs serve more than one function. If you see two (or more) functions at work in a single paragraph, feel free to say so.

2. How does the writer unify and organize the paragraph? Note especially the opening and closing sentences and their relation to the rest of the paragraph.

3. How does the writer create a sense of continuity in the paragraph? Is there linkage between sentences?

SAMPLE PARAGRAPHS

1. When Harley gave the signal, Johnny released the net into the water. After about forty-five minutes, Johnny pulled up the net and untied the bottom, releasing the catch into the *Donna.* He then took a small hand-held net, scooped up some of the fish, and placed them on a flat wooden board. With his hands, he skillfully pushed the larger shrimp into a wooden box and tossed on the deck the small shrimp and the other fish, which washed out the side holes and back into the water. He did this until all the catch was sorted. Then he tossed in the net, starting the process again.*

2. We think of males as large and powerful, females as smaller and weaker, but the opposite pattern prevails throughout nature—males are generally smaller than females, and for good reason, humans and most other mammals notwithstanding. Sperm is small and cheap, easily manufactured in large quantities by little creatures. A sperm cell is little more than a nucleus of naked DNA with a delivery system. Eggs, on the other hand, must be larger, for they provide the cytoplasm (all the rest of the cell) with mitochondria (or energy factories), chloroplasts (for photosynthesizers), and all other parts that a zygote needs to begin the process of embryonic growth. In addition, eggs generally supply the initial nutriment, or food for the developing embryo. Finally, females usually perform the tasks of primary care, either retaining the eggs within their bodies for a time or guarding them after they are laid. For all these reasons, females are larger than males in most species of animals.[18]

3. When you are inside the jungle, away from the river, the trees vault out of sight. It is hard to remember to look up the long trunks and see the fans, strips, fronds, and sprays of glossy leaves. Inside the jungle you are more likely to notice the snarl of climbers and creepers round the trees' boles, the flowering bromeliads and epiphytes in every bough's crook, and the fantastic silk-cotton tree trunks thirty or forty

122

feet across, trunks buttressed in flanges of wood whose curves can make three high walls of a room—a shady loamy-aired room where you would gladly live, or die. Butterflies, iridescent blue, striped, or clear-winged, thread the jungle paths at eye level. And at your feet is a swath of ants bearing triangular bits of green leaf. The ants with their leaves look like a wide fleet of sailing dinghies—but they don't quit. In either direction they wobble over the jungle floor as far as the eye can see. I followed them off the path as far as I dared, and never saw an end to ants or to those luffing chips of green they bore. [19]

4. Like other beers, Coors is produced from barley. Most of the big Midwestern brewers use barley grown in North Dakota and Minnesota. Coors is the single American brewer to use a Moravian strain, grown under company supervision, on farms in Colorado, Idaho, Wyoming and Montana. At the brewery, the barley is turned into malt by being soaked in water—which must be biologically pure and of a known mineral content—for several days, causing it to sprout and producing a chemical change—breaking down starch into sugar. The malt is toasted, a process that halts the sprouting and determines the color and sweetness (the more the roasting, the darker, more bitter the beer). It is ground into flour and brewed, with more pure water, in huge copper-domed kettles until it is the consistency of oatmeal. Rice and refined starch are added to make mash; solids are strained out, leaving an amber liquid malt extract, which is boiled with hops—the dried cones from the hop vine which add to the bitterness, or tang. The hops are strained, yeast is added, turning the sugar to alcohol, and the beer is aged in huge vats at near-freezing temperatures for almost two months, during which the second fermentation takes place and the liquid becomes carbonated, or bubbly. (Many breweries chemically age their beer to speed up production; Coors people say only naturally aged brew can be called a true "lager.") Next, the beer is filtered through cellulose filters to remove bacteria, and finally is pumped into cans, bottles or kegs for shipping. [20]

5. Protectionism remains a potent political force in the U.S., but it makes increasingly less sense. More and more Japanese companies are now intent on exporting from, not to, the United States. On March 7 of this year, Honda made a landmark shipment of 540 Accord coupes from Portland, Oregon, to Tokyo. Fujitsu America is sending some $3 million worth of disk drives, cellular car phones and modems manufactured at its Hillsboro, Oregon, and other U.S. factories to Canada, New Zealand, South America and Western Europe. Sanyo is shipping 5,000 television sets from the Arkansas plant that it operates in

a joint venture with Sears. Toshiba is exporting microwave ovens and TV sets from its Lebanon, Tennessee, plant to Japan.[21]

6. Gothic was originally a term of abuse hurled at the architecture of the Middle Ages by a pupil of Michelangelo whose object was to advance the interests of the "new" style (now known as Renaissance) at the expense of the old. The style he wrongly termed Gothic actually began in twelfth-century France and flourished over much of Europe, especially the north, for the following four centuries. It is now used to describe a splendid, soaring style typified by the pointed arches and rose windows of cathedrals, and found repeated in miniature on much of the furniture that has survived.[22]

7. There are, of course, many differences between private and public schools, and we can't be sure which differences are most important. But in light of what we know about literacy, an important factor must be that curricula of private schools impart more literate information than those of public schools. Private schools offer fewer nontraditional and vocational courses and give each student proportionally more academic courses. This interpretation is supported by Walberg and Shanahan, who suggest, in commenting on the new Coleman report, that the crucial factor is "time on task." In private schools, both middle-class and disadvantaged students spend more time in content courses and are exposed to more of the information that belongs to literate culture. The implication is that many more students could become highly literate if they were presented with the right sort of curriculum, particularly in their early years.[23]

8. In the first act of Henrik Ibsen's play *A Doll's House,* Nora Helmer adopts a different personality for each character she talks with. To her husband, Torvald, Nora is a "songbird." She constantly whirls around him and does everything possible to win his praise, acting coy, flirtatious, and helpless. When she first talks with Mrs. Linde, a childhood friend, Nora acts like a young high-school girl. She brags about her husband's promotion at work much like a cheerleader might brag about her boyfriend's being named captain of the football team. But when it comes to conversing with Mr. Krogstad, Torvald's employee, Nora is no longer a "songbird" or a cheerleader; she now becomes a serious, forceful woman."*

9. During June and July, commercial orchardists in the Yakima valley thin the small apples that grow on their trees, spacing the fruit four to six inches apart. Though costly and time consuming, thinning has two desirable effects on fruit production. First, it causes the apples to grow to the standard "eating" size preferred by most people—

neither too small nor too large. Second, thinning causes apples to attain better color. When buying red apples, shoppers usually look for the deepest possible crimson. Thinning prevents closely bunched apples from shading one another, thus giving the fruit the sun exposure it needs to color properly.[24]

10. The assigning of traditional grades (A through F) in a freshman writing course often works against the purpose of the course—to help students learn to write better. One problem with such grades is that they discourage rather than encourage progress and improvement. At the beginning of a writing course, many students earn low grades because they are inexperienced writers. They simply don't know how to write an effective essay, and in the process of learning to do so, they make mistakes—and low grades. Such grades affect the students' confidence and morale, making writing an unpleasant task associated with anxiety and failure. As a result, students are discouraged; instead of working seriously on their writing, they spend time worrying about the easiest way to earn a better grade on the next paper—usually by writing "safe" papers that are simple and correct but lacking in thought.*

11. The interviewer asked Winston about the D on his transcript, the one in algebra. Feeling suddenly defensive, Winston explained that he was a freshman at the time, was unprepared for the course, and had spent too much of his time pledging a fraternity. The interviewer made a sound suggesting that he wasn't very impressed by the explanation. There was a long pause, which Winston interrupted by saying that his subsequent math grades, while not outstanding, were somewhat higher. The interviewer looked tired, shrugged his shoulders, and suddenly asked Winston why he wanted to work for the IRS.

12. A house remains standing not because it is nailed or cemented together but because of the process by which it transfers weight to the ground. The roof, which shields the house from weather, carries not only its own weight but also the weight of snow and rain. This weight is transferred downward to the second major structural element, the vertical supports, which include the outside walls, the load-bearing partitions inside the house, and any support columns built into the structure. These supports, in turn, transfer their weight to the floor, which also carries the weight of the people and furniture in the house. Finally, all the weight from the first three structural elements—roof, vertical supports, and floor—is transferred to the foundation, which rests on the earth.

13. A slicing knife has a narrow blade that is six to eight inches in length.

It is moved freely up and down, its only guide being the knuckles of the hand steadying the object being sliced. A chopping knife (which can also serve perfectly well for slicing) has a deep blade, the point of which forms a fulcrum, remaining always in contact with the work surface, while the depth of the blade prevents the knuckles of the working hand from rapping against the surface. The blade of a practical chopping knife will be eight to ten inches in length, with a depth of one-and-a-half to two inches.[25]

14. Furniture tells all. Just as a paleontologist can reconstruct a prehistoric animal from a fragment of jawbone, one can reconstruct the domestic interior, and the attitudes of its inhabitants, from a single chair. A Louis XV *fauteuil* reflects not only the decor of the room for which it was intended, but also the delightful elegance of the period. A gleaming mahogany Georgian Windsor chair, with its gracefully carved stickwork, is the essence of gentlemanly restraint. An overstuffed Victorian armchair, with its deeply tufted, rich fabrics and lace antimacassars, represents both the conservatism of that period and its desire for physical ease. An Art Deco chaise lounge, upholstered in zebra skin and encrusted with mother-of-pearl, exhibits a tactile and voluptuous enjoyment of luxury.[26]

15. Just about every herb known in the Middle Ages, whether cultivated in a garden or gathered from the wild, had at least one, and usually several, medicinal uses. Betony, for instance, according to Walahfrid and the herbalists, was good for just about everything. Rosemary is listed in an herbal of 1525 as a cure for asthma, evil swellings, cankers, gout, coughs, poisoning, worms in the teeth, and bad dreams. Parsley was recommended for fever, heart pains, stitch, weak stomach, stones, and paralysis, and onions were said to be good for the eyesight and for dog bites, skin discoloration, and baldness; they also cleared the head and increased sexual prowess. The herbals tell us that periwinkle was supposed to cure toothaches and fevers and that concoctions containing strawberry juice could be gargled for throat ulcers. Some plants induced a general sense of well-being. Rue sharpened the vision, elecampane strengthened the stomach, dates made a sick person stronger, and quinces promoted cheerfulness. As for violets, one had only to smell them to feel better.[27]

16. The real problem with forecasting the generation of a storm such as this is gauging its severity. It is not like following a fully developed storm for several days as it moves across the ocean, watching it weaken or strengthen with some sort of regularity. It is more like watching a car about to crash into a brick wall; you know there is

126

going to be a crash, there is an 80 percent chance the gas tank will explode, but you don't know how much gas is in the tank! Just as with the car, the measure of a storm's severity is gauged by its ingredients: the existence of a front (the brick wall), the amount of cold air coming down behind the front (speed of the car), and the degree of circulation in the upper air approaching the front (amount of gas in the tank).[28]

17. It takes a conscious effort to realize how constricted the space is on a basketball court. Place a regulation court (ninety-four by fifty feet) on a football field, and it will reach from the back of the end zone to the twenty-one-yard line; its width will cover less than a third of the field. On a baseball diamond, a basketball court will reach from home plate to just beyond first base. Compared to its principal indoor rival, ice hockey, basketball covers about one-fourth the playing area. And during the normal flow of the game, most of the action takes place on about the third of the court nearest the basket. It is in this dollhouse space that ten men, each of them half a foot taller than the average man, come together to battle each other.[29]

18. I begin my compost heap with a layer of twigs and small dead branches. These allow excess moisture to drain from the heap during heavy rains. Next, I alternate layers of different kinds of vegetation. This type of "sandwiching" is necessary to ensure that the heap decomposes properly. One layer must contain "carbonaceous" materials (mainly autumn leaves, straw, and dried hay), the other "nitrogenous" materials (mainly grass clippings and spent garden plants). Between layers, I usually toss a light covering of soil. Vegetable peelings and trimmings from the kitchen also go onto the pile as they are available, as do egg shells and coffee grounds. Every few weeks I turn the layers with a pitch fork to keep the pile from matting down. In dry weather, I sprinkle the material with a garden hose to speed decomposition.*

19. My grandmother, my mother, and I are philatelists—just three of the many thousands of philatelists living in the United States. No, we don't belong to a secret cult, nor do we practice strange rituals. While the word may sound strange, its meaning is very simple. A philatelist is a stamp collector, one who loves postage stamps. Philatelists collect and study postage stamps, stamped envelopes, postmarks, postcards, and all the paraphernalia connected with postal history. Most people know at least something about stamp collecting, if only from recent efforts by the U.S. Postal Service to promote the hobby. But philately today is far more than a hobby; it is a big business in

which investors spend millions of dollars speculating in rare stamps.*

20. Route 301, an inland route—to be taken in preference to the coast road, with its lines of trucks from the phosphate plants—passes through a lot of swampland, some scraggly pinewoods, and acre upon acre of strawberry beds covered with sheets of black plastic. There are fields where hairy, tough-looking cattle snatch at the grass between the palmettos. There are aluminum warehouses, cinder-block stores, and trailer homes in patches of dirt with laundry sailing out behind. There are Pentecostal churches and run-down cafes and bars with rows of pickup trucks parked out front.[30]

9.2   Practicing Paragraph Functions (*BHW* 9a–i)

Select four of the functions discussed in Chapter 9 of *The Borzoi Handbook for Writers,* and write a paragraph illustrating each one. Draw your topics from the following list, or develop topics of your own. The sample paragraphs in Exercise 9.1 and in Chapter 9 of the *Handbook* may be useful models.

TOPICS

A.   Create a vivid description
   1. Describe a person. Concentrate on physical appearance, clothing, or mannerisms. Use concrete details to give the reader a dominant impression of the person.
   2. Describe a place—a room, a view from the window of a moving car, a quiet spot in the park. Give the reader a vivid sense of the place, its sights, sounds, and smells.
   3. Describe an orange, an apple, a banana, or another fruit or vegetable for someone who has never seen it before. Give a vivid impression that appeals to sight, touch, smell, taste, and maybe even hearing (e.g., the sound of someone biting into a crisp apple).
B.   Recount an event
   4. Recall a childhood memory, a brief incident that caused you to see something in a new light. The insight or point of the story can be stated at the beginning or saved for the end.
   5. In a paragraph, tell a good joke or brief story that ends with a punch line.
C.   Illustrate a point with details

6. Write a paragraph illustrating one of the following points:
   - Recent movies demonstrate Americans' fascination with violence.
   - Several buildings on campus illustrate the best (or worst) in contemporary architecture.
   - Television advertisements present stereotypical, and often degrading, images of women (or men).

D. Support a point with reasons
   7. Write a paragraph giving reasons to support one of the following points:
      - It *is* possible to get a well-balanced meal at a fast-food restaurant.
      - Blue jeans are the most versatile article of clothing in a college student's wardrobe.
      - Procrastination is the worst vice of college students.

E. Draw a comparison or contrast
   8. Write a paragraph comparing or contrasting one of the following:
      - Two similar pieces of equipment or two tools (tennis rackets, corkscrews, ink pens, etc.)
      - Two ways of doing something (taking lecture notes, studying for a test, baiting a fishing hook, frying an egg, etc.)
      - Your current attitude toward something and your attitude in the past

F. Analyze causes or effects
   9. Write a paragraph on one of the following:
      - Effects of aging as you observe them in yourself or in someone you know
      - Effects of falling in love (feel free to treat this topic seriously or humorously)
      - Causes for the popularity of a particular singer, actor, or politician
      - Causes for your success in accomplishing something difficult (giving up cigarettes, passing calculus, learning to speak French)

G. Clarify the meaning of a term or concept
   10. Write a paragraph in which you introduce a hobby, trade, or profession by defining its technical name. Use the unfamiliar term to spark the reader's curiosity. Then proceed with your definition and discussion. Suggested terms: *spelunker, numismatist, lapidarist, discographer, ichthyologist.*

11. Define one of the following slang terms (or one of your own choice) for someone who has never heard it before: *turkey, dude, teenybopper, yuppie, burnout.* Use examples to make the definition sharp and vivid.

H. Show the parts or steps that make up a whole

12. Write a paragraph explaining how to do one of the following:
    - The best way to study for an exam or another academic assignment
    - A foolproof way to cook something (see the "strawberry shortcake" paragraph in Exercise 7.8, page 110)
    - The way *not* to do something (try a humorous approach)

I. Develop an analogy:

13. Write a paragraph in which you develop one of the following analogies:
    - _____ is like going to the dentist.
    - _____ is like floating in a swimming pool all day.
    - _____ is like watching a football game while wearing ear plugs.
    - Eating pizza is like _____.
    - Choosing a career (or major) is like_____.
    - Writing a paper is like_____.

10

Opening
and Closing
Paragraphs

OPENING PARAGRAPHS

10.1 Evaluating Opening Paragraphs
(*BHW* 10a–g)

Evaluate the following opening paragraphs, deciding how effectively each one engages the reader's interest, establishes the writer's voice and stance, and announces a main point. Does the opening invite you to continue reading? Why? Be prepared to discuss your findings in class. The notes in brackets will help you determine whether an opening is appropriate for the type of essay indicated.

1. [A student essay about the changing roles of men and women]

    Many people believe that the women's movement has come and gone without making even a dent in society at all. I believe differently.

Anyone can look around and find evidence that the women's movement has made a difference, and it is not yet dead or gone. Before the
movement, everyone's role was clear and defined. Today, things are
not quite so simple. People actually have to stop and think about their
roles as men and women in the workplace, the family, and the community. In my view, this increased awareness of gender roles has been a
healthy side effect of the women's movement.*

2. [An article, published in *National Geographic*, about the popularity
   and commercial success of the kiwifruit]

   Thirty years ago, growing up in New Zealand, I often sliced into a
   brown berry that looked like a duck's egg in a bristly hair shirt.
   Repulsive? Not really, for I knew a secret: The berry's odd appearance
   disguised an equally exotic interior, a sunburst of neat white streaks
   radiating from a cream-colored core, past tiny black seeds and into
   shimmering green flesh. Sweet-tart in taste, it seemed a succulent
   blend of strawberry, banana, melon, and pineapple flavors. Delicious!
   I loved the kiwifruit.

   I still do, and today this peculiar product of a woody vine is
   captivating palates outside New Zealand at an extraordinary pace. In
   1986 more than a billion kiwifruit, once called Chinese gooseberries,
   were tucked into trays and shipped to at least 30 nations. Thousands
   of acres are newly planted each year in a dozen countries, including
   the United States, France, Japan, and Italy, the leading producers after
   New Zealand. [31]

3. [A student essay arguing for improvements in marriage and family
   development courses]

   In recent years there have been many marriage and family development courses organized on both the high school and college levels.
   Most of these courses emphasize the emotional relationship of husband and wife; often, they stress the importance of child rearing. Of
   course, this type of information can be very helpful to the couple in
   the future, but I believe that the more immediate need for a beginning
   family is a practical understanding of financial matters. Without the
   proper management of money, it is difficult for a couple to start out
   on a solid footing. I believe, therefore, that marriage and family
   development courses should be designed to emphasize the financial
   situation of the couple instead of the emotional one.*

4. [A student paper summarizing the first book reviews of George Orwell's *1984*]

In 1949 George Orwell published his anti-utopian novel *1984*. The first critics to read the book had diverse reactions. They disagreed about the book's purpose and criticized Orwell's skills as a novelist. Some were appalled by the picture of the future created in the book, while others praised Orwell for exposing the evils of totalitarianism. Although Orwell confused some reviewers with his style and technique, most critics agreed that his purpose was to illustrate the dangers of political power.*

5. [A magazine article describing "straight-A illiterates," well-educated people unable to write simply and clearly enough to communicate]

Despite all the current fuss and bother about the extraordinary number of ordinary illiterates who overpopulate our schools, small attention has been given to another kind of illiterate, an illiterate whose plight is, in many ways, more important, because he is more influential. This illiterate may, as often as not, be a university president, but he is typically a Ph.D., a successful professor and textbook author. The person to whom I refer is the straight-A illiterate, and the following is written in an attempt to give him equal time with his widely publicized counterpart.[32]

6. [A student essay on the theme of charity in Eudora Welty's story "A Worn Path"]

It is interesting to consider the various meanings of the word "charity." Everyone has a different idea of what charity is. *Webster's New World Dictionary* defines it as "love for one's fellow men" or "leniency in judging others." These definitions are applicable to the main character in Eudora Welty's "A Worn Path," but they don't fit all the other characters.*

7. [A magazine editorial urging better treatment for nurses]

The media are pretty unkind to nurses. Either they are disingenuously insulted by those who urge women to study medicine instead of nursing, or they are gratuitously patronized when they use militant tactics to improve their pay and conditions.

It's time to reassess nurses' status, their image, and, most urgent of all, their appalling pay and working conditions.[33]

8. [A magazine article about the ingredients included in hot dogs]

I used to wonder what goes into a hot dog. Now I know and I wish I didn't.[34]

9. [A magazine article evaluating the Strategic Defense Initiative]

It seemed like a good idea at the time. In a speech on March 23, 1983, President Ronald Reagan described his vision of "intercept[ing] and destroy[ing] strategic ballistic missiles before they reached our own soil . . . an effort which holds the promise of changing the course of human history." Nicknamed "Star Wars," the defense shield would replace the terror of mutually assured destruction (MAD) with the promise of demolishing any missiles coming America's way. From the start, though, many physicists and military officers warned that Star Wars was technologically impossible. Now, $30 billion later, there's evidence that the Strategic Defense Initiative Office (SDIO), as the Star Wars command is known, saw the flaws all along—and knowingly masked the program's failures and overstated its progress just to keep the money rolling in.[35]

10. [A student essay on an assigned topic: Explore a word that intrigues you, using information found in the *Oxford English Dictionary* (*OED*)]

There it was, rolling and tumbling down the mountainside. A boulder had worked itself loose, and now, trailed by pebbles and dust, it bounded off a ledge and sailed through the air. Gaining speed, it quickly crashed through the branches of the tall pines. In seconds it was over. There was no echo: the monstrous boulder had landed in the hot sand with only a dull thump.

Thump. A simple word—a noun and a verb—that, according to the *OED,* is a "mere imitation of a noise." But like most words, *thump*'s simplicity is deceptive. Besides having a 400-year history, it has a marvelous sound; saying it requires a unified action of the teeth, tongue, lips, vocal chords, and, above all, the stomach.*

11. [A student essay on the same topic as item 10]

When assigned a paper on a word, I had no idea where to begin. How could I write 500 words about a single word? Most words have several meanings and interesting histories. I was surprised to find that the OED includes thirteen volumes with thousands of words. English has the largest vocabulary of any language, and the *OED* is the largest dictionary. After browsing through a volume of the *OED*, I finally decided to write about the word *pumpkin* because it has such an interesting history and so many different meanings.*

12. [A one-page article on world temperatures in 1990, published in *Science News*]

Planet Earth steamed straight into the 1990s with record-setting temperatures that extended the warming trend of the last two decades. In separate statements released last week, two groups of researchers reported that the global average surface temperature during 1990 was the highest in more than a century of weather measurements. [36]

13. [A student essay on the advantages of constructing a two-story home]

This essay will discuss the advantages of building a two-story home instead of a one-story home. I will discuss three benefits of two-story construction: lower building costs, better use of available lot space, and reduced energy costs.*

14. [A book review published in *The New Republic,* a journal of commentary on politics, society, and the arts]

Harold Bloom will appreciate better than anyone the fate of being misread. Having devoted the better part of his career as a literary critic to explicating the necessity of misreading as a prerequisite for what he calls "strong" poetry, it seems poetically just that Bloom's own writing—*The Book of J* in particular, his most recent and best book—should be misinterpreted by nearly everybody, misconstrued as a work of literary criticism about the Bible when in fact it is an audacious if flawed attempt at theology. [37]

15. [A student essay explaining five theories about the cause of depression]

Alex sits alone, quietly listening to the tick of the clock. Each minute seems longer than the one before. He waits. But for what? His only companions are the faceless shadows lurking in the room. It is dusk now. He has nowhere to go, nowhere to turn.

    Alex suffers from depression, a condition that afflicts thousands of Americans each year. Its effects are dramatic, ranging from the disruption of day-to-day living to suicide—the ultimate plea for relief.*

10.2 Finding Effective Openings
(*BHW* 10a–g)

Locate three effective openings in magazines, newspapers, or the essay collection used in your composition course. Look in particular for funnel and baited openers or for introductions that use other tactics recommended in *The Borzoi Handbook for Writers*. Bring the introductions to class, and be prepared to explain why you selected them.

10.3 Revising an Opening (*BHW* 10a–g)

Review the opening paragraphs of the essays you have written thus far in your composition course. Take what you judge to be one of your weaker efforts and revise it, using one of the approaches recommended in *The Borzoi Handbook for Writers*. Bring your revision to class along with the original, and be prepared to discuss the changes.

10.4 Writing an Opening (*BHW* 10a–g)

For the essay you are now drafting, write an opening using one of the approaches recommended in *The Borzoi Handbook for Writers*. If you are an inexperienced writer, a funnel opener (10a) may be the simplest approach, but consider other tactics as well, choosing one that is most likely to engage the reader's interest and establish your voice.

10.5 Evaluating Opening Sentences
(*BHW* 10h)

Imagine that you are an instructor reading these opening sentences from student essays on the general topic of education. Decide which sentences make you want to read further and which do not. What is wrong with the sentences that do not?

1. As a homemaker returning to school after thirty-two years in the kitchen, I expected the worst, and that is just what I got.
2. In this modern world of ours today, every student has a right to his or her own opinion about education.

3. Today's high school graduates and their parents face a nearly insurmountable challenge: paying for a college education.
4. Education is an important part of our society.
5. I feel that a college education is a very meaningful experience.

10.6 Writing Opening Sentences
(*BHW* 10h)

Review the essays you have written thus far in your composition course. Rewrite the opening of one essay, paying particular attention to the first sentence. Do whatever you can to make that sentence as engaging as possible. Remember, however, that a measured, well-crafted sentence is often more engaging than a contrived "shocker" or an artifically clever opening.

CLOSING PARAGRAPHS

10.7 Evaluating Closing Paragraphs
(*BHW* 10i–m)

Read the essays identified below and evaluate their closing paragraphs. Does each essay end with an appropriate sense of completion? Does each writer succeed in leaving a strong impression? Explain.

1. "Teachers' Tests," p. 39 (Review 10m in *The Borzoi Handbook for Writers.*)
2. "Death from the Sky," p. 45
3. The essay on page 66, Exercise 5.4 (Compare the draft with the final version.)
4. "Death of a Canyon," p. 77
5. "Behind the Scenes," p. 81
6. "My Parents: Playing in Harmony," p. 86
7. "Turning Citizens into Suckers," p. 90
8. "When It Rains It Pours," p. 389
9. "Clever Hans and His Effect: Horse Sense about Communicating with Animals," p. 400

10.8 Finding Effective Closing Paragraphs (*BHW* 10i–m)

Locate three effective closing paragraphs in magazines, newspapers, or the essay collection used in your composition course. Bring the paragraphs to class, and be prepared to explain why you selected them.

10.9 Revising Closing Paragraphs (*BHW* 10i–m)

Review the closing paragraphs of the essays you have written thus far in your composition class. Take what you judge to be one of your weaker efforts and revise it, following the advice in *The Borzoi Handbook for Writers*. Bring your revision to class along with the original, and be prepared to discuss the changes.

10.10 Review Exercise: Exploring Paragraphs in Context—Student Essays (*BHW* Chapters 7, 8, and 10)

Read one of the student essays listed below and mark several paragraphs that illustrate the principles covered in Chapters 7, 8, and 10 of *The Borzoi Handbook for Writers*. Specifically, locate admirable examples of (1) paragraph unity and continuity, (2) paragraph structure and development, and (3) opening and closing paragraphs (you may have already located closing paragraphs for Exercise 10.7).

1. "Death of a Canyon," p. 77
2. "Behind the Scenes," p. 81
3. "My Parents: Playing in Harmony," p. 86
4. "Turning Citizens into Suckers," p. 90
5. "When It Rains It Pours," p. 389
6. "Clever Hans and His Effect: Horse Sense about Communicating with Animals," p. 400

III

SENTENCES

11

Sentence Clarity

11.1 Identifying Independent Clauses (*BHW* 11a, 17c)

For each sentence in the following passage, underline the "grammatical core"—the independent clause(s), including any modifying elements that are not set off by punctuation. If a sentence contains two independent clauses joined by a coordinating conjunction, circle the conjunction. The first sentence is done for you as an example.

When Nixon agreed to debate Kennedy in a series of national telecasts, the Vice President and his lieutenants were certain that Nixon would enhance his advantage. The Vice President had used the medium to good effect in 1952, and he could now count on a

5   phenomenally large audience. In the 1950s, the number of American families who owned television sets had risen from 4.4 million to 40 million, 88 percent of the nation's families. Millions of Americans—estimates ran as high as 70 million—tuned in to watch the first contest.

10   The outcome was a major surprise. While Nixon seemed

constantly on the defensive, obsessed with scoring debater's points against his rival, Kennedy ignored the Vice President and spoke directly to the nation, enunciating his major theme of national purpose: "I think it's time America started moving again."

15 While Kennedy appeared calm and self-possessed, Nixon seemed tense and haggard (TV cameras were unkind to his features).

Although three more debates followed, they were largely unilluminating encounters in which various issues were so fuzzed over that neither man's position was distinct; it was the first debate

20 that made its mark and, many thought, determined the outcome of the election. Almost all observers agreed that Kennedy had scored a clear triumph; at the very least, he had drawn even with Nixon and could no longer be dismissed as a callow upstart.[1]

11.2 Identifying Independent Clauses in Your Own Writing (*BHW* 11a, 17c)

Copy a page from one of your own essays. Then underline the "grammatical core" of each sentence—the independent clause(s) and any modifying elements that are not set off by punctuation.

11.3 Identifying Clear Sentences (*BHW* 11a–d)

Circle the subjects and verbs in the following sentences; then decide which sentence in each pair has a clearer main idea—a stronger alignment between meaning and grammatically important words. Circle the letter of the sentence you choose.

Example: (a) There (was) (agreement) by the candidates to answer all questions.

(b) The (candidates) (agreed) to answer all questions.

142

1. (a) Our expectation was to finish the job in three months.

   (b) We expected to finish the job in three months.

2. (a) A report from the Commission on Central America received study by the president.

   (b) The president studied a report from the Commission on Central America.

3. (a) After receiving complaints from several people, the FBI investigated Bilko's mail-order division.

   (b) An investigation of Bilko's mail-order division was initiated after the FBI received complaints from several people.

4. (a) The senator voted against the bill because he believed that the dairy industry was already burdened by needless government regulation.

   (b) The reason for the senator's negative vote in regard to the bill was his belief that the dairy industry was already burdened by needless government regulation.

5. (a) The hiring of unskilled workers to fill the positions necessitates an investigation by the agency.

   (b) The agency must find out why unskilled workers were hired to fill the positions.

11.4 Revising Sentences to Align Meaning with Subjects and Verbs (*BHW* 11a–d)

Revise the following sentences to clarify main ideas. For sentences 1–5, use the underlined word to form the subject. Your goal should be to make each sentence as readable as possible.

Example: The use of computers is now increasing in many <u>professional</u> fields.

Today, more and more professionals use computers.

1. A <u>presidential</u> warning was issued in order to stop further news leaks at the Justice Department.

   _____

   _____

2. Humans are sometimes attacked and eaten by <u>lions</u> that are too old to attack their usual prey.

   _____

   _____

3. The main type of music played by the <u>group</u> is bluegrass music.

   _____

   _____

4. The change to a later time for <u>our</u> second meeting was thought to be necessary because the first meeting, which was held early, was poorly attended. [Change *our* to *we.*]

   _____

   _____

   _____

5. The thing that should be of most concern to <u>instructors</u> is that students sometimes are unable to synthesize the many facts they are given in courses.

   _____

   _____

   _____

144

For sentences 6–10, convert the underlined noun into the main verb of the sentence. Make any other changes necessary to clarify main ideas.

Example: The <u>filing</u> of legal proceedings against the dog's owner occurred after Patrick was attacked.

After he was attacked by the dog, Patrick filed a lawsuit against its owner.

6. I finally reached an <u>understanding</u> of the point being made by the lecturer.

_____

_____

7. The <u>discovery</u> of how to make cheese occurred thousands of years ago in human history.

_____

_____

8. <u>Revisions</u> of departmental policy occur at the director's level.

_____

_____

9. A <u>need</u> exists for the university to make improvements in the quality of food in the dormitories.

_____

_____

10. The scientists conducted an <u>investigation</u> into the relationships within a large herd of giraffes in order to arrive at a determination of the strength of the bonds between female giraffes and their calves.

_____

_____

_____

Note: As you will see in the following exercise, using active voice often clarifies main ideas. Keep in mind, however, that passive voice has legitimate uses—in some scientific writing, for example, or when the writer wishes to shift emphasis from the performer of the action to the thing being acted upon. For additional practice in recognizing and using passive forms, see Exercises 31.3 and 31.4, pages 335–338.

11.5 Revising Sentences to Eliminate Passive Voice (*BHW* 11e)

Underline passive verb forms in the following sentences. Then rewrite each sentence, making the verbs active. If you consider the passive form preferable in a particular sentence, put a check mark in the left margin, and be prepared to justify your choice. (In some cases—as in the example—you will need to supply a subject for the sentence.)

Example: During the three years of study in Africa, it <u>was observed</u> that wildebeests <u>were killed</u> by lions more often than any other prey.

During three years of study in Africa, one scientist observed that lions killed wildebeests more often than any other prey.

1. A pride of lions is formed by one or more family groups.

2. Cooperation is often used by pride members when they hunt.

3. Prey is sometimes chased by one lion toward another one waiting in ambush.

146

4. The lion—king of beasts—is often feared more than the tiger, but tigers are, in fact, larger and fiercer than lions.

_____

_____

5. It is often thought that lions kill freely and easily.

_____

_____

6. In fact, they often fail to catch their prey; on rare occasions they are even killed by the intended victim.

_____

_____

7. We know, for example, that a lion can be killed by blows from an adult giraffe's powerful legs.

_____

_____

8. When lions do manage to kill a giraffe, the carcass can be used as a source of food for several days.

_____

_____

9. Young giraffes rather than adults are killed most often.

_____

_____

10. Though it is a fairly rare occurrence, giraffes are sometimes pulled into rivers or pools and drowned by hungry crocodiles.

_____

_____

_____

11.6   Revising Sentences to Eliminate Deferred Subjects (*BHW* 11f)

Revise the following sentences by eliminating subject-deferring expressions such as *it is, it was, there is, there was*. Make any other changes necessary to clarify the sentences.

Example: There were barely twenty years between the two world wars.

Barely twenty years elapsed between the two world wars.

1.   It is usually the case that children learn to swim faster if they are taught early.

_____

_____

2.   Some say that it is the television that is to blame for poor reading skills today.

_____

_____

3.   It is argued by others that there has not been any serious decline in reading skills.

_____

_____

4.   It is one of her points in the essay that there are similarities between the political systems of the two countries.

_____

_____

_____

5.   It is obvious in the first chapter of the novel that there is a failure of communication between the main characters.

_____

11.7 Review Exercise: Revising for Sentence Clarity (*BHW* 11a–g)

The following paragraphs are sluggish and hard to read, partly because of sentences that lack clear main ideas. Underline the key words in each sentence—the ones that should carry the main meaning. Then revise for maximum clarity.

PASSAGE 1

The failure of public school education is becoming a highly publicized issue in the media. Educators and politicians are concerned by the increasing evidence of low test scores and the number of unprepared high school graduates. This concern has led to feder-
5   ally and locally funded studies of improvements that could be used to improve the system. One such study is being conducted in Austin, Texas, by the Select Committee on Public Education. Among the committee's many recommendations is a suggestion which Texans will find hard to accept. The Select Committee has
10   determined that the extreme emphasis on athletics in the Texas public schools is part of the problem. Strong evidence has been presented in an attempt to convince the public that cutbacks in athletic programs are necessary.*

PASSAGE 2

As predicted, results in the present study show very clearly that a smile could make a person more likeable. Moreover, a smile literally increased one's face value. This positive evaluation effect is shown by the several attributes, apparently unrelated to smiling
5   (being intelligent, good, bright, nice, pleasant), being ascribed to the smiling person. The fringe benefits of smiling seemed generous. The present study also found that the attraction effect of smiling tended to be more obvious on the male face.[2]

11.8   Review Exercise: Peer Editing
for Sentence Clarity (*BHW* 11a–g)

Exchange drafts with a classmate—either a paragraph or a complete essay—and read each other's work for unclear sentences. First, underline the "grammatical core" (independent clause) of each sentence, as you did for Exercise 11.1. Then circle the subject and verb. Finally, study the underlined part of the sentence in isolation, checking to see whether meaning is aligned with grammatically important words, especially the subject and verb. Mark any unclear sentences and return the draft to your classmate for revision.

Besides looking for poor alignment between meaning and grammatically important words, check for these additional signs of unclear expression:

1. Excessive use of the verb *to be* (*is, are, was, were, has been,* etc.)
2. Unnecessary use of passive voice
3. Unnecessary use of deferred subjects (*it is, there is, there are, there were,* etc.)
4. Unnecessary use of *that* or *what* clauses

12

Subordination

12.1 Identifying Subordination (*BHW* 12a)

Look in a book or magazine for a passage that contains subordination. Photocopy or write out the passage and underline the subordinate material. Be prepared to explain how the author uses subordination to achieve economy and to emphasize main ideas.

12.2 Identifying Subordination in Your Own Writing (*BHW* 12a)

Photocopy or write out a page from one of your own essays. Underline the subordinate material, and be prepared to explain how the subordination helps emphasize main assertions. Make note of any passage where your writing might be improved by further subordination.

12.3 Revising to Eliminate Vague Subordination (*BHW* 12b)

Rewrite the following sentences to eliminate vague subordination. Make any other changes necessary to clarify the sentences. (Your revisions need not contain free subordinate elements.)

Example: In terms of greatness, historians regard Abraham Lincoln as
one of our best presidents.

*Historians regard Abraham Lincoln as
one of our greatest presidents.*

1. With regard to Susan's request for a vacation in July, we decided to
postpone it until August.

   _____

   _____

2. In the area of grades, I did very well last semester.

   _____

   _____

3. Seeing as how we were best friends ten years ago, why can't we get
along now?

   _____

   _____

4. As far as math, I have nothing to worry about.

   _____

   _____

5. I don't think you and I are in full agreement in connection with your
plan to spend the summer living rent-free at my parents' beach house.

   _____

   _____

12.4 Subordination: Combining Pairs
of Sentences (*BHW* 12a–d)

Combine each pair of sentences, turning one into a phrase or subordinate
clause in the other.[3]

Example: Michael Hutchins and Victoria Stevens spent several years studying mountain goats in Olympic National Park. They hoped to help the National Park Service develop a plan for managing the animals.

In an effort to help the National Park Service develop a plan for managing its mountain goats, Michael Hutchins and Victoria Stevens spent several years studying the animals in Olympic National Park.

or

Because Michael Hutchins and Victoria Stevens spent several years studying mountain goats in Olympic National Park, they may be able to help the National Park Service develop a plan for managing the animals.

1. Cougars, bobcats, coyotes, and golden eagles inhabit the Olympic Mountains. Hutchins and Stevens found little solid evidence that these animals prey on mountain goats.

   _____

   _____

   _____

   _____

2. An essential feature of the mountain goat's habitat is the alpine meadows. These meadows provide the animal's major food resource.

   _____

   _____

153

3. Mountain goats are like most animals inhabiting temperate regions. They must cope with seasonal fluctuations in food availability.

4. Food is abundant in the summer. Mountain goats then consume quantities in excess of their daily needs.

5. Mountain goats have a craving for salt. Mineral licks are an important part of the mountain goat's ecology.

6. National Park Service officials stopped providing salt for goats several years ago. They noticed that excessive trampling in the area of the salt lick was destroying plant life.

7. Mountain goats are particularly susceptible to overheating. Their digestive system has a built-in furnace.

8. Goats have colonies of microorganisms in their stomachs. These microorganisms generate heat as a result of their own metabolic processes.

9. This heat is combined with the goat's own heat and with solar radiation. The excess heat can cause thermal stress.

10. A mountain goat is often overheated and harassed by insects. It may lie in dirt and throw cool soil over its body with a foreleg.

12.5 Using Free Subordinate Elements
(*BHW* 12a–d)

Write ten sentences that contain free subordinate elements. Put brackets around the subordinate material. (Suggested topics: politics, popular music, reading and writing, required college courses.)

For sentences 1–6, use a free element at the beginning of the sentence to explain or place a condition on the main idea.

Example: [After the senator spoke with a group of her constituents,] she decided to vote for the farm bill.

155

1. _____
_____
_____

2. _____
_____
_____

3. _____
_____
_____

4. _____
_____
_____

5. _____
_____
_____

6. _____
_____
_____

For sentences 7–8, use a free element at the end of the sentence to add a further thought.

Example: The president called the bill a boon for the economy, [a measure that would greatly increase farm production.]

7. _____

_____

_____

8. _____

_____

_____

For sentences 9–10, use a free element in the middle of the sentence to modify a particular word.

Example: *Most farmers agreed that the bill, [a measure to lower interest rates], would greatly increase farm production.*

9. _____

_____

_____

10. _____

_____

_____

12.6   Gaining Clarity through Free Subordination (*BHW* 12a–d)

The following sentences are awkward because of excessive bound subordination. Underline the bound elements. Then rewrite each sentence, converting all or part of the underlined material into free subordinate elements. Make any other changes necessary to clarify the sentence.[4]

Example: An academic achievement test that was given to 600 sixth-graders from eight countries resulted in the finding that U.S. students scored last in mathematics, sixth in science, and fourth in geography.

In an academic achievement test given to 600 sixth-graders in eight countries, U.S. students scored last in mathematics, sixth in science, and fourth in geography.

1. More than a fifth of the students from one U.S. school that participated in the part of the test designed to determine whether students had a knowledge of geography could not locate the United States on a map of the world.

    _____

    _____

    _____

    _____

2. The warming of the Pacific Ocean called *El Niño* that spawned so much bad weather on the West Coast last winter also slowed the earth's rotation, according to meteorologists from Boston's Atmospheric and Environmental Research, Inc.

    _____

    _____

    _____

158

3. The warm waters from *El Niño* created atmospheric pressures that were greater on the eastern side of mountain ranges and slowed the earth enough that the phenomenon created an extra one-fifth of a millisecond per day.

4. Researchers at the University of Western Australia have invented a robot to shear sheep that has been used on hundreds of sheep during four years of testing while breaking the skin of the animals only a dozen or so times.

5. The developers of the machine are working on a new model that may raise the amount of wool shorn per sheep from 70 to 95 percent that they hope will help fill the dwindling ranks of people who shear sheep.

12.7 Review Exercise: Using Subordination to Combine Sentences (*BHW* 12a–d)

Combine each group of sentences into a single sentence, using at least one subordinate element, either bound or free. Experiment with several combinations until you find one that states the point clearly and concisely. Write your final version in the space provided.[5]

Example: The dandelion spreads rapidly. One year a single plant may grow in a field. A few years later the field may be covered with dandelions.

> *Because dandelions spread so rapidly, they may cover an entire field only a few years after a single plant has taken root there.*

1. Dandelion leaves have jagged "teeth." The French called the plant *dent-de-lion*. This means "lion's tooth."

2. The French name for the plant was adopted into the English language. *Dent-de-lion* came to be known as dandelion. The plant's scientific name is *Taraxacum officinale*.

3. Dandelion stalks are hollow. A white, sticky sap oozes out from the cut end of this stalk. At one time scientists tried to make rubber out of this sap.

_____

_____

_____

_____

4. Scientists had little success in making rubber. There is a Russian dandelion known as *kok-saghyz*. This plant does yield rubber.

_____

_____

_____

_____

5. Dandelions have their uses. The fleshy root is a food for some people. They scrape the roots. Then they slice them. Then they boil them in salt water.

_____

_____

_____

_____

6. The island of Minorca is east of Spain. The people there once stayed alive by eating dandelions. A swarm of locusts had destroyed all other green plants on the island.

_____

_____

_____

_____

7. Dandelions are also used to make a beverage. The roots are cleaned. Then they are baked and ground. The result of this process is used as a coffee substitute or mixed with regular coffee.

_____

_____

_____

_____

8. Many consider young dandelion leaves a tasty vegetable. The leaves of plants are gathered in early spring. They haven't flowered yet. The leaves are mixed with other greens in salads.

_____

_____

_____

_____

9. The leaves of older plants are not used. They are too bitter. Seed houses have been developing new dandelion strains. These have larger leaves. The leaves taste better than wild dandelion leaves.

_____

_____

_____

_____

10. Dandelion leaves can be cooked like spinach. When cooked, they lose some of their vitamin value. The leaves are rich in vitamins A and B. They also contain calcium, phosphorus, and iron.

_____

_____

_____

_____

12.8 Review Exercise: Using Subordination in a Paragraph (12a–d)

Combine the following sentences into a paragraph that contains several free subordinate elements. You may want to combine each numbered group of sentences into a single sentence, but you need not do so. There is no single correct answer; the example suggests one possible combination for the first group.*

Example: When light came, I spotted two deer, a doe and a fawn.

1. Light came. I spotted two deer. One was a doe. The other was a fawn.

2. They highstepped through the grass. The grass was tall. They were in a clearing. They walked as if they were trying not to make a sound.

3. Suddenly they became frisky. Maybe the cold weather made them playful. Maybe it was the sun. It now shone through the tall grass. It seemed to raise their spirits.

4. Then something happened. The two deer vanished. Another one appeared. It was a magnificent buck.

5. The deer strutted. He was like a king. He came through an opening in the brush. He gradually moved closer.

6. My hands shook. I eased the gun up. I eased it up to my shoulder. I squeezed off a shot.

7. The shot broke the silence. The buck was startled. He crashed through the dense brush. He disappeared among the trees.

12.9 Review Exercise: Peer Editing for Improved Subordination (12a–d)

Exchange drafts with a classmate—either a paragraph or a complete essay—and read each other's work to identify passages that could use further subordination. In particular, mark sentences that might be combined to highlight key ideas while giving lesser emphasis to minor points. After you have finished, return the drafts and discuss them.

13

Sentence Emphasis and Variety

EMPHASIS

Note: The next three exercises will help you identify and use parallel elements. For additional practice with parallelism, see Exercises 23.1–23.3, pages 273–277.

13.1   Recognizing Parallel Elements (*BHW* 13a)

Underline parallel elements in the following sentences. Then arrange the elements in groups to indicate parallel relationships, numbering each group as indicated in the example.[6]

Example: Let every nation know, whether it wishes us <u>well</u> or <u>ill</u>, that

we shall <u>pay any price,</u> <u>bear any burden,</u> <u>meet any hardship,</u>

support any friend, oppose any foe to assure the <u>survival</u> and the <u>success</u> of liberty.

① well/ ill② pay any price/ bear any burden/ meet any hardship/ support any friend/ oppose any foe③ survival/ success

1. We observe today not a victory of party but a celebration of freedom, symbolizing an end as well as a beginning, signifying renewal as well as change.

2. If a free society cannot help the many who are poor, it cannot save the few who are rich.

3. Together let us explore the stars, conquer the deserts, eradicate disease, tap the ocean depths, and encourage the arts and commerce.

4. Now the trumpet summons us again—not as a call to bear arms, though arms we need; not as a call to battle, though embattled we are; but a call to bear the burden of a long twilight struggle, year in and year out, "rejoicing in hope, patient in tribulation," a struggle

against the common enemies of man: tyranny, poverty, disease, and war itself.

_____

_____

_____

_____

5. And so my fellow Americans, ask not what your country can do for you; ask what you can do for your country.

_____

_____

13.2 Using Anticipatory Patterns
(*BHW* 13b)

Write five sentences using the anticipatory pattern indicated in parentheses. (Suggested topics: teachers, clothing styles, holiday customs.)

Example: (more *x* than *y*) *There is more reason to doubt his motives than to count on his financial support.*

1. (both *x* and *y*) _____

_____

_____

2. (either *x* or *y*) _____

_____

_____

3. (neither *x* nor *y*) _____

_____

_____

4. (not only *x* but also *y*) _____

_____

_____

5. (so *x* that *y*) _____

_____

_____

13.3 Using Series (*BHW* 13c)

Use each of the following series in a sentence. Make the series consistent, and arrange it in a climactic order.

Example: (madly in love, very photogenic, rich)

> *They were everything a celebrity couple should be: rich, madly in love, and very photogenic.*

1. (liberty, the pursuit of happiness, life)

_____

_____

_____

2. (discipline, hard work, persistence)

_____

_____

3. (school, home, work)

_____

_____

_____

4. (navy blue, hot pink, gray, black)

_____

_____

_____

5. (go home, get a good night's rest, take my medicine)

_____

_____

_____

VARIETY

13.4 Identifying Sentence Variety
(*BHW* 13f–l)

In the space provided, list several features that give sentence variety to each passage. Be prepared to discuss your findings in class. An item in the first passage is identified as an example.

PASSAGE 1

I drove to Brattleboro to read poems at the new Unitarian church there in a state of dread and exhaustion. How to summon the vitality needed? I had made an arrangement of religious poems, going back to early books and forward into the new book not yet
5 published. I suppose it went all right—at least it was not a disaster—but I felt (perhaps I am wrong) that the kind, intelligent people gathered in a big room looking out on pine trees did not really want to think about God. His absence (many of the poems speak of that) or His presence. Both are too frightening.[7]

lines 2–3——author uses a question _____

_____

_____

PASSAGE 2

Among the vices of age are avarice, untidiness, and vanity, which last takes the form of a craving to be loved or simply admired. Avarice is the worst of those three. Why do so many old persons, men and women alike, insist on hoarding money when they have
5   no prospect of using it and even when they have no heirs? They eat the cheapest food, buy no clothes, and live in a single room when they could afford better lodging. It may be that they regard money as a form of power; there is a comfort in watching it accumulate while other powers are dwindling away. How often
10   we read of an old person found dead in a hovel, on a mattress partly stuffed with bankbooks and stock certificates! The bankbook syndrome, we call it in our family, which has never succumbed.[8]

PASSAGE 3

There are many ironies to the English colonization of Ireland. Politically, Ireland is a trauma. English armies have trampled on Irish sovereignty for over eight hundred years and have shed much blood there. Culturally, the Irish are the traditional butt of "Irish
5   jokes": envied for their eloquence, they are almost in the same breath scorned for their "stupidity." In England, as we have seen, the Anglo-Saxons and the Celts hardly mixed. In Ireland, the strange and sometimes tragic fusion of their two languages has made a culture, spoken and written, that is one of the glories of the
10   English language. The story of English in Ireland throws up many questions: What is the source of our fascination with the Irish

voice? Why *is* Irish literature in English so impressive? And, most elusive of all, what has been the exact influence of the Irish on the English language itself?[9]

_____

_____

_____

_____

_____

_____

13.5 Revising to Eliminate Choppiness (*BHW* 13f–l)

The following passages are taken from elementary school textbooks.[10] Since the writing is aimed at young readers, it consists largely of brief, plain statements with few internal pauses. Revise the passages, varying lengths and types of sentences and using subordination to highlight main ideas. Your goal should be to "raise" the reading level of the passages, making them suitable for a more sophisticated audience. Doing so may involve omitting some information (e.g., the definition of *raft* in the first passage).

PASSAGE 1

Pioneers traveled west in covered wagons. These were pulled by horses or strong cattle called oxen. Families often traveled together in a wagon train, with one covered wagon behind another in a long line.

5   The trip west was not easy. There were no roads across the mountains or through the forests. There were no bridges across the rivers. Sometimes pioneers built large wooden rafts to travel on a river or a lake. Rafts are flat boats. People loaded their wagons onto the rafts and floated along.

10   Travel was very slow. The wagon trains traveled 12 hours a day. Sometimes the pioneers had to stop to make a path for the wagons to cross. Wagons often broke or got stuck in the mud. Then other families would stop to help. The trip west might take as long as six months.[11]

PASSAGE 2

One drug in all tobacco products is **nicotine.** Nicotine makes the heart beat faster. Nicotine also makes the openings of blood vessels smaller than they should be. This makes it hard for blood to flow easily. When the blood vessels become smaller, the heart
5   must pump much harder to move blood throughout the body. The blood pressure rises. High blood pressure can harm the circulatory system.

The smoke of burning tobacco contains a sticky, dark brown substance called **tar.** Sometimes you can see tar spots on windows
10   and walls in rooms where people smoke. Inside a smoker's body, tar coats the tubes leading to the lungs, as well as the lungs. Tar that builds up in the lungs makes it hard for oxygen to pass into the smoker's blood. Because of this, a smoker's body cells get less oxygen than they need for good health.

15   Smokers also get less oxygen because they breathe the carbon monoxide in tobacco smoke. **Carbon monoxide** is one of many poisonous gases made by burning tobacco. Carbon monoxide takes the place of oxygen in the blood when a smoker breathes it. The result is that a smoker's body cells get less oxygen. Cells
20   need oxygen to stay healthy and grow. [12]

PASSAGE 3

But most people in Europe during the Middle Ages were not nobles. They were common people. Most of them lived on the land of the nobles. There were two main groups of commoners: free people and serfs.
5   Free people rented their land from the lord. They were free to leave the land when they chose to do so. They could travel or move to a town. Serfs, on the other hand, were not free. They were tied to the land. A serf needed the lord's permission to leave the land. Serfs were not exactly slaves. They were not completely
10   owned by another person. Sometimes, a serf would get rich enough to buy his or her freedom. [13]

13.6   Varying Sentence Length (*BHW* 13g)

Write a very short sentence to follow each of the long sentences or passages given below. Be prepared to explain the effect you achieved by doing so.

Example: On their second try, after standing in the rain for over an hour, Casey and Karen finally approached the ticket window, confident that *this* time they would see the play.

They didn't.

1. After two weeks on vacation in Nova Scotia, Mr. Wiegand felt more relaxed than he had in years. But the long drive home had tired him, and as he pulled the car around the corner, he thought how wonderful it would be to sleep in his own bed again. As he came to a stop in the driveway, he shuddered at what he saw.

2. After lecturing for nearly two hours on inert gases, Professor Parks turned to the class, pointed to the blackboard, and smiled.

3. Many colleges and universities today claim that they have high admissions standards, that they offer strong preparation in the liberal arts, and that their graduates always find jobs.

4. The Fulmers watered their lawn every week, fertilized it three times during the summer, trimmed it, pampered it, all but talked to it. The next winter was mild, so in the spring they waited patiently for the first sprouts to appear.

5. Besides working full-time as a biologist, Jerry Farr served on the City Council, directed a local charity, and spent what little spare time he had doing volunteer work.

13.7 Practicing Varied Sentence Patterns (*BHW* 13h–l)

Write sentences using the patterns named below. (For model sentences, see the indicated sections of *The Borzoi Handbook for Writers.*)

1. A question, paired with a related declarative sentence (13h)
2. An exclamation, paired with a related declarative sentence (13h)
3. A sentence with a dramatic interruption (13i)
4. A sentence with inverted syntax 13j)
5. A cumulative sentence (13k)
6. A suspended sentence (13l)

13.8 Review Exercise: Exploring Sentences in Context—Student Essays (*BHW* Chapters 11–13)

Read one of the student essays listed below and mark several sentences that illustrate principles covered in Chapters 11 through 13 of *The Borzoi Handbook for Writers*. Specifically, locate admirable examples of distinct expression, subordination, sentence emphasis, and sentence variety. Be prepared to discuss your findings in class.

1. "Death of a Canyon," p. 77
2. "Behind the Scenes," p. 81
3. "My Parents: Playing in Harmony," p. 86
4. "Turning Citizens into Suckers," p. 90
5. "When It Rains It Pours," p. 389
6. "Clever Hans and His Effect: Horse Sense about Communicating with Animals," p. 400

IV
WORDS

14

Appropriate Language

14.1 Using a College Dictionary
(*BHW* 14a)

In order to better understand the features of your college dictionary, use it to complete this exercise.

Name of dictionary _____

A. ABBREVIATIONS AND LABELS

Where does your dictionary explain the abbreviations used in its entries?

_____

_____

How does it abbreviate the following terms?

Example: adjective   *adj.*_____

1. noun   _____

2. conjunction   _____

3. verb _____

4. plural _____

5. transitive verb _____

List five restrictive labels used in your dictionary.

Example: <u>slang</u>_____

6. _____

7. _____

8. _____

9. _____

10. _____

B. PRONUNCIATION

List the pronunciations given by your dictionary for the following words.

Example: Augustine _ô'gəstēn'_   _ô gus'tin_

1. protein _____

2. literature _____

3. harass _____

4. Caribbean _____

5. hangar _____

6. often _____

7. poinsettia _____

8. miniature _____

9. mononucleosis _____

10. New Orleans _____

C. DERIVATION

Use the information given in your dictionary to explain the derivation of the following words.

Example: dandelion *Derived from Middle French, modification of dent de lion, literally tooth of (a) lion, translation of medieval Latin dens leonis, in allusion to the toothed leaves.*

1. daisy _____

2. bloomer (article of clothing) _____

3. astronaut _____

4. optic _____

5. biology _____

6. liberty _____

7. canine _____

_____

_____

8. Catholic _____

_____

_____

9. Jew _____

_____

_____

10. Protestant _____

_____

_____

D. SYNONYMS

Define the word *naive* and the synonyms that follow. Take care to distinguish each word from the others in the list.

1. naive _____

_____

_____

2. innocent _____

_____

_____

3. unsophisticated _____

_____

_____

4. unaffected _____

_____

_____

5. guileless _____

_____

_____

Use your dictionary to locate several synonyms for each of the following words.

Example: social *amiable, companionable, genial, affable*

6. disaster _____

7. wind (noun) _____

8. sensuous _____

9. hide (verb) _____

10. talkative _____

14.2 Editing a Passage for Unidiomatic Expressions (*BHW* 14c)

Edit the following passage to eliminate errors in the use of idiomatic expressions. Consult *The Borzoi Handbook for Writers* or a dictionary as necessary. The first error is corrected for you as an example.

Jane was angry *with* at Martha, her designer. Martha had promised to consult Jane in regards to every change of the project, but when the design was finished, there were dozens of details that didn't conform with Jane's directions. The wall space in the new kitchen was equal with that of the old kitchen, and Martha had been told to reserve space on one wall for Jane's collection of wicker baskets. Instead, Martha had devoted the wall for shelving. When Jane asked Martha why she had departed with the plan, Martha said crisply, "I'm a professional. My judgment is superior than yours." Annoyed of Martha's outrageous condescension (not to mention her unidiomatic English), Jane fired her and hired a new designer who would comply to her wishes. Meanwhile, Jane's husband, Mike, who was oblivious of the whole project, accidentally destroyed Jane's entire wicker collection with leaving a faucet running in the basement where the wicker was stored. Mike, an artist, was preoccupied at the time by his latest work, a 128" by 48" acrylic called *Homage à G. F. Will.* Things eventually worked up. By the advice of her new designer, Jane decided not to replace the wicker. Instead, she agreed—reluctantly— on Mike's proposal to hang his massive canvas where the wicker used to be.

14.3 Identifying Middle Diction
(*BHW* 14d)

Provide a middle diction equivalent for each slang or formal word in the following list. Consult your dictionary as necessary.

Examples: nefarious *evil*

stuck-up *conceited*

1. nerd _____
2. icky _____
3. commence _____
4. buddy _____
5. cheapskate _____
6. misprize _____
7. pernicious _____
8. pulchritude _____

9. imbibe _____

10. mix-up _____

11. booze _____

12. flagellate _____

13. super (adjective) _____

14. masticate _____

15. hyper (adjective) _____

14.4 Recognizing Formal Diction
(*BHW* 14d)

Underline the formal diction in the following passages. Is the diction appropriate given its context? Explain. Note any other features that make the writing formal. Then rewrite one of the passages in a less formal style, relying mainly on middle diction.

1. [Article III, Section 1, of the U.S. Constitution]

   The judicial Power of the United States, shall be vested in one supreme Court, and in such inferior courts as the Congress may from time to time ordain and establish. The Judges, both of the supreme and inferior Courts, shall hold their Offices during good behavior, and shall, at stated Times, receive for their Services, a Compensation, which shall not be diminished during their Continuance in Office.

2. [Abraham Lincoln speaking about the Civil War in his Second Inaugural Address]

   Neither party expected for the war the magnitude or the duration which it has already attained. Neither anticipated that the cause of the conflict might cease with, or even before, the conflict itself should cease. Each looked for an easier triumph, and a result less fundamental and astounding.

3. [A wedding invitation]

> Mr. and Mrs. Alexander Bennington request the honor of your presence at the marriage of their daughter, Christina Lynne, to Mr. Gilbert Everett Fulmer, Saturday, the eighth of November, nineteen hundred and ninety-two, at ten o'clock in the morning, St. David Church, 8500 Ridgeway, Great Neck, New York.

14.5 Recognizing Informal Diction
(*BHW* 14d)

Underline the informal diction or slang in the following passages. Is the diction appropriate given its context? Explain. Note any other features that make the writing informal. Then rewrite one of the passages in a more formal style, relying mainly on middle diction.

1. [Huckleberry Finn, the young narrator of Mark Twain's novel, describing his life after the Widow Douglas adopts him]

> At first I hated the school, and by-and-by I got so I could stand it. Whenever I got uncommon tired I played hookey, and the hiding I got the next day done me good and cheered me up. So the longer I went to school the easier it got to be. I was getting sort of used to the widow's ways, too, and they warn't so raspy on me. Living in a house, and sleeping in a bed, pulled on me pretty right, mostly, but before the weather was cold I used to slide out and sleep in the woods, sometimes, and so that was a rest to me. I liked the old ways best, but I was getting so I liked the new ones, too, a little bit. [1]

2. [American journalist Tom Wolfe describing whiskey runners]

> Whiskey running certainly had a crazy gamelike quality about it, considering that a boy might be sent up for two years or more if he were caught transporting. But these boys were just wild enough for

that. There got to be a code about the chase. In Wilkes County nobody, neither the good old boys or the agents, ever did anything that was going to hurt the other side physically.[2]

3. [A handwritten invitation to a party]

   Tom and I are planning a get-together this Friday night—nothing fancy, just a few folks from the neighborhood. Why don't you drop by for a drink and a bite to eat—around 8 or 8:30. Give us a call if you can't make it.

14.6 Revising to Eliminate Mixed Diction (*BHW* 14d)

The following passage contains an incongruous mixture of formal and informal language. Cross out the inappropriate words and replace them with words that make the passage consistent in its use of middle diction. Make your changes in the space above the lines. One expression is revised for you as an example.

Many British Romantic writers ~~inveighed against~~ *attacked* the established political and social order in their poetical compositions. Blake, for example, really blasts the use of child labor in his poems about the plight of chimney sweeps, little kids who were forced to support themselves because of poverty and government indifference. In "London," Blake goes after a wider range of social ills, criticizing the government, the church, and the military for engendering an atmosphere of repression in nineteenth-century London.

In his lyrical endeavors, Shelley also criticizes the established social order, especially the bigwigs in power. His "England in 1819" is a stinging attack on the King and Parliament, in which he prognosticates a future revolution. In "Song: Men of England,"

Shelley openly calls for English workers to rise up and get rid of the industrial system that puts them down. Even though this poem was written a really long time ago, it is still regarded as an important verbalization about the plight of the British working class.

14.7 Revising to Eliminate Fad Words (*BHW* 14d)

The following passage contains a number of fad words—words generally used as one part of speech that have been awkwardly wrenched into service as another part of speech. Rewrite the passage to eliminate the inappropriate diction.

When he passed out the midterm exam, Professor Frolick announced that he was in no hurry time-framewise. He wanted the exam to be a fun experience that wouldn't stress out anyone in the class. He suggested that we prioritize the questions and then answer the two or three about which we felt most together. The professor said he had authored the exam not to intimidate us but to see how much we had learned informationwise. His goal, he said, was to teach as impactful a course as possible.

14.8 Changing Connotations within a Sentence (*BHW* 14e)

A. Replace the italicized words in the following sentences with words that have more favorable connotations. Write your answers in the space provided.

Example: Nancy's score was *mediocre.*   *average*

1. Ralph has *concocted* another theory about his missing pet raccoon.   _____

2. Art is *finicky* about what he will eat for breakfast.   _____

186

3. The dinner featured a *hodgepodge* of foods
from the Middle East. _____

4. My uncle gave me a *lecture* on the evils of
using snuff. _____

5. I hadn't seen my grandmother in years; I was
surprised by how *decrepit* she had become. _____

B. Replace the italicized words in the following sentences with words
that have less favorable connotations. Write your answers in the space
provided.

Example: Her behavior was *childlike*.   *childish*

6. Mary Jo looked *slender* in her new designer
body stocking. _____

7. Dennis, the *timid* fellow in the corner, needs
a lesson in self-defense. _____

8. What's that horrible *odor*? _____

9. In less than five minutes, Harry *drank* three
large glasses of milk. _____

10. Terry is *plumper* than Tony. _____

14.9   Selecting Words with Appropriate Connotations (*BHW* 14e)

Circle the word in parentheses that carries the appropriate connotation for
the context in which it appears. Be prepared to explain why you selected
the word you did. Consult your dictionary as necessary.

Example: Lydia is the sort of (person/individual) everyone admires.

1. The baker (withdrew/removed) the hot loaves of bread from the oven.

2. The (scent/aroma) of freshly baked bread filled the room.

3. The (aroma/fragrance) of her perfume lingered in the car after she had gone.

4. Ken and Mary Grant were generous people, sharing their (opulence/wealth) with the entire Baraboo community.

5. We all admired the dignity and (pride/arrogance) with which Emma handled her fall from power.

6. In his notes, the biologist observed that the animal exhibited typical (catty/feline) behavior.

7. Dan had little (flair/aptitude) for decorating a room.

8. Despite his effort to make it cozy, the den still felt somewhat (cold/frigid).

9. The king was an imposing presence, (portly/stout) in body and lofty in carriage.

10. Although your paraphrase is generally accurate, it slightly (distorts/falsifies) what I said.

14.10 Eliminating Sexist Language
(*BHW* 14f)

Edit the following sentences to eliminate sexist language and pronouns that needlessly suggest bias. Make your changes in the spaces above the lines.

Example: ~~If~~ A dentist who ~~fails~~ the licensing exam on ~~his~~ first attempt, ~~he~~ the may take it again in six months.

1. The university employs a staff of fifty cleaning ladies.

2. Each student is expected to finish his exam within two hours.

3. The NOW convention featured one session on women in the professions, which included speeches by several lady doctors.

4. According to the standard contract, the landlord or his agent will collect the rent on the first of each month.

5. Emily Dickinson is regarded today as an important poet. During her lifetime, however, Miss Dickinson published almost none of her work.

6. Even if a poet has published widely in periodicals, he will find it difficult to convince someone to publish his first book.

7. Until recently, a beginning grade school teacher in this state could expect her annual salary to be no more than $10,000.

8. The college hired several coeds to work at the bookstore during the first week of school.

9. The invention of movable type is one of man's greatest achievements.

10. As every housewife knows, the price of groceries has risen steadily in the past ten years.

14.11 Translating Jargon into Plain English
(*BHW* 14g)

The following sentences mimic the wordy, pompous kind of jargon often used by government bureaucrats. Translate each sentence into the well-known saying hidden beneath the jargon.

Example: A period of pre-eminence is passed through by each and every canine.

Every dog will have its day.

1. Pulchritude does not penetrate the dermal plane.

   _____

2. It is fruitless to become lachrymal due to scattered lacteal material.

   _____

3. Articles which coruscate are not fashioned from aureate materials, at least not necessarily.

   _____

4. A feathered creature clasped in the manual members is the equivalent valuewise of a brace in the bosky growth.

   _____

5. Immature gallinaceons must not be calculated prior to their being produced.

   _____

6. One can induce an equine quadruped to approach liquid refreshment, but one cannot induce said quadruped to imbibe.

   _____

7. The totality is aright that finalizes aright.

   _____

8. Rapidity of motion spawns detritus.

   _____

9. The slender-leaved plants rooted beyond the barrier appear to possess in nearly all cases enhanced qualities colorwise.

   _____

10. The individual who reclines with canine creatures shall assume an upright posture with insect-type creatures.

    _____

14.12   Translating Plain English into Jargon
        (*BHW* 14g)

Try translating the following sayings into the type of jargon illustrated in
the preceding exercise. A thesaurus may help you find "appropriate"
language.

1. Don't judge a book by its cover.
2. She who laughs last laughs best.
3. A fool and his money are soon parted.
4. A penny saved is a penny earned.
5. All's fair in love and war.

14.13   Revising a Passage to Eliminate
        Jargon (*BHW* 14g)

Underline the jargon in the following passages. Then translate each passage into plain English, eliminating jargon, wordiness, overused expressions, and any other problems that cloud meaning.

PASSAGE 1

    The Department of Systems Management is seeking input from all

personnel regarding the installation of an upgraded, cost-effective

system of telephone-calling instruments in all corporate offices.

The department is prepared to up-front enough funding to upgrade

5   the instruments that are operative at this point in time.

    The decision-making process regarding upgrade-planning

will proceed during the time frame of the next two months. At this

point in time, personnel must initiate a determination of strategies

that will maximize telephone usage efficiency. This office will (1)

10   prioritize those strategies, (2) determine how the strategies will

impact the company, and (3) anticipate ways to facilitate the

installation of new instruments.

This project will attempt to determine the effect of classroom management strategies on the behaviors of learners at the third-grade elementary level. Group A will be managed by means of nonthreatening feedback provided by the classroom teacher: the

5 teacher will ignore negative behaviors and will reward positive behaviors with positive oral feedback. Group B will be managed by punitive retention in the classroom during the recess period. At the end of experimentation, an oral assessment will be obtained from classroom teachers in order to determine experimental out-

10 comes. As a result of the experiment, suggestions will be made to help teachers maximize the effectiveness of classroom management strategies.

14.14 Using Jargon for a Comic Effect
(*BHW* 14g)

In the following piece of writing, a student retells Aesop's fable of the fox and the grapes, using jargon to achieve a comic effect. Study the piece, and be prepared to discuss how the writer's language changes the familiar story: What kind of writing is the student trying to parody? How does she do so? Then write your own version of a fable or fairy tale, trying for a similar effect. Possible topics: the three little pigs, the tortoise and the hare, Goldilocks, Cinderella.

A Particular Fox and Some Grapes

One of the fox's desires is for ambulation, and in an excessively thermal, post-meridianic latitude one particular fox was exercising this quadruped means of self-transportation. While implementing this program of ambulation, he was awakened to the fact that the environment was abundantly populated by both herbaceous annual plants and temperate deciduous varieties.

A species of flora that came to immediate attention was the fruity by-products of V. vinifera's propagatory instincts, lingering above as they always must. Upon spying these, the fox asked himself, "Would these fruits not satisfy my dehydrated condition?" And upon reaching an affirmative internal attitude, the fox adopted an upright posture and propelled himself upward in an effort to achieve his zenith. No luck, for gravity made nadir's approach much more efficient. Again and again he tried to resolve this classic approach-avoidance conflict exemplified by his desire for the fruity byproducts, but his inability to expend sufficient kinetic energy to propel himself within reach resulted in frustration and a violent decline to terra firma.

The conflict was, in essence, resolved when the fox postulated that he was either experiencing a visual hallucination, manifested in the form of grapes and induced by heat prostration and dehydration, or that in the event of their actual existence, said grapes were inclined to be immature and thus highly stimulatory to the bitterness sensors of the tongue surface. And besides, everyone knows that grapes are carcinogenic.*

15

Efficient Language

15.1 Identifying Concrete Language (*BHW* 15a)

Underline examples of concrete language in the following passage, and be prepared to discuss how such language contributes to the effectiveness of the writer's description.

A high school marching band was playing "Yankee Doodle." The air was a confusion of pungent odors: barbecued ribs, wet straw, tacos, and horse manure. In the sky, hovering over a Ferris wheel and the 4-H barns, a blimp advertised a hot tub company. My friend Melanie and I had driven an hour out of the city to go, for the first time, to the Great Geauga County Fair, a classic rural American event.

We started by strolling down the main strip, a street lined with carnival games and food joints. Most of the latter served the usual carnival delicacies: corn dogs, cotton candy, and caramel apples. Others offered more exotic-sounding cuisine: Buffalo Burgers, curly fries, Birch Beer and, for dessert, elephant ears and funnel cakes. The games, advertised by shouting, bored-looking carnies, included everything from a basketball toss to a pellet gun range—all with as much light, sound, and gaudy color as possible.

Near the basketball toss, we stopped to listen to Sister Jean the Ragtime Queen and her partner Laundry Fat. Sister played the piano, Laundry the washboard.

At the end of the strip, we drifted into the 4-H barns. In the first one, massive draft horses with names like Peanut Butter and Jellybean were loaded down with delicate ribbons and streamers. Next door in the swine barn, a pig named McKenzie had taken first prize. Above his stall was a hand-written sign informing us that he weighed forty pounds last April and now, a little over six months later, tipped in at 220 pounds—an average weight gain of almost one pound a day. Beneath the sign, the proud owner had taped a recent Polaroid of McKenzie.*

15.2   Revising for Concreteness (*BHW* 15a)

Because it states a broad conclusion, the following paragraph is necessarily abstract. Write another version of the paragraph in which you rely more heavily on concrete language. You need not follow the order of the original passage sentence by sentence. Instead, try to communicate the same general points, adding detail wherever possible to give the writing more sensory appeal.

Eventually American institutions will have to adjust to the new realities of family life. If families are to be healthy and stable units, the home as well as the economic realm must be more flexible to allow for greater sharing of responsibilities and more available options to men as well as women. Until that time individual women and men will need to negotiate the terms of their private lives in the face of public or institutional constraints and archaic beliefs about what it means to be a man or a woman in American society, and what a stable, happy, and healthy family requires.[3]

15.3 Revising for Concreteness in Your Own Writing (*BHW* 15a)

In a draft of your current essay, find a passage that could be improved by greater concreteness. Revise it and submit a copy of the original along with the revision.

15.4 Revising to Eliminate Wordiness (*BHW* 15b–d)

Revise the following passages to eliminate wordiness. Try several revisions on your own paper. Then copy the most concise version into the space provided. Watch for (1) redundancies, (2) circumlocutions, (3) needless intensifiers, and (4) statements cast in negative form.

Example: Due to the fact that each and every person who came into the showroom would not have anything to do with the salesman, he did not sell a single, solitary car last weekend.

Because every customer in the showroom ignored him, the salesman sold no cars last weekend.

1. Maria said that the possibility exists that she might have the capacity to attend the party with a personal friend.

   _____

   _____

2. As far as the growing expansion of grain surpluses is concerned, it is quite likely that the Secretary of Agriculture might call upon the Congress to give its approval to the sale and exportation of grain to the Russian Republic.

3. In the area of books on scientific subjects, the public library is not without an ample supply of material.

4. Despite the fact that she is only two years of age, Bridget has the ability to do simple arithmetical problems that are more or less an impossibility for most children of her age.

5. It is not possible at the present time to make contact with the people who were witnesses at the time of the accident.

6. We circled around the incredibly steep mountain on a simply horrible road that was very narrow, but when we reached the very top of the mountain, the sensational view was certainly beautiful—not unlike some of the views I had seen in the Alps.

7. The press secretary said, "At this point in time, the president sees no reason to believe that there is cause for alarm in the matter concerning the placement of missiles in Cuba."

8. Each individual person at the seminar was asked to discuss his or her future plans and to explain what the end result of those plans would most likely be.

_____

_____

9. "First and foremost," said Casper, "I really do love your daughter Shirley, and I do so hope, Mr. Mueller, that you understand that I am desirous of asking you to make me the happiest man in the world by giving your blessing to the fact that your daughter and I wish to enter into the state of matrimony . . ." "Cease and desist," shouted Mr. Mueller. "Can't you manage to be less wordy and verbose?"

_____

_____

_____

10. To make a long story short, eliminating excessive wordiness is quite simply a matter of careful revision. First, read and study your rough-draft prose in order to cut and excise verbose redundancies. Second, where circumlocutions are concerned, it is necessary that you find a somewhat shorter and more economical way to replace a needless phrase. Third, try to avoid the awful habit of adding an incredible number of perfectly useless intensifiers that just serve the quite unnecessary purpose of greatly fortifying and exaggerating simple statements that need no fortification or exaggeration. Finally, it is not a good idea to cast statements in a negative form unless it cannot be avoided; the negative form usually does not get the point across in a way that is as uncloudy as the positive form. Sometimes it is even not undifficult for the reader to grasp your meaning.

_____

_____

_____

_____

_____

_____

_____

_____

_____

_____

15.5 Revising to Eliminate Wordiness in Your Own Writing (*BHW* 15b–d)

Check the rough draft of your current essay and find five sentences that could be more concise. Revise them and submit the original sentences with the revisions.

15.6 Eliminating Euphemisms and Clichés (*BHW* 15e–f)

Revise the following passages to eliminate euphemisms and clichés. Try several drafts on your own paper before copying the final version into the space provided. For many passages, you will need to supply new details and thoroughly rewrite the sentences in order to make the language fresh.

Example: My high school graduation is a day I shall never forget. I had the privilege of giving the valedictory address. Unfortunately, I had butterflies in my stomach, and during my speech I felt my heart in my throat. Right in the middle of the speech, I burst into a flood of tears.

Everytime I'm asked to speak before a large group, I think about my high school graduation. I was so nervous about giving the valedictory address that I started crying halfway through the speech.

1. The bumper stickers were selling like hotcakes, which gave John high hopes of earning enough cold, hard cash to pay for his long-awaited vacation at South Padre Island.

_____

_____

_____

_____

2. Mrs. Honeychurch passed away on Tuesday and will be committed to her final resting place on Friday.

_____

_____

3. Travis and Tiffany were head over heels in love, and we all waited with bated breath to see whether they would tie the knot. When we could stand the suspense no longer, Travis explained that they would not be married in the near future because they simply didn't have enough money to make ends meet.

_____

_____

_____

4. Jessie, who had never been on a boat before, spent the day leaning over the railing. She was experiencing a bit of motion discomfort.

_____

_____

5. Because of unforeseen circumstances in his negotiations with the Teamsters, the long-suffering union boss was forced to announce that a strike was a foregone conclusion.

_____

_____

_____

6. In today's modern society, many people get trapped in a vicious circle of earning and spending money.

7. It goes without saying that a nuclear holocaust would pose a grave danger to humanity; we must do everything in our power to see that such a tragedy never occurs.

8. "And I'll be an old-fashioned Virginia housewife again," said Martha. "Steady as a clock, busy as a bee—and cheerful as a cricket." [4]

9. Having sown his wild oats, Pat decided once and for all to settle down and devote himself fully to his career.

10. We heard a bloodcurdling scream in the bedroom. Mother said not to worry. It was just Dwight coming to terms with his feelings. He had been studying with a local primal scream therapist, learning how to handle aggression in a positive way.

16

Figurative Language

16.1 Recognizing Figurative Language (*BHW* 16a–d)

Underline the figurative language in the following passages. Be prepared to point out examples of simile and metaphor and to discuss how the figurative language contributes to the effectiveness of the writing. "Translate" some of the figurative language into literal language and see what is lost in the translation.

1. I was walking by the Thames. Half-past morning on an autumn day.
   Sun in a mist. Like an orange in a fried fish shop.[5]

2. What does education often do? It makes a straight-cut ditch of a free,
   meandering brook.[6]

3. On the smoking skillet he poured the buckwheat batter. It spread like
   lava, the grease spitting sharply. Around the edges the buckwheat
   cake began to firm, then brown, then crisp.[7]

4. As Dan Quayle knows all too well, the vice presidency is the sand trap of American politics. It's near the prize, and designed to be limiting. [8]

5. Clutter is the disease of American writing. We are a society strangling in unnecessary words, circular constructions, pompous frills and meaningless jargon. [9]

6. Women have served all these centuries as looking-glasses possessing the magic and delicious power of reflecting the figure of a man at twice its natural size. [10]

7. When teachers complain of an essay that it lacks detail—a frequent complaint—they usually lament the lack of examples. . . . Examples are necessary to clarify and also to keep the reader from falling asleep. Without generality we lack statement or idea; but without example we lack salt to make the baked idea palatable. [11]

8. But while all those advances [in energy-saving devices and nonpolluting sources of energy] are being perfected, extending the life of the Oil Era remains humanity's best insurance policy against a declining standard of living. We need to hang onto the trapeze we're riding until we get a firm grip on the next trapeze. [12]

9. Watching a newsreel or flipping through an illustrated magazine at the beginning of the American war [WW II], you were likely to encounter a memorable image: the newly invented jeep, an elegant, slim-barrelled 37-mm gun in tow, leaping over a hillock. Going very fast and looking as cute as Bambi, it flies into the air, and behind, the little gun bounces high off the ground on its springy tires. [13]

10. The partitions in the camp were thin and did not extend clear to the

top of the rooms, and as I was always the first up I would dress softly so as not to wake the others, and sneak out into the sweet outdoors and start out in the canoe, keeping close along the shore in the long shadows of the pines. I remembered being very careful never to rub my paddle against the gunwale for fear of disturbing the stillness of the cathedral. [14]

16.2 Evaluating Figurative Language (*BHW* 16a–d)

Underline the figurative language in the following passages, and be prepared to discuss why it is or is not effective. Note any examples of mixed metaphor.

1. When he saw his father's face, Tom's confidence melted like ice cream in August.

2. As time went on, new values were born in the country, and this rebirth shed its light on the old morality.

3. Frank's ideas are like cotton candy—a little bit of sugar and a lot of hot air.*

4. Like all British police officers in Lower Burma, George Orwell lived in a pressure cooker.*

5. The ship of state is drifting off course, and it is the president's responsibility to get us back on the road again.

6. During a spring rain, the attic was a place of wonder. My sister and I would climb the steep pull-down stairs just to hear the rain dancing on the tin roof. At one end of the room we could see the wind-tossed

tree tops licking against the window panes. And when the wind blew up, it whistled merrily under the eaves.*

7. When these students initiated the first sit-ins, their spirit spread like a raging fire across the nation, and the technique of non-violent direct action, constantly refined and honed into a sharp cutting tool, swiftly matured. [15]

8. From the far side of the room, his face looked like the soft, drooping face of a bloodhound. The cheeks sagged heavily under their own weight. The eyes were buried under folds of loose skin. But up close, his face became an intricate roadmap, highways cutting across his forehead, tiny back roads branching out from the corners of his mouth and eyes and twisting their way down his cheeks.*

9. The coffee table bore its household harvest of books, periodicals, half-emptied coffee cups scummed over with cream, a dash of cigarette ashes for good measure, and a heel of French bread. . . . An oval platter served as ashtray, heaped with a homey Vesuvius of cigarette butts, ashes, bits of cellophane from discarded packs, a few martini-soaked olive pits, and a final cigarette stub issuing a frail plume of smoke from the top of the heap, signature of a dying volcano. [16]

10. I had never been in a more outlandish place. Skinny horses covered with heavy red trappings pushed past, loaded down with wood or carpets or scrap metal. Ornate, immensely crowded buses roared their engines. Absurd rickshaws powered by motor scooters squawked like chickens. Fish-sellers wheedled passing customers to consider their wares: strange, scaly objects that had been caught off Karachi, 1500 miles and a good four days away.

There were stalls selling copper pots, or golden slippers that curled at the toes, or lengths of glorious scarlet and purple cloth. A money-changer displayed a jagged scar running from his naked foot almost to his knee. A revolver was tucked into his waistband, over which flowed a generous stomach. Spice merchants dug deeply into small pyramids of yellow saffron and carnelian-colored paprika, leaving overhanging cliffs that could collapse at any time in clouds of pungent, aromatic dust. [17]

16.3 Evaluating Extended Figures of Speech (*BHW* 16c)

Study each of the following extended figures of speech. Do the writers rely on simile or metaphor? Do their images seem natural and unstrained? Does the figurative language contribute to the effectiveness of the passage? Be prepared to discuss your answers in class.

1. Let us take a peek twenty years down the road. But be forewarned; the view is fog-shrouded and the route is laced with unseen hollows and hairpin curves that can send the traveler spinning into the weeds. Such are the hazards of prognostication and I will therefore qualify what follows with a disclaimer: Futurism is bunk. [18]
2. Astrology has something frowsy about it. It comes to the door in hair curlers. It looks through the screen with squint-shrewd eyes. The caller who rang the doorbell stares in at crackpot mystery in the half-light, and senses there a kind of disreputable plausibility. The dogs on the porch get restless and slink away. A universe of surreal connections unfolds. [19]
3. The ivory tower, as college students—and psychiatrists—across the country will testify, is not nearly so pleasant an abode as it appears from the outside. It shelters its inhabitants from some of life's pedestrian difficulties, but at the same time creates new traumas and problems, which take on, in such closed quarters, an importance of which the real world cannot conceive. The legendary tower of learning is not a stable structure: it is buffeted by the high winds of exam periods, by the gales of preprofessional competition; it shakes with the constant

underground rumblings of adolescent crises. What shall I be? What shall I do? Will I succeed? At times it sways so forebodingly that the unfortunate standing on top sees his future in a heap of broken bones and ivory rubble.[20]

16.4   Creating Similes (*BHW* 16a–b)

Working alone or with a group of classmates, use the following phrases to create several fresh similes (avoid clichés: "as flat as a pancake," "as smooth as silk"). List a number of possibilities for each phrase, even if some of them sound forced or ungainly. Then use three of your best similes in sentences. You might want to try for a humorous effect in one sentence.

Example: as flat as . . .

> *the Kansas prairie, yesterday's Coke, a warm beer, a tomato under a truck tire, a soprano with a bad head cold*

Sentence:

> *David was always the class clown, but his pranks were usually as flat as yesterday's Coke.*

1. as red (or green, blue, yellow, etc.) as . . .

2. as messy as . . .

3. as confusing as . . .

_____

_____

_____

4. as smooth as . . .

_____

_____

_____

5. as wrinkled as . . .

_____

_____

_____

SENTENCES

1. _____

_____

_____

2. _____

_____

_____

3. _____

_____

16.5 Changing Literal Language to Figurative Language (*BHW* 16a–d)

In each of the following sentences, the italicized word is used in its literal sense. Write a sentence in which you use the same word figuratively.

Example: The children *played* in the yard for over an hour.

The day was nearly gone, but the sunlight played on the face of the cliff for a few more minutes before slipping away.

1. Andrew and Sarah *danced* gracefully across the floor.

2. Max *swam* twenty laps at the natatorium.

3. Open your *mouth* and take a bite.

4. *Eat* less and live longer.

_____

_____

_____

5. The flowers *wilted* in the afternoon sun.

_____

_____

_____

16.6   Review Exercise: Exploring Words in Context—Student Essays (*BHW* Chapters 14–16)

Read one of the student essays listed below, and mark several examples of effective diction. Specifically, look for examples of (1) apt word choice, (2) concrete language, (3) conciseness, and (4) figurative language. Be prepared to discuss your findings in class.

1. "Death of a Canyon," p. 77
2. "Behind the Scenes," p. 81
3. "My Parents: Playing in Harmony," p. 86
4. "Turning Citizens into Suckers," p. 90
5. "When It Rains It Pours," p. 389
6. "Clever Hans and His Effect: Horse Sense about Communicating with Animals," p. 400

V

USAGE

17

Complete Sentences

17.1 Recognizing Subjects and Verbs (*BHW* 17a–b)

Circle the main verb and underline the subject in each of the following sentences. [1]

Example: Beavers (live) in colonies, one or more family groups to a lodge.

A family usually (consists) of a mated pair and two sets of offspring.

1. Beavers are thickset animals with small, rounded ears, short legs, and large, webbed hindfeet.

2. Musk glands in both sexes produce a liquid used in perfumes.

3. The beaver's coat, consisting of a dense, fine underfur overlaid with many coarse guard hairs, is glossy tan to dark brown above, paler below.

4. The search for this fur stimulated some of the early 19th-century explorations of western North America.

5. Beavers show preference for streams and small rivers.

6. Their dams of sticks, stones, and mud may last for years, creating ponds that sometimes cover many acres.

7. Eventually, silt fills these ponds.

8. In rivers and lakes, beavers often burrow into banks.

9. Their food usually consists of the tender bark and buds of trees.

10. Branches, twigs, and small logs are anchored in the bottom mud in deep water for winter food.

17.2 Recognizing Independent Clauses
(*BHW* 17c)

Put brackets around the independent (or main) clause in each of the following sentences. (Some sentences may have two independent clauses joined by a coordinating conjunction.)[2]

Example: [Wool cloth was slightly easier to produce than linen.]
After the sheep were sheared, [the fleece was picked through and brambles and other dirt removed.]

1. While some women by the late eighteenth century might have turned their skeins of thread over to a professional weaver, many still made their own cloth at home.

2. If the household was very large, a special weaving house might have been built to accommodate the loom.

3. The weaving itself consisted of pressing a foot treadle to separate the warp threads.

216

4. Since this work was done in spare moments between other chores, it might easily have taken a year for a wife to make her husband a cloth suit.

5. Such a garment was highly valued by its owner.

6. If producing a family's clothing might have been a pleasure, cleaning was never anything but drudgery.

7. Fortunately for the colonial woman, who already had great demands on her time, the standards of the eighteenth century were not high.

8. People washed their hands and faces, but they bathed only rarely.

9. Too much bathing was considered unhealthy—which it probably was when done in cold water in an unheated house during a New England winter.

10. Most people did not own many garments, and wash day came only once or twice a year.

17.3 Recognizing Subjects, Verbs, and Independent Clauses in Your Own Writing (*BHW* 17a–c)

Photocopy or write out a page from one of your own essays. Circle the main verb and underline the subject in each sentence. Then put brackets around each independent clause.

17.4 Sentence Practice: Joining Fragments and Independent Clauses (*BHW* 17c–d)

The following items are fragments—dependent clauses treated as complete sentences. In the space provided, connect each fragment to an independent clause to form a complete sentence.

Example: As soon as she finished the history exam.

As soon as she finished the history exam, Natalie began to study for her math quiz.

or

Dustin said that he would talk to Rachel as soon as she finished the history exam.

1. After two years on the baseball team.

_____

_____

_____

2. Which caused Heidi to quit smoking.

_____

_____

_____

3. Before his tax refund arrived.

_____

_____

_____

4. Although many women now work outside the home.

_____

_____

_____

5. If you bite into that peach.

_____

_____

17.5 Repairing Sentence Fragments
(*BHW* 17c–d)

Eliminate fragments in the following passages by combining the elements into a single sentence or by rewriting fragments as independent clauses.

Example: Most banks now offer high-interest certificates of deposit. Along with passbook savings accounts.

Along with passbook savings accounts, most banks now offer high-interest certificates of deposit.

1. Asian and African elephants differ in size. The African elephant being larger.

_____

_____

_____

2. The albatross, like most sea birds, lays only one egg a year. Both parents helping to care for the single chick when it hatches in February or March.

_____

_____

_____

3. Mars has two satellites, Phobos and Deimos. Which are both closer to Mars than the moon is to Earth.

_____

_____

_____

4. Many types of fruit thrive in the Yakima Valley. Such as apples, peaches, apricots, and cherries.

_____

_____

_____

5. Many are leaving the teaching profession today. Partly as a result of low salaries and poor working conditions.

_____

_____

_____

17.6 Editing a Passage to Repair Sentence Fragments (*BHW* 17c–d)

Edit the following passages to eliminate sentence fragments. Make the necessary changes by underlining each fragment and writing your revisions in the space above the lines. Two fragments are corrected as examples.

PASSAGE 1

Scientists have recently discovered 6,000,000-year-old ice on a

It is by

glacier in Antarctica. ~~By~~ far the oldest ice ever found.

, e

New ice near the surface of the glacier is evaporating/ ~~E~~xpos-

ing layer upon layer of ancient ice that contains volcanic dust,

5   carbon dioxide and other materials that have accumulated over the

years. Usually, such complete records are obtained only by dril-

ling deep ice cores. Such as the 6,500-foot-long vertical shaft that

researchers obtained in Greenland last year. The stratified layer of

that core providing a continuous climatic history of the world for

10   the past 125,000 years. The oldest such information now on re-

cord.

The Antarctic glacier is littered with hundreds of meteorites. Some of which are 7,500,000 years old. From these remnants, Ian Whillans of Ohio State University and other scientists were able
15 to establish the age of the ice.[3]

PASSAGE 2

Americans are now using 450 billion gallons of water a day. According to a recent report from the U.S. Geological Survey. The figures represent a 200-percent increase in water use over the past 30 years, but the survey says daily use falls far short of the 1,200
5 billion gallons the country can supply every day. Not including extensive groundwater resources.

The figures, which cover the 1975–1980 period, include water used for all purposes. Public supply, industry, irrigation, rural and commercial. Industry makes the biggest drain on the
10 water supply—260 billion gallons a day. Eighty-three percent of which goes to thermoelectric power. Idaho uses more water than any other state. Rhode Island using the least water.[4]

PASSAGE 3

A French company tried to construct a canal across Panama in the 1880s, but the project ended when thousands of workers died from disease. Malaria and yellow fever. Mosquitoes spread these diseases. Americans set out to build a canal in 1907. But first devel-
5 oped a plan to control the insects. It took seven years to complete the project. Involving the removal of nearly a quarter of a million cubic yards of earth. Workers used steam shovels for much of the work. While the canal was under construction, President Theodore

Roosevelt visited Panama and posed for photographers. Sitting at
10   the controls of a steam shovel.

The canal is a marvel of technology. Although some people
imagine it to be little more than a massive open ditch. It is fifty-
one miles long. Its locks raise or lower ships eighty-five feet on
the passage through the waterway. Completion of the project was
15   a boon for shippers. Shortening the trip from Boston to San Francisco by 9,000 miles. Some modern ships have outgrown the
canal. Especially oil supertankers. However, the canal can still
accommodate most ships.[5]

17.7   Evaluating Intentional Sentence Fragments (*BHW* 17e)

The following passages contain intentional sentence fragments. What, if
anything, do the authors gain by using them? Underline the fragments, and
be prepared to discuss their effects.

1.   The lunch was a yuppie cardiologist's dream. Sprouts and fiber ga-
lore.*

2.   After living in Los Angeles for five years, Mary longed to see her
hometown again. The courthouse square, the neatly trimmed lawn, the
tidy house in which she had grown up.*

3.   What do the ancient civilizations of China, Greece, and Egypt have in
common with college students everywhere? Is it their intense thirst for
knowledge? Not quite. Whether you've just built a pyramid or passed
that last final, the sundial and the campus clock tower send the same
message: it's time for a cold beer.*

4.   They float on the landscape like pyramids to the boom years, all those

Plazas and Malls and Esplanades. All those Squares and Fairs. All those Towns and Dales, all those Villages, all those Forests and Parks and Lands. Stonestown. Hillsdale. Valley Fair, Mayfair, Northgate, Southgate, Eastgate, Westgate. Gulfgate. They are toy garden cities in which no one lives but everyone consumes, profound equalizers, the perfect fusion of the profit motive and the egalitarian ideal, and to hear their names is to recall words and phrases no longer quite current. Baby Boom. Consumer Explosion. Leisure Revolution. Do-It-Yourself Revolution. Backyard Revolution. Suburbia.[6]

5. One of the things that makes the French Revolution so confusing to read about is the great number of names that appear on every page, and disappear without a trace. Worse than a Russian novel. And the reason for this is that for almost ten years it produced no great men, except perhaps Robespierre.[7]

223

18

Joining
Independent
Clauses

18.1 Sentence Practice: Joining
Independent Clauses (*BHW* 18a)

Write ten sentences, using two independent clauses in each. For sentences 1–5, join the independent clauses with a comma and the coordinating conjunction given in parentheses. (Suggested topics: sports, dangerous occupations, politicians.)

Example: (but) *A 1967 study listed astronauts as the worst insurance risk, but race car drivers were not far behind.*

1. (and) _____

_____

_____

2. (but) _____

3. (for) _____

_____

4. (so) _____

_____

5. (yet) _____

_____

For sentences 6–10, join the independent clauses with a semicolon.

Example: President Richard Nixon took office
on January 20, 1969; he resigned on
August 9, 1974.

6. _____

_____

7. _____

_____

8. _____

_____

9. _____

10. _____

18.2 Sentence Practice: Joining Independent Clauses with Sentence Adverbs and Transitional Expressions (*BHW* 18a)

Write five sentences, each containing two independent clauses joined by a semicolon and the word or phrase in parentheses. (Suggested topics: women and careers, television, current events.)

Example: (therefore) *Mina does the same work as Patrick; therefore, she should receive the same salary.*

1. (however) _____

2. (furthermore) _____

3. (thus) _____

4. (for example) _____

5. (on the other hand) _____

_____

_____

18.3 Repairing Comma Splices and Fused Sentences (*BHW* 18a–c)

In the space provided, indicate whether each sentence is correct (C), is a fused sentence (FS), or contains a comma splice (CS). Then eliminate the errors, using one of the two methods illustrated in the examples. Make the necessary changes in the space above the lines. (Watch for sentence adverbs or transitional phrases that may disguise errors.)[8]

Examples: (comma and coordinating conjunction)

Pigs are herd animals, but we seldom notice it because we keep the animals confined.   *FS*

(semicolon)

Pigs are like other flocking or herding animals; they follow that system of bosses and underlings known as a "pecking order."   *CS*

1. A senior boar will lead the herd, when there is no boar loose with the sows, an older and experienced sow rules the sty.   _____

2. Pigs can be as absolutely brutal to one of their number as can a bunch of chickens bent on pecking a sickly pullet to death.   _____

3. Pigs are famous for wallowing they wallow by choice when the weather is hot.   _____

4. They wallow both to cool themselves and to help thwart external parasites. _____

5. Tanned pigskin is tough, however, the skin while on the pig is hardly more resistant to scratches or bites than our own. _____

6. Slap a white pig, your hand leaves a red welt. _____

7. Fly and mosquito bites leave the red spots and blotches characteristic of a bad case of the measles. _____

8. Pigs are not well equipped to cope with either high or low temperatures, in fact, piglets are totally incapable of regulating their body temperatures for the first two or three days after birth. _____

9. Adult pigs have few sweat glands, and most of those are on their snouts. _____

10. When the weather is hot, they must seek a cool spot in which to lie, they seek shade and/or a wallow. _____

18.4   Repairing Comma Splices
(*BHW* 18a–c)

Eliminate the comma splices in the following sentences, using one of the two methods illustrated in the examples. In each case, use the method that seems best suited for showing the logical relationship between the two clauses. Be prepared to justify your choices. Make the necessary changes in the space above the lines.*

Examples: (comma and coordinating conjunction)

but

A well-designed résumé may get you job interviews,ʌit cannot get you a job.

(semicolon)

229

A well-designed résumé may get you job interviews; it cannot get you a job.

1. A résumé is a summary of your qualifications for employment, it is usually no more than a page long.

2. A résumé includes personal information, you should limit this information to your name, address, and telephone number.

3. Information about your age, health, and marital status will probably do you little good, it may actually undermine your chances for an interview.

4. For recent college graduates, "education" is naturally an important category on the résumé, however, many students overemphasize their schooling.

5. It is best to state educational accomplishments simply and briefly, a long list of course work isn't likely to get much attention.

6. Employers would rather know what you can do for them, give them a list of your skills.

7. You can include your skills in a category about work experience, you might want to put them in a separate part of the résumé.

8. Employers look for a well-rounded applicant, in fact, they often single out a résumé that lists extracurricular activities, volunteer work, memberships, even hobbies.

9. Be careful not to include too much detail, major points can get lost in a sea of trivia.

10. End the résumé with the address of your college placement service, your letters of recommendation should be available there.

18.5 Using Subordination to Repair Comma Splices (*BHW* 18a–c)

Five items from the preceding exercise are reprinted below. This time, eliminate the comma splices by converting one part of each sentence into a phrase or a subordinate clause. Write your revisions in the space provided. You might want to compare your corrections to the ones you did for Exercise 18.4, noting how meaning is altered, however slightly, by a change in sentence structure.

Example: A well-designed résumé may get you job interviews, it cannot get you a job.

Although a well-designed résumé may get you job interviews, it cannot get you a job.

1. A résumé is a summary of your qualifications for employment, it is usually no more than a page long.

_____

_____

_____

2. Employers would rather know what you can do for them, give them a list of your skills.

_____

_____

_____

3. You can include your skills in a category about work experience, you might want to put them in a separate part of the résumé.

_____

4. Employers look for a well-rounded applicant, in fact, they often single out a résumé that lists extracurricular activities, volunteer work, memberships, even hobbies.

5. Be careful not to include too much detail, major points can get lost in a sea of trivia.

Note: The preceding exercise illustrates how to eliminate comma splices by bringing out the logical relationships within a sentence—subordinating one element to another. For further practice in using subordination, see Chapter 12.

18.6 Editing a Passage to Repair Comma Splices and Fused Sentences (*BHW* 18a–c)

Edit the following passage to eliminate fused sentences and comma splices. Make the necessary changes in the space above the lines. The first error is corrected for you as an example.[9]

The Vikings had many reasons for their reckless pursuits; it would

seem that they engaged in dangerous ventures to prove themselves

valiant and courageous. Upon returning from one of their many

fierce voyages, they were warmly welcomed by their native peo-

5   ple, who celebrated their return with exuberance, usually for days

232

at a time. Women served horns filled with mead amid drinking and laughter the Vikings would play games of chance, using dice and counters. Sometimes they sent up burnt offerings to the gods, they always sang of their forefathers' achievements, lustily drinking to

10   even greater deeds in days to come.

Every hardy Norseman was expected to engage in war, the customary weapons were battle-ax, sword, and bow. Wearing a conical helmet with nose cover and a coat of mail or leather garment, the warrior felt well protected, however, at times he

15   would show his courageous nature by removing his shirt *(serk)* before a battle. Armed only with a club, he would engage his enemy in combat, the term *berserk,* meaning "without a shirt," stems from this demonstration.

19

Joining Subjects and Verbs

SUBJECT-VERB COHERENCE

19.1 Repairing Mixed Constructions and Faulty Predication (*BHW* 19a–b)

Edit the following sentences to eliminate mixed constructions and faulty predication. Make the necessary changes in the space above the lines.

Example: (a) Even though my nine brothers and sisters are scattered across Canada, ~~is not enough to stop our annual meeting~~ *we meet every year* in Toronto.

(b) Joe's aggressiveness sometimes ∧ *causes him to* behaves in antisocial ways.

1. When designing a house was the best part of the architecture course I took last fall.

2. His uncle Jaime gave it to him the beagle he had seen in the pet shop.

3. Dan's reluctance to lead the hike canceled the outing.

4. Whenever the four of them got together was the time they talked for hours about their college days.

5. Mr. Daeger's ideas stated a point that none of us had considered before.

6. The audience, they roared their approval as the singer leapt onto the stage.

7. Dr. Robert Gorman won it for the second time, the President's Award for Excellence in Teaching and Research.

8. Dr. Torok and her husband, they were honored for their contributions to the hospital's building fund.

9. In helping David study for the exam was when I learned the material myself.

10. A lecture I heard last week believed that the Dow would reach 5,000 by the turn of the century.

SUBJECT-VERB AGREEMENT

19.2 Matching Subjects and Verbs
(*BHW* 19c)

Circle the verb in parentheses that agrees with the subject.

Example: dolphins (is valued, are valued)

1. a whale (lives, live)

2. whales (swims, swim)

3. there (is, are) whales

4. whales of this type (survives, survive)

5. school of whales (consists, consist)

6. whale and dolphin (is hunted, are hunted)

7. neither a whale nor a dolphin (has been found, have been found)

8. every whale and dolphin (survives, survive)

9. Flipper, along with many other dolphins, (performs, perform)

10. *Moby-Dick,* a book about whales, (is read, are read)

19.3 Changing Subjects and Verbs: Singular and Plural (*BHW* 19c)

Rewrite each sentence, making singular subjects and verbs plural, plural subjects and verbs singular. Circle the words you change.[10]

Example: The (potato) (is) high in fiber.

Potatoes are high in fiber.

1. The potato was first cultivated in South America nearly 2,000 years ago.

_____

_____

2. Today, it is a major world food staple. _____

_____

3. Potatoes are earthy, starchy, immediately accessible.

_____

_____

4. They somehow fill the heart as well as the belly.

5. Potatoes are the world's best vegetable.

6. The tomato also comes from South America. _____

7. When first introduced in Europe, it was thought to be poisonous.

8. Today tomatoes are an important food source in Europe.

9. They are a staple in the Italian diet.

10. The tomato has become almost compulsory in the American dinner salad.

19.4 Identifying Subject-Verb Agreement (*BHW* 19c–n)

Underline the subject and circle the correct verb form in each of the following sentences. In the space provided, indicate whether the verb you circle is singular (S) or plural (P). [11]

Example: The <u>absence</u> of trees (makes, make) the Arc-

tic landscape appear lifeless, bare, and deso-

late.   *S*

1. But there (is, are) unexpected richness of life.   _____

2. Lichens, mosses, grasses, and flowering plants
    (forms, form) a continuous cover over the thin
    humus layer.   _____

3. But the mammals (is, are) most impressive, from
    the little Arctic mouse to polar bears, caribou, the
    musk oxen and lemmings.   _____

4. And there (a) (is, are) innumerable birds, many of
    which (b) (remains, remain) in the Arctic only dur-   (a) _____
    ing the summer.   (b) _____

5. Whether plant or animal, every living organism (has
    adapted, have adapted) in its own way to the ex-
    treme environment.   _____

6. As everywhere, the soils of the Arctic (represents,
    represent) the basis of all life on land.   _____

7. High Arctic desert soils commonly (displays, dis-
    play) ephemeral salt crusts.   _____

8. The chemical reaction of these soils (is, are) usually
    neutral to alkaline.   _____

9. The low soil temperatures, even in summer,
    (a) (means, mean) that nitrogen-producing bacteria   (a) _____
    (b) (breaks, break) down the organic material ex-
    tremely slowly.   (b) _____

10. Where bird droppings or animal carcasses (a) (fer-
    tilizes, fertilize) the soil, a remarkably luxuriant   (a) _____
    vegetation soon (b) (flourishes, flourish).   (b) _____

19.5 Eliminating Errors in Subject-Verb Agreement (1) (*BHW* 19c–n)

In the following sentences, circle any verbs that do not agree with their subjects. Then write the correct verb form in the space provided. Write C in the space if there is no error. [12]

Example: Most stars in the universe (has) masses of
one-tenth to fifty times the mass of our
sun.   *have*

1. Just a few light-years from our solar system lie a cold, dark, invisible object. _____

2. Only a twentieth of the sun's mass, it still retain the small planetary system that was born with it. _____

3. But these planets whirl about their sun in darkness, for the star does not shine. _____

4. Any light that touches their chill surfaces come from other stars.

5. This dark star are neither a black hole nor a neutron star. _____

6. It is a black dwarf—a star so small its core never grew hot enough to ignite. _____

7. Stars of all kinds are born in dusty gas clouds like the Orion and Lagoon Nebulae. _____

8. Some of these has many times the sun's mass, while others are smaller. _____

9. The nebula's temperature and density determines how large or small a given star will turn out to be. _____

10. The laws of physics shows that a star below a certain critical mass will never become hot enough to initiate thermonuclear fusion of hydrogen in its core. _____

19.6 Eliminating Errors in Subject-Verb Agreement (2) (*BHW* 19c–n)

The following sentences contain the type of subject-verb agreement errors that writers often overlook in revising first drafts. Review the rules for agreement; then carefully locate and circle each incorrect verb form. Write the correct form in the space provided.

Example: Each of the winners (were) honored at a reception following the competition. *was* _____

1. The number of degrees granted by American colleges and universities have increased steadily over the past twenty years. _____

2. Unfortunately, the college graduate who enter the job market today may well be underemployed. _____

3. There is more and more stories about cab drivers who display their diplomas on the dashboards of their cabs. _____

4. Even having three degrees—a B.A., an M.A., and a Ph.D.—do not guarantee a job, as many unemployed college professors will testify. _____

5. Despite the surplus of graduates, the number

of new students are still growing every year at
some colleges. _____

6. At some universities, a virtual army of first-
year students enlist in computer courses, hop-
ing to enter a new and lucrative job market. _____

7. English and history, once popular fields of
study, now gives way to more "practical"
disciplines. _____

8. Neither art nor music are required in many
college curriculums today. _____

9. What is the likely results of the current trend
toward narrow technical training? _____

10. Some complain that intense specialization,
along with a lack of preparation before college, too often result in graduates without
basic skills in reading, writing, and thinking. _____

19.7 Editing a Passage to Eliminate Errors in Subject-Verb Agreement (*BHW* 19c–n)

Edit the following passages, correcting errors in subject-verb agreement.
Make the necessary changes in the space above the lines. One error is
corrected as an example.[13]

PASSAGE 1

According to the World Health Organization in Geneva, physicians makes up a relatively small proportion of the community at
large. In none of the countries listed are there more than one

doctor per 200 people. Clearly, an abundance of doctors are a
5   good thing, but it do not necessarily follow that the general health
of the inhabitants of a country improve as doctors become more
plentiful. For example, the Soviet Union, with the highest proportion of physicians among the countries listed, are currently beset
by serious health problems, a high infant-mortality rate, and a
10   declining life expectancy.

PASSAGE 2

Using a genetically engineered form of interferon administered by
nasal-spray dispensers, a group of British and French scientists
have proved that the substance is effective in blocking a common-
cold virus. Previous studies has shown that the much more expen-
5   sive form of interferon, which is derived from human cells, also
work against colds, but this is the first time that interferon cloned
from bacteria have been tested.

PASSAGE 3

J. Kevin Thompson, a psychologist at the University of South
Florida, conducts research on the way people perceive—or mis-
perceive—their bodies. Each of us have a mental image of our
physical self, and sometimes that image has little relation to our
5   actual size or shape. The most extreme cases of distorted body
image occurs in those with anorexia or bulimia, two eating disorders that mainly affects young women. Anorexics—people who
starve themselves to a dangerously low weight—nearly always
has an exaggerated image of body size, perceiving themselves as
10   much heavier than they are.

Thompson's research in recent years concern the body im-

243

ages of people without eating disorders. With his colleagues, he has developed methods to determine how people perceive various parts of their bodies. In one experiment, nearly all of the one

15   hundred women tested overestimated body size; the estimates, in many cases, was 25 percent over actual measurements. For some women, there is particularly strong concerns about the size of their cheeks, waist, thighs, or hips. A woman with a thin or average face, for example, may see her cheeks as puffy and unattractive.

20   Does misperceptions of body size stem from actual perceptual problems, or do emotions interfere with our judgments? There is no definitive answers, but common sense tell us that emotions do affect self-image. For most people, minor distortions in body perception causes no serious psychological problems. After all,

25   few of us is fully satisfied with the way we look. But if the problem in any way threaten physical or psychological health, then we should seek professional help.*

19.8 Review Exercise: Editing a Passage for Fragments, Comma Splices, Fused Sentences, and Subject-Verb Agreement (*BHW* Chapters 17–19)

Edit the following draft, correcting fragments, comma splices, fused sentences, and errors in subject-verb agreement. Make the necessary changes in the space above the lines.

He thunder across the glossy pages of every popular magazine. He and his trusty steed alone in the wilderness, at one with nature, a symbol of everything masculine, a man in the purest sense of the word. He is the Marlboro Man who, along with his cohorts the Camel

Man and the Chaz Guy, have become a symbol of the American male. An image for all men to emulate.

Newspapers, magazines, and television spends millions of dollars each year selling this image to the public, thus they shapes the way we view ourselves. Giving us a highly inaccurate picture of what it means to be "masculine." The media man is cool, aloof, and rugged he is so secure in his own maleness that female companionship, tenderness, and sensitivity is seldom, if ever, a part of his image.

We've all seen the infamous Old Spice Man. Making his glorious return from the sea. After ten months aboard ship, he seem cool and assured when welcomed by his waiting girl, she kept herself busy by knitting her man a sweater. After all, why should she entertain thoughts of an affair, her man uses Old Spice.*

20

Modifiers

20.1 Editing a Passage for Errors in Degrees of Adjectives and Adverbs (*BHW* 20a–b)

Edit the following passage for errors in degrees of adjectives and adverbs. Make corrections by crossing out words and, if necessary, writing the accurate forms in the space above the lines. One error is corrected for you as an example.

Last Sunday, to celebrate the end of the ~~most~~ coldest winter on record, Max and Hiroko Warshauer invited everyone on the third floor to their apartment for an Italian buffet. The evening started with two antipasto trays; the more larger one was a combination

5   of smoked meat and fish, tomatoes, olives, peppers, and cheese. The other, without fish or meat, disappeared quickliest; apparently, the smoked tuna didn't appeal to the vegetarian family from 3-C.

Next, Hiroko brought out an array of the most richest looking

10   pasta dishes I'd ever seen. The crowning glory was Max's spa-

ghetti carbonara, which he declared to be the best in Cleveland.

Mr. Spencer, a rather persnickety man from 3-E, bluntly stated

that the carbonara was spoiled because the pasta had been cooked

much more longer than it should have been.

15   After sampling the various pastas, we were served a main

dish of chicken cacciatore, which even Mr. Spencer liked, though

he did make a passing remark about preferring his chicken a bit

less spicier. Toward the end of the evening, he also evaluated the

Chianti: ''Somewhat more drier than desirable.'' The best part of

20   the evening was the good company. The worse was Mr. Spencer's

dropping his bowl of spumoni on the Warshauers' new Belgian

rug.

CHOOSING AND PLACING MODIFIERS

20.2   Recognizing Modifiers: Words, Phrases, and Clauses (*BHW* pp. 250–251)

In each group of sentences, underline the type of modifier indicated.

Examples: (words)

Macel often gave her husband red roses or a box of rich chocolate candies.

(phrases)

At the last minute, Judy changed her plans for the Christmas party.

(subordinate clauses)

The girl who <u>was dressed as a bunch of grapes</u> won the prize for the most original costume.

SENTENCES 1–4: WORDS

1. Sometimes the best way to impress people is to remain absolutely silent.

2. The brightest room in the house was Dorothy's, a big second-floor study with six windows and a high ceiling.

3. Unfortunately, the police acted too quickly and arrested the wrong man.

4. She opposed capital punishment because of its often unfair and erratic application.

SENTENCES 5–7: PHRASES

5. In some elections, the candidate with charm defeats the one with ideas.

6. The cook sighed, looking with pride at the dozen pumpkin pies lining the shelf.

7. Unable to resist any longer, Amanda took out her wallet and bought the coat with her rent money.

SENTENCES 8–10: SUBORDINATE CLAUSES

8. When they added up the time they had spent playing Trivial Pursuit, they decided to throw the game away.

9. Most scientists believe that Pluto, which was discovered in 1930, is the outermost planet in our solar system.

10. Although he is short and small-framed, Pablo is a good athlete.

20.3 Using Modifiers: Phrases and Clauses
(*BHW* pp. 250–251 and 20i–q)

Write five sentences in which you use the following phrases or clauses as modifiers. Punctuate as necessary.

Example: while looking for his glasses

While looking for his glasses, Frank found his missing notebook.

or

Frank was mugged while looking for his glasses.

1. after finding a rattlesnake in his dorm room

_____

_____

_____

2. who is now more than a hundred years old

_____

_____

_____

3. although Coke is Tanya's favorite breakfast drink

_____

_____

_____

4. by climbing to the top of the flagpole

_____

_____

_____

5. that Jack built

_____

_____

_____

20.4 Sentence Practice: Using Phrases and Clauses as Modifiers (*BHW* pp. 250–251 and 20i–q)

Write five sentences using phrases or clauses as modifiers. Underline the modifiers and punctuate as necessary. (Suggested topics: teachers, clothing styles.)

Example: <u>Always in style</u>, blue jeans can be formal or casual, <u>which is one reason for their popularity</u>.

1. _____

_____

2. _____

_____

3. _____

_____

4. _____

5. _____

_____

_____

_____

20.5 Sentence Combining: Using Phrases and Clauses as Modifiers (*BHW* pp. 250–251 and 20i–q)

Combine the following pairs of sentences, using the underlined part of the second sentence as a modifier in the first. There are no single "correct" answers. Work with each pair until you devise a combination that seems clear and effective. Write your final version in the space provided, punctuating as necessary.

Example: Beethoven conducted the first performance of his Ninth Symphony in 1823. He was <u>totally deaf at the time.</u>

> *Although he was totally deaf at the time, Beethoven conducted the first performance of his Ninth Symphony in 1823.*

or

> *Beethoven, totally deaf at the time, conducted the first performance of his Ninth Symphony in 1823.*

1.   The krubi plant grows so quickly that it sprouts and reaches a height of ten feet in a matter of days. The krubi <u>is found in the jungles of Indonesia.</u>

_____

2. The ampersand (&) was invented by an ancient Roman, Marius Tiro. Tiro also devised thousands of other shorthand symbols.

3. About 35 percent of the people in India speak Hindi. Hindi is the country's official language.

4. An underwater railway tunnel links the Japanese islands of Honshu and Kyushu. The tunnel is more than eleven miles long.

5. King Sobhuza II enjoyed the longest reign of any monarch in history. He ruled Swaziland from 1900 to 1983.

6. The cuttlefish ejects an inky liquid into the water. It does this in order to hide itself from predators.

7. Thomas Jefferson and John Adams died on July 4, 1826. This day was the fiftieth anniversary of American Independence.

8. Coffee is regarded by some today as a potentially harmful stimulant. Coffee was <u>once used in Arabia as a medicine</u>.

_____

_____

_____

9. _The Sun,_ a British newspaper, commemorated Queen Victoria's coronation in 1838. The newspaper did so by <u>printing an entire issue in gold ink</u>.

_____

_____

_____

10. The Order of the Garter was founded in 1347. It is <u>the oldest order of knighthood</u>.

_____

_____

_____

20.6 Repairing Dangling and Misplaced Modifiers (*BHW* 20c–d)

Underline the dangling and misplaced modifiers in the following sentences. Then revise each sentence, relating modifiers clearly and effectively to the words they modify. If a sentence contains no problems with modification, write C in the space provided.*

Examples: (misplaced modifier)

The company says that there is little evidence to link ''second-hand smoke'' with disease in nonsmokers <u>in its advertisement</u>.

**In its advertisement, the company** _____

says that there is little evidence to link "second-hand smoke" with disease in nonsmokers.

(dangling modifier)

But when <u>smoking in public places</u>, greater consideration is needed.

But when smoking in public places, smokers should show greater consideration.

1. Like the other advertisement, the reader will find this one puzzling.

   _____

   _____

   _____

2. After comparing the three ads, the one with muted colors had the greatest effect.

   _____

   _____

   _____

3. Once placed in a magazine, readers will stop and read this advertisement.

   _____

   _____

   _____

4. The black background of the page may be the key to the advertisement's success; being black, the bright orange letters stand out.

_____

_____

_____

5. Lewis Thomas, a medical doctor, writes movingly in his essay, "The Long Habit," about death.

_____

_____

_____

6. Offering scientific information about the nature of dying, anecdotes are used as well.

_____

_____

_____

7. By using a personal tone to relate scientific information, our fear of death is placed in a new light.

_____

_____

_____

8. One of the most important functions of the doctor was to provide comfort at the moment of death in the past.

_____

_____

_____

9. Some scientists theorize that all creatures are equipped with a physiological mechanism that takes effect and induces tranquility when dying.

_____

_____

10. In concluding his essay about death, a humorous touch is used.

_____

_____

_____

20.7 Placing Adverbs for Precise Meaning (*BHW* 20f)

Each sentence in this exercise is followed by an adverb that could be inserted at more than one place in the sentence. Indicate two or more possible locations with a slash (/), and be prepared to discuss how each location affects meaning.

Example: /Jenny was/ asked/ to manage/ the bookstore.

    (only)

1. Half the tourists got lost on the way to the museum.

    (nearly)

2. One man wanted to see the Picasso collection.

    (just)

3. The woman from Akron wanted to see the Asian art.

    (even)

4. Everyone else insisted that we see the David Hockney exhibit.

    (almost)

5. I was interested in the kinetic sculpture.

    (only)

20.8 Punctuating Modifiers: Words, Phrases, and Clauses (*BHW* 20i–q)

In the following sentences, underline any modifying words, phrases, or clauses that require punctuation. Then add commas where necessary, circling each one as shown in the example. Circle the number of any sentence that requires no additional commas.[14]

Example: Huge aggregations of garter snakes◯ at times numbering 10,000 to 15,000◯ have drawn the attention of herpetologists to the Interlake region of southern Manitoba.

1. Since the snakes cannot withstand freezing temperatures they must hibernate during the winter.

2. The study of the red-sided garter snake which ranges the farthest north of any snake in North America sheds light on how reptiles have adapted to cold environments.

3. The garter snakes emerge from hibernation in late April or early May.

4. First large numbers of males appear.

5. Soon after females leave the communal den emerging singly or in small groups over a period of several weeks.

6. The mass emergence of male snakes as opposed to the delayed staggered emergence of females may have adaptive value.

7. With the ratio of males to females as high as 50 to 1 the probability of females being fertilized is virtually 100 percent.

8. Also if females were to emerge together, mate, and disperse early in the season unpredictable freezing temperatures might destroy much of the breeding population.

9. The staggered return to activity of the females ensures that some will survive.

10. As soon as they have mated females leave the den site and disperse to summer feeding areas.

11. Consequently the total time they are exposed to predators at the den site is reduced.

12. The bulk of the population that remains around the den for any length of time is male—and somewhat more expendable.

13. As soon as a female appears on the surface she is mobbed by male suitors.

14. The male's vigorous courtship behavior is triggered by the sudden change in body temperature coincident with emergence from the den.

15. In the laboratory male red-sided garter snakes court females within ten minutes after a transfer from a cold dark environment to a warm lighted one.

16. This sequence simulates the normal transition from hibernation to immediate posthibernation conditions.

17. When they are kept cold and merely transferred from darkness to light male garter snakes fail to exhibit courtship behavior.

18. The change in body temperature irrespective of light conditions appears to be the principal factor in triggering mating behavior.

19. Male courtship behavior lasts for three to four weeks waning over time.

20. Surprisingly enough the snakes do not eat during the mating period.

20.9 Review Exercise: Placing and Punctuating Modifiers (*BHW* 20c–q)

Edit the following draft for errors in the placement and punctuation of modifiers. Make the necessary changes in the space above the lines. You may want to copy your revised version onto a separate sheet of paper before submitting it. One sentence is revised for you as an example.*

Although changed by several drastic remodeling projects over the
                      our home on Belvin Street always makes me
years, ~~I always~~ feel comfortable.~~in our home on Belvin Street.~~ My

family has many good memories of the house, even though we've

only owned it for eleven years. Affectionately called "the old

5   stack of boards" by my father, my mother who is more sentimen-

tal than he is speaks of its warmth and security fondly.

Built around 1900 by modern standards the foundation of the

house is inadequate; the structure rests on piers made of huge old

cedar stumps not of concrete. Extending out to four full-length

10   columns, at one time there was a balcony. It was removed long

ago judged structurally unsound.

Five large bedrooms but one bath only are upstairs. Down-

stairs the living room is in the front part of the house. A large

elegant room, it has a fireplace in the middle of a varnished

15   wooden wall which is made of red bricks. Behind the living room

just beyond a hand-carved wooden door is the dining room. From

here one can see the modern kitchen a room that still retains a hint

of its turn-of-the-century charm. Finally used in the past as a

parlor or library on the other side of the kitchen is a small office.

21

Noun and Pronoun Case

21.1 Identifying Correct Pronoun Case (*BHW* 21a–i)

Review the rules governing case; then circle the correct pronouns in the following sentences.

Example: My roommate and (**I**, me) had an argument last week about (**who**, whom) would control the volume of the stereo.

1. He argued that if the stereo doesn't disturb (his, him) studying, then it shouldn't disturb the studying of the student (who, whom) lives next door.

2. Having lived in the apartment long before (he, him), I insisted that I could better judge (who, whom) the stereo would disturb.

3. A rabid advocate of tenants' rights, he believed that (we, us) renters had the right to do whatever we chose to do in our apartments.

4. I reminded him that *our* rights were probably in conflict with (them, those) of the people (who, whom) lived around us.

5. "Besides," I said, "the rules about loud music are not for (us, we) tenants to decide; Mr. Ronan, the landlord, spelled out the rules to you and (I, me) when we signed the lease."

6. Enraged, he insisted that (he, him) and (I, me) should discuss the matter with Mr. Ronan.

7. Just then the phone rang; it was the building manager, (who, whom) had warned us about loud music twice before.

8. A moment later there was a knock on the door. "(Whom, Who) in the heck is that?" yelled my roommate.

9. "It is (I, me)," said the student (who, whom) lived next door, a pompous fellow who spent most of his time correcting my room-mate's grammar. My roommate opened the door in a fit of rage.

10. Standing beside two police officers, our pompous neighbor said to us, "It is time for you and (I, me) to have a talk."

11. "Your music," said one of the officers, "is disturbing (him, his) studying."

12. As it turned out, our neighbor hadn't even filed a complaint against my roommate and (I, me).

13. The building manager said that (he, him) and his wife had heard the music in their apartment, three flights down.

14. One of the police officers said that (she, her) and her partner had heard the music from the street.

15. My roommate and (I, me) moved out the next week.

21.2 Eliminating Errors in Pronoun Case (*BHW* 21a–i)

Edit the following sentences for errors in pronoun case, making the necessary changes in the space above the lines. Circle the number of any sentence that contains no error.

Example: Paul and ~~me~~ worked all last summer in an apple orchard.
I

1. Him and me decided to leave Seattle right after spring quarter and spend the rest of the vacation at his uncle's place in Wenatchee, Washington.

2. His uncle Joe, who has been farming for thirty years, owns a forty-acre orchard.

3. He was skeptical about us surviving the rigors of apple farming for a whole summer.

4. The first job he gave Paul and I was "thinning."

5. For us city types, the hot summer job was indeed physically demanding and tedious.

6. Along with the rest of the work crew, Paul and me spent eight hours a day plucking tiny green apples from the trees, spacing the fruit four to six inches apart.

7. Thinning the apples in the summer helps assure them growing to a marketable size by fall.

8. The hardest part of the job for Paul and me was climbing the ten-foot ladders to reach the high branches.

9. One of the workers, whom we got to know fairly well, had been thinning every summer since he was thirteen years old.

10. There were few people, he said, whom were willing to hire someone
    that young.

21.3 Eliminating Errors in the Use of *Who* and *Whom* (*BHW* 21a–i)

Edit the following sentences for errors in pronoun case, making the necessary changes in the space above the lines. Circle the number of any sentence that contains no error.

        Whom
Example: ~~Who~~ did you talk to about driving the tractor?

1. Paul is the one who told me about the job.

2. Joe will give the job to whomever shows the most skill at using the
   forklift.

3. Who will earn more money, the driver or the pickers?

4. Anyone whom can pick five or more bins of apples a day will earn
   more than the driver.

5. Whoever gets the driving job will be the envy of the slower pickers.

22

Pronoun Agreement and Reference

PRONOUN AGREEMENT

22.1 Using Personal Pronouns Consistently (*BHW* 22a)

In the following passages, change all personal pronouns from first to third person. After doing so, read each passage carefully, making sure that all pronouns are consistent in person and gender. The first pronoun in each passage is changed for you.

PASSAGE 1

When ~~I~~ **he** wrote the following pages, or rather the bulk of them, I

lived alone, in the woods, a mile from any neighbor, in a house

which I had built myself, on the shore of Walden Pond, in Con-

cord, Massachusetts, and earned my living by the labor of my
5   hands only. [15]

PASSAGE 2

She
~~I~~ had awakened at five and decided to fish for a few hours. I rowed
the dinghy out to the boat on that lovely foggy morning and then
headed around my side of Martha's Vineyard into the heavy
waters of West Chop. Up toward Lake Tashmoo I found the quiet
5   rip where the flounders had been running, put out two lines, and
made myself some coffee. [16]

22.2   Eliminating Errors in Pronoun Agreement (1)(*BHW* 22a–h)

In the following sentences, cross out any pronoun that does not agree in
number with its antecedent. Write the correct pronoun in the space provided. If a sentence contains no error, write C in the space.

Example: Elephants use their trunks to carry water
to their mouths and to hose ~~itself~~ down.   *themselves*

1. In the wild, African elephants feed mainly on
    grass, but they will eat dozens of other foods as
    well.   _____

2. The Asian elephant, on the other hand, eats
    from the trees and bushes found in their native
    forests.   _____

3. Neither the African nor the Asian elephant di-
    gests their food very efficiently.   _____

4. In fact, every elephant consumes about double
    the amount of food their body actually needs.   _____

266

5. Anyone interested in keeping an elephant as a pet would certainly find themselves with an enormous grocery bill; a pair of elephants in the backyard would probably consume about a quarter of a million pounds of food a year.

    _____

6. Elephants use their trunks to feed itself.

    _____

7. An African elephant has two "fingers" at the end of its trunk; it uses these in feeding.

    _____

8. These fingers are so flexible that the elephant can use it to pick a single leaf.

    _____

9. Their tusks also help an elephant find food.

    _____

10. The tusks serve as probes; with it the elephant digs roots out of the earth and finds water in the riverbeds, even when they are completely dry.

    _____

22.3 Eliminating Errors in Pronoun Agreement (2) (*BHW* 22a–h)

In the following sentences, cross out any pronoun that does not agree in number with its antecedent. Write the correct pronoun in the space provided. If a sentence contains no error, write C in the space.

Example: The team won ~~their~~ third consecutive game last week.   *its*_____

1. After the jury delivered their verdict, the judge scheduled a date for sentencing.

    _____

2. The mob wound its way angrily toward the site of the accident.

    _____

3. Each girl on the soccer team is required to take their turn playing goalie. _____

4. Every dog will have its day. _____

5. Economics justly deserves its reputation as a dry discipline. _____

6. The United States urged its allies to support the treaty. _____

7. After the fireworks, the crowd broke up and moved slowly toward their cars. _____

8. Neither of the two women would allow their name to be placed in nomination. _____

9. Neither Fred nor Tom made his vote public. _____

10. After they quit singing as a group, each of the Beatles made recordings on their own. _____

22.4 Revising Sentences for Pronoun Agreement (*BHW* 22a–h)

Revise the following sentences, using the directions given in parentheses. Make all changes necessary to bring pronouns into agreement with antecedents and subjects with verbs. Make your revisions in the space above the lines.

Example: A singer—however talented or untalented—is always welcome to compete in the Greater Milwaukee Irish Songfest. (Change *singer* to *singers*.)

(handwritten edits: "A" changed, "singer" to "Singers"; "is" changed to "are")

1. Either Bridget or Nora must decide whether she plans to sing "Who Put the Overalls in Mrs. Murphy's Chowder?" at next week's Irish songfest. (Delete *Either;* change *or* to *and.*)

268

2. Kevin had no trouble deciding that he would do his famous imitation of Richard Nixon singing "When Irish Eyes Are Smiling." (Change *Kevin* to *The O'Meara brothers.*)

3. Entering the songfest for the first time, Mary decided to take her chances with "I'll Take You Home Again Kathleen." (Change *Mary* to *The Sullivan twins.*)

4. A person is almost transported to Dublin when she hears Patrick Kennedy Joyce sing "Danny Boy." (Change *person* to *people.*)

5. The Caffrey-Sullivan Singers usually take first prize with their spirited rendition of "Finnegan's Wake." (Change *The Caffrey-Sullivan Singers* to *Brendan Prendergast.*)

22.5 Eliminating Agreement Errors with Indefinite Pronouns (*BHW* 22f)

In the following sentences, pronouns fail to agree in number with the indefinite pronouns that serve as their antecedents. Revise each sentence in the space provided, making pronouns agree with antecedents, while avoiding the use of masculine pronouns to refer to both men and women. Usually, the best solution is to recast the entire sentence to eliminate one of the pronouns.

Example: Everyone has a right to their own opinion.

Everyone has the right to an opinion.

1. None of the students volunteered their time for the fundraiser.

_____

_____

2. Anybody should be able to solve the puzzle by themselves.

_____

_____

3. Neither of them has earned their keep.

_____

_____

4. Each student has a bluebook in which to write their exam.

_____

_____

5. Someone had their phone number carved in the top of the desk.

_____

_____

_____

PRONOUN REFERENCE

22.6 Eliminating Errors in Pronoun Reference (*BHW* 22i—m)

In each of the following passages, underline any pronoun that lacks a clear, explicit antecedent. Then, in the space above the lines, make whatever changes are needed to correct the problem. In some cases you may have to supply antecedents.

Example: Tomatoes were once believed to be poison. ~~In Europe they~~ *Europeans* grew them as a curiosity before <u>they</u> grew them as a food.

1. Primitive people often used vegetables in their fertility rites. This survives today in our marriage custom of throwing rice on newlyweds.

2. Instead of rice, some Europeans use peas. They throw it into the bride's lap, which increases her fertility—at least according to folklore.

3. They say that eating carrots improves one's eyesight. It is probably not just a myth.

4. Carrots do, in fact, have a high vitamin A content. This is known to help correct the problem of night blindness.

5. Some vegetables, including asparagus and onions, were once thought to be aphrodisiacs. They were eaten to stimulate their ardor for lovemaking.

6. Today onions are often credited with the opposite effect. Eating it makes one's breath rather unromantic.

7. They keep introducing "new" vegetables to the supermarket shelves.

8. Spaghetti squash is an example of this trend. They are a low-calorie replacement for pasta.

9. The meat is scraped out of the shell after the squash has been boiled whole—in a big pan since the vegetable is about the size of a large eggplant. This makes it look like spaghetti.

10. But how does it taste? Spaghetti lovers' opinions differ on it.

22.7 Review Exercise: Editing a Passage for Pronoun Errors (*BHW* Chapters 21–22)

Edit the following paragraphs to eliminate problems with pronoun case, agreement, and reference. Underline any pronoun that is in the wrong case; that fails to agree with its antecedent; or that lacks a clear, explicit antecedent. Make the necessary changes in the space above the lines. The first sentence is done for you as an example.

People

~~They~~ discovered cucumbers in India thousands of years ago. It was later grown by Greeks and Romans whom used forcing tech-

niques for a year-round crop. Columbus brought it to America on
one of their early voyages, and they gradually spread throughout

5   the New World.

In Buddhist lore it symbolized fertility. Egyptians and Jews
delighted in the refreshing fruit. This was not true of the English,
whom remained fearful of its "natural coldness" for centuries.
(This is caused by its high water content.) Early American settlers

10   believed that dreaming about the cucumber when one was ill
would bring them good health, and that a person whom ate cucumbers would have a sharper appetite. They also applied it in oint-
ment form to soothe and cool the skin. [17]

23

Parallelism

JOINING PARALLEL ELEMENTS

Note: The following exercises are designed to help you locate and correct faulty parallelism. For practice in using parallelism to make your writing more effective, see Exercises 13.1–13.3, pages 165–169.

23.1 Identifying Correct Parallel Construction (*BHW* 23a)

Decide which sentence in each pair contains a *correct* parallel construction. Circle the letter of the correct sentence, and underline its parallel elements.

Example: (a) Critics of "plastic money" believe that credit cards have

become too easy to get and too painless to use.

(b) Critics of "plastic money" believe that credit cards have

become too easy to get and are too painless to use.

1. (a) Major credit companies earn millions of dollars each year from

consumers who prefer to buy now and later to pay the bills.

(b) Major credit companies earn millions of dollars each year from consumers who prefer to buy now and pay later.

2. (a) Widely accepted both in the United States and abroad, credit cards enable users to travel with ease, to eat at the best restaurants, and to shop at the finest stores.

(b) Widely accepted both in the United States and abroad, credit cards enable users to travel with ease, eating at the best restaurants, and to shop at the finest stores.

3. (a) Nowadays credit cards are used not only to purchase luxury items but also to buy essential services.

(b) Nowadays credit cards not only are used to purchase luxury items but also to buy essential services.

4. (a) For example, some hospitals now display signs inviting patients to pay either with MasterCard or with Visa.

(b) For example, some hospitals now display signs inviting patients to pay either with MasterCard or paying with Visa.

5. (a) Some complain that the ease of using a credit card now exceeds the ease of cash.

(b) Some complain that the ease of using a credit card now exceeds the ease of using cash.

23.2 Identifying and Revising Faulty Parallelism (*BHW* 23a–i)

In the following sentences, underline any instances of faulty parallelism. Then revise the problem, writing your correction in the space above the lines. Circle the number of any sentence that requires no revision.

Example: Even those who dislike the taste of milk consume it whenever
~~they eat butter, cheese, ice cream, and eating a variety of other~~
foods.

Handwritten correction: a variety of other foods.

1. The Jersey, a fawn-colored cow, and the Holstein, a black and white cow, are among the most popular dairy breeds.

2. Milk varies in color and composition, depending on the breed of cow and the nature of its diet.

3. For example, the milk of Holsteins is whiter than Jerseys'.

4. Whichever breed produces it, cows' milk is a nearly ideal food, containing fats, proteins, carbohydrates, and it contains several vitamins and minerals.

5. Virtually all milk sold in the United States is both pasteurized and it is homogenized.

6. During pasteurization, milk is heated to destroy disease-causing organisms and to eliminate some of the bacteria that promote souring.

7. Developed and named after Louis Pasteur in the 1860s, pasteurization helped control the spread of tuberculosis.

8. Today, pasteurization may seem more a precaution, rather than a necessity, but even with modern handling methods, some nonpasteurized milk would undoubtedly become contaminated.

9. Unlike pasteurization, homogenization is not so much a necessity, but rather a convenience.

10. Whether necessary or it is not necessary, the homogenization process is used widely in the United States.

11. Homogenized milk is blended so thoroughly that its cream will not separate and rising to the top.

12. Long before they knew about pasteurization and homogenization, people drank milk; they also used it to make butter, cheese, and yogurt.

13. Milk can, and indeed always has been, used to make such products.

14. Today most Americans, and indeed most people throughout the world, drink cows' milk.

15. But in some countries, other animals provide part of the milk supply: the buffalo in India, the goat in several Mediterranean countries, and in northern Europe reindeers are still used for milk.

PUNCTUATING PARALLEL ELEMENTS

23.3 Using Commas with Parallel Elements (*BHW* 23j–l)

The following sentences contain some parallel elements that require punctuation and others that are punctuated unnecessarily. Add commas where appropriate and circle any punctuation that should be omitted.

Example: He has forbidden his Government to pass laws of immediate and pressing importance.

1. We hold these truths to be self-evident that all men are created equal, that they are endowed by their Creator with certain unalienable Rights that among these are Life Liberty and the Pursuit of Happiness.

2. The history of the present King of Great Britain is a history of repeated injuries, and usurpations.

3. He has called together legislative bodies at places unusual uncomfort-
    able and distant from the depository of their Public Records.

4. He has plundered our seas ravaged our Coasts burnt our towns, and
    destroyed the lives of our people.

5. We have reminded them of the circumstances of our immigration, and
    settlement here. [18]

24

Relations between Tenses

24.1 Establishing Correct Relations between Tenses within a Sentence (*BHW* 24a–b)

In each of the following sentences, circle any verb whose tense is not properly related to the tense of the underlined verb. Then write the correct verb form in the space provided. If the sentence contains no error, write C in the space. [19]

Example: The Book of Lists <u>includes</u> an entry that (described) fifteen well-known love offerings.

describes

1. When his wife <u>died</u> in 1631, Shah Jahnan, emperor of the Moguls, builds the magnificent Taj Mahal in her honor.

   _____

2. After Marc Antony and Cleopatra <u>became</u> lovers, he presents her with Cyprus, Phoeni-

279

cia, Coele-Syria, and parts of Arabia, Cilicia, and Judea.

3. Since most present-day lovers <u>own</u> far less real estate than Marc Antony, they had to give more modest gifts.

4. Richard Burton, however, gives several love offerings that <u>would have impressed</u> Cleopatra herself.

5. Elizabeth Taylor <u>was given</u> a $1,050,000 gem that Burton has purchased from Cartier.

6. "Diamond Jim" Brady <u>gave</u> actress Lillian Russell a gold-plated bicycle; its spokes have been encrusted with chips of diamonds, emeralds, rubies, and sapphires.

7. When Russell <u>went</u> on tour, the bicycle—kept in an expensive morocco case—travels with her.

8. Most lovers, of course, <u>cannot afford</u> a gold-plated bicycle (or an ordinary ten-speed, for that matter), so they gave much more modest gifts.

9. Most of us <u>settle</u> for a box of candy or a dozen roses, or we took our beloved out for a fancy dinner.

10. But just in case we do <u>strike</u> it rich, *The Book of Lists* offers a few suggestions for more expensive gifts.

24.2 Changing the Governing Tense of a Passage—Present to Past (*BHW* 24a–b)

Edit the following passage so that its governing tense is past rather than present. Make sure that the tense of every verb is correctly related to the tense of the first verb, which has been changed for you as an example.

It ~~is~~ **was** long past midnight when she arrives at the Hotel Thompson

which stands like the only living thing in the shuttered street. Lise

parks the little black car in a spot near the entrance, takes her book

and her zipper-bag and enters the hall.

5   At the desk the night-porter is on duty, the top three buttons

of his uniform unfastened to reveal his throat and the top of his

undervest, a sign that the deep night has fallen and the tourists

have gone to bed. The porter is talking on the desk telephone

which links with the bedrooms. Meanwhile the only other person

10   in the hall, a youngish man in a dark suit, stands before the desk

with a brief-case and a tartan hold-all by his side. [20]

24.3 Changing the Governing Tense of a Passage—Past to Present (*BHW* 24a–b)

Edit the following passage so that its governing tense is present rather than past. Make sure that the tense of every verb is correctly related to the tense of the first verb, which has been changed for you as an example.

At first Dad and I ~~stood~~ **stand** on the deck of the boat quietly taking in

everything. But when Dad saw how simple it was to sort the catch,

he started to help, and I followed to get a better view. Most of the

catch was shrimp, but the nets contained many other fish that we

5   tossed back. It was these that interested me. Baby catfish that

looked like miniature sharks, eels, and jellyfish were most common. An occasional rockfish, trout, or red speckled squid turned up. Johnny told me the names of the various fish and taught me to pick up a jellyfish without getting stung.

10   Suddenly Dad placed a big trout in my hands. It squirmed out onto the deck, and I chased after it clumsily. My legs got wet, and my tennis shoes squeaked. I laughed and felt like a little kid again.*

24.4 Matching Verb Forms to a Governing Tense (*BHW* 24a–b)

In the space provided, change each verb in parentheses to its correct form. Make sure that all verbs are consistent with the governing tense established in the first sentence. One verb is supplied for you as an example.

Every day, during breaks and after lunch, Speyer fed bits of bacon to the blue lizards that (live) 1. *lived* outside the barracks. He soon (concentrate) 2._____ on one bold lizard, and after a week he (have) 3._____ us as an audience. Sitting on the barracks steps, he (put) 4._____ his hand on the ground, palm up. He then (set) 5._____ bacon pieces in it, placing more in the crook of his arm and on his shoulder. Soon the lizard (come) 6._____ from under the steps, moving quickly, then stopping to do a sort of push-up and pant in its throat like a frog. It (take) 7._____ the food in his palm, then (run) 8._____ easily up to his elbow and finally all the way to his shoulder.

After a few days, we (press) 9._____ Speyer to expand his performance. During afternoon break, he (repeat) 10._____ the usual sequence. But this time, as the lizard (eat) 11._____ from his shoulder, Speyer slowly (turn) 12._____ his face to it.

Tensed to run, the lizard suddenly (thrust) 13._____ its body toward Speyer's extended tongue. It (come) 14._____ away with a shred of bacon, then (flash) 15._____ down his arm and out of sight.[21]

24.5 Correcting Shifts in Verb Tense within a Passage (*BHW* 24a–b)

The following paragraph contains unacceptable shifts in verb tense. Correct any verb that does not follow in a correct sequence from the tense established at the beginning of the passage. One verb is corrected for you as an example.

A fertilized female tarantula lays from 200 to 400 eggs at a time; thus it ~~was~~ *is* possible for a single tarantula to produce several thousand young. She takes no care of them beyond weaving a cocoon of silk to have enclosed the eggs. After they hatched, the
5   young walked away, found convenient places in which to dig their burrows and spend the rest of their lives in solitude. Tarantulas feed mostly on insects and millipedes. Once their appetite was appeased, they digest the food for several days before eating again. Their sight is poor, being limited to sensing a change in the
10 intensity of light and to the perception of moving objects. They apparently had little or no sense of hearing, for a hungry tarantula would have paid no attention to a loudly chirping cricket placed in its cage unless the insect happens to touch one of its legs.[22]

24.6 Using Verb Tense in Direct and Indirect Discourse (*BHW* 24c)

Rewrite the following quotations as indirect discourse. Make sure that you change verb tenses as necessary.

Example: "I have decided not to return to college this term," said Hamlet.

Hamlet said that he had decided not to return to college this term.

1. "I never wanted to go to college in Germany in the first place," he protested.

_____

_____

2. "I plan to go to a vocational school where I can pick up a useful trade," he said.

_____

_____

3. "I have had it with the curriculum at Wittenberg," he insisted.

_____

_____

4. "No matter what Uncle Claudius wants," he added, "I will study clothmaking."

_____

_____

5. "If I had worked at the trade since boyhood, I would be a master clothmaker today," he concluded.

_____

_____

24.7 Review Exercise: Editing a Passage for Errors in Parallel Construction and Shifts in Verb Tense (*BHW* Chapters 23–24)

Edit the following passage to eliminate errors in parallel construction (including faulty punctuation) and shifts in verb tense. Make the necessary changes in the space above the lines. You may want to copy your revised version onto a separate sheet of paper before submitting it. Two errors are corrected for you as an example.*

Every serious student can expect to write a major research project at one time or another during her academic career. Planning, organizing, and ~~to write~~ **writing** such a paper ~~was~~ **is** an invaluable experi-ence. It not only gave a student practice in research and writing,
5   but also self-confidence is promoted as the student develops the ability to complete a major task. However, the student is likely to appreciate these benefits only after the paper is finished. During the course of the research and while she was writing the paper, the student can expect to spend an enormous amount of time, and
10   energy. She may also experience a great deal of worry and could be frustrated as well. But these problems diminish if the student had organized her time wisely, and effectively gathered material.

So far during my college career, I have written my research papers at the last possible moment. However, with the size, and
15   importance of the project I am now doing, continuing this practice would mean a poor performance a case of ulcers and I would probably end up with a low grade. Obviously, to plan carefully and pacing my work was more productive than a last-minute effort. Since my main problem with writing a paper is managing
20   my time efficiently, I planned to make a definite schedule for this project, planning each phase of my research, and to start my writing as early as possible.

VI
PUNCTUATION

25

Periods, Question Marks, Exclamation Points

25.1 Using Periods, Question Marks, and Exclamation Points (*BHW* 25a–j)

Some of the following sentences contain errors in the use of periods, question marks, and exclamation points. Correct the errors in the space above the lines. Circle the number of any sentence that is punctuated correctly.

Example: "Will having an M.B.A. help you find a better job?" I asked.

1. Last year I asked my business professor why she had resigned from the college faculty?

2. She said that she planned to return to graduate school.

3. "Why," I asked?

4. She explained that she could eventually earn more money working in industry than she could in teaching, especially if she had an M.B.A.

5. I told her that I was surprised (!) to learn that business people made more than college professors.

6. She laughed.

7. I asked her how she planned to make a living while earning an M.B.A.?

8. She said "night school," thought for a minute, and then made a strange remark.

9. Was she merely pulling my leg when she asked, "Do you think I can get a part-time job as an actress?"?

10. A year later I saw her on a soap opera; she was playing the part of an out-of-work teacher.

26

Commas

26.1 Using Commas to Join Independent Clauses (*BHW* Chapter 26, 18a)

Underline all coordinating conjunctions in the following sentences. Then insert a comma before each conjunction that joins two *independent clauses*. Circle any commas that are used incorrectly between coordinate elements. [1]

Example: More than forty species of termites can be found in the United States and Canada, but the most destructive is the subterranean termite.

1. These voracious insects are often called white ants yet their appearance is actually very different from that of the ant.

2. The body of the termite is comparatively straight, and of approximately equal thickness throughout its length.

3. The ant has a narrow-waisted body that is shaped like an hourglass, and hind wings that are shorter than its forewings.

4. Termites live off cellulose, or rotting plant material in the soil but they also attack wooden objects such as house timbers or furniture.

5. In colder climates the subterranean termite stays below the frost line, and can live for as long as ten months without a taste of the cellulose found in wood but in areas where there is no frost it can eat the year round.

6. This species is especially fond of softwoods such as pine but it will just as eagerly attack any type of wood.

7. The destruction wrought by termites is hidden from view, and may take place slowly over a long period of time but it can be devastatingly thorough.

8. Termites eat only the interior sections of a timber or they hollow out a piece of furniture, leaving just a shell.

9. They often go undetected for no opening ever shows on the surface of the wood they attack.

10. Worker termites cannot endure exposure to light, and open air so they often build mud tunnels from the ground to a new source of food.

26.2 Sentence Practice: Using Commas to Join Independent Clauses (*BHW* Chapter 26, 18a)

Write five sentences in which you use a comma and the conjunction in parentheses to join two independent clauses. (Suggested topics: fast-food restaurants, politics, your hometown.)

Example: (yet) *The senator claimed that he had no interest in the nomination, yet he continued to promote speculation about his candidacy.*

1. (and) _____

_____

_____

_____

2. (but) _____

_____

_____

_____

3. (or) _____

_____

_____

_____

4. (for) _____

_____

_____

_____

5. (so) _____

_____

_____

_____

26.3 Using Commas to Set Off Introductory Elements (*BHW* Chapter 26, 20i–k)

In the following sentences, add commas where necessary to set off introductory modifying elements—words, phrases, or clauses. Consider the comma optional if the introductory element is brief and if the sentence is clear without the added comma.

Example: Like bees and ants, termites are social insects.

1. Highly organized they live in colonies consisting of a queen, winged reproductives, soldiers, and workers.

2. During her lifespan of forty years or more a single queen lays millions of eggs.

3. In one day she may produce as many as 35,000.

4. Although they are blind, sterile, and unable to stand exposure to light or dryness worker termites can be incredibly destructive.

5. In nature they enrich the soil by speeding the decay of vegetable matter.

6. Unfortunately they are not discriminating.

7. When conditions are right they will invade the timbers in a home just as readily as they will a rotting stump in the woods.

8. Building tunnels they work steadily and methodically, destroying support timbers, framing lumber, or even the paper surface on sheetrock.

9. Causing extensive damage each year in the United States they cost homeowners millions of dollars.

10. Although few people realize it homeowners pay far more each year to repair termite damage than they do to repair the ravages of hurricanes and tornadoes.

26.4 Sentence Practice: Using Commas to Set Off Introductory Elements (*BHW* Chapter 26, 20i–k)

Write five sentences in which you use commas to set off the type of introductory element named in parentheses. (Suggested topics: pressures on college students, the expense of raising children, television commercials.)

Examples: (phrase) *Along with the pressure to do well academically, most students feel a great deal of pressure to succeed socially.*

(clause) *If raising children is expensive today, imagine what it will cost at the turn of the century.*

(word) *Nevertheless, most people still say they want to have children, despite the cost.*

1. (phrase) _____

_____

_____

2. (phrase) _____

_____

_____

3. (clause) _____

4. (clause) _____

   _____

   _____

   _____

5. (word) _____

   _____

   _____

   _____

26.5 Using Commas with Nonrestrictive Elements (*BHW* Chapter 26, 20k–n)

In the following sentences, add commas where necessary to set off nonrestrictive elements, including sentence adverbs, transitional expressions, appositives, and parenthetic elements. Underline any material that you set off. Then circle commas that are used incorrectly to set off restrictive elements. Finally, circle the number of any sentence that is punctuated correctly.[2]

Examples: Africanized bees, <u>which have devastated the beekeeping in-</u>
<u>dustry in many Latin American countries,</u> continue to move
toward the United States.

There is growing concern among the 200,000 people who
raise bees in the United States.

1. Killer bees the Africanized honeybees that have stung hundreds of
people to death in recent years have just entered Costa Rica on their
steady move north.

2. The scientists, who have been studying Africanized bees, predict that they will arrive in the United States by the end of the decade.

3. In 1957, twenty-six swarms of African queen bees, which are more aggressive than European varieties, escaped from a laboratory in São Paulo, Brazil.

4. The African bees rapidly took over docile bee colonies, that lived in the region.

5. According to David Roubik a Smithsonian bee biologist most colonies along the Atlantic coast of South America are now Africanized.

6. There are claims Roubik up to 300,000 bees per square mile.

7. Africanized bees look just like the European bees, that are common in the United States.

8. They are however much more likely to react to an intruder.

9. In fact, they react up to thirty times more quickly and are up to ten times more likely to sting.

10. Some scientists doubt whether the killer bees accustomed to the warm southern climate will be able to withstand northern temperatures, and others contend that the bees will become gentler as they interbreed with European varieties.

26.6 Sentence Practice: Using Commas with Nonrestrictive Elements (*BHW* Chapter 26, 20k–n)

Write five sentences using correctly punctuated nonrestrictive elements. (Suggested topics: popular music and musicians, home cooking.)

Example: <u>The bass player, a distinguished-looking man with a Mohawk haircut, jumped onto the stage from a suspended platform.</u>

1. _____

_____

_____

2. _____

_____

_____

3. _____

_____

_____

4. _____

_____

_____

5. _____

_____

_____

26.7 Using Commas to Separate Coordinate Modifiers and Items in a Series (*BHW* Chapter 26, 20o–p, 23k)

In the following passages, supply commas where necessary to separate coordinate modifiers and items in a series. (The passages are adapted from an 1898 book of advice for young women.)[3]

PASSAGE 1

I knew one girl, supposed to be a very fine student, who brought on "fits" by overstudy while away at college. I had the opportunity to investigate this sad disheartening case, and I discovered that she had been eating from morning till night. She carried nuts

5   candy and apples in her pocket and pickles and cake in her room and studied and munched until it was no doubt a disturbed digestion rather than an overused brain that caused the "fits."

PASSAGE 2

If you eat regularly of plain meat vegetables fruits cereals milk and eggs, and if you avoid rich pastries cakes puddings pickles and sweet-meats, you will have compassed the round of healthful wholesome diet. I would like to emphasize the fact, however, that

5   tea and coffee are not foods. They are irritants stimulants nerve-poisons. If you are wise you will avoid them. You will also avoid the use of alcohol in all forms, whether wine ales beer or cider.

26.8 Sentence Practice: Using Commas to Separate Items in a Series and Coordinate Modifiers (*BHW* Chapter 26, 20o–p, 23k)

Write three sentences using commas to separate items in a series and two sentences using commas between coordinate modifiers. (Suggested topics: favorite desserts, flowers, famous athletes.)

Examples: (series) *The senator promised to have the tulip declared the state flower, an endangered species, and a national treasure.*

(coordinate modifiers) *The sundae was topped with a puff of rich, thick whipped cream.*

1. (series) _____

_____

_____

_____

2. (series) _____

_____

_____

_____

3. (series) _____

_____

_____

_____

4. (coordinate modifiers) _____

_____

_____

_____

5. (coordinate modifiers) _____

_____

_____

_____

26.9 Review Exercise: Editing a Passage for Comma Errors (*BHW* Chapter 26, 18a, 20i–p, 23k)

Edit the following passages by adding commas where necessary and circling those that are not needed. The first sentence is done for you as an example. (Some commas are used correctly; some are optional.)[4]

PASSAGE 1

The oceans' legendary mists have long swirled with tales of exotic beasts, but stories, whether based on fact or fantasy, tell of no creature with as much age-old charm as the mermaid. The idea of near-humans—both male and female—inhabiting the sea, and

5   inland waters has captured imagination since people first ventured seaward and for a very long time mermaids seemed every bit as real, as flying fish.

PASSAGE 2

The folklore of mermaids is ancient, and widespread crossing cultures continents and centuries. Mer-people have been called by diverse names—Sirens nixies and Nereids among others.

PASSAGE 3

Like all folkloric characters, each group of mer-people has specific traits, and habitats but there are some features, that we have come to associate with the generic mermaid. The part-woman part-fish charmer gives room for a great deal of artistic variation,

5   but most mermaids tend to merge woman with fish near, or below the waist. At that point, the torso starts to taper with scaly grace to a fish's tail.

PASSAGE 4

In overall form their bodies are designed for open-water seductions, and quick getaways, and mermaids are as the story goes as soulless as water. Traditionally the only way for a mermaid to acquire a soul, is by marrying a mortal.

PASSAGE 5

The moon goddess Atargatis known also as Derceto and worshiped by Syrians Philistines and Israelites is the earliest female fish deity. As a moon goddess Atargatis added many facets to the fish-god profile. She was associated with the more mysterious
5 attributes of the night, and she went on to acquire an aura of seductiveness vanity beauty cruelty and unattainable love.

PASSAGE 6

There has always been a discrepancy in the descriptions of the mermaids cited by naturalists, and sea captains and those representing the poetic truths of artists. Compare for example the lovely sea-maid of ''dulcet breath'' that Shakespeare wrote of in *A Mid-*
5 *summer Night's Dream* with the Amboina Mermaid, that appeared in natural history volumes in the early 1700s. Although the mermaid of Amboina is given the glamour of exotic coloring she is still described as a monster. In an original color drawing by Samuel Fallours published in 1717 she has copper-colored skin
10 highlighted with a green, that matches the hula skirt of fins around her hips.

PASSAGE 7

By the middle of the 19th century stuffed mermaids had become spectacles in Victorian London. Showmen bought most of these so-called preserved specimens usually trumped-up monkey-fish composites from Japanese fishermen.

PASSAGE 8

The vitality of the mermaid legend indicates, that there may be a substratum of fact an animal that may appear mermaidlike, from a distance. Several possibilities have been suggested: the sea cows of the order Sirenia, including the manatee and the dugong, and,

5   of course, the many varieties of seals.

PASSAGE 9

While these animals hardly have the beauty to sink a ship, or even attract a sailor long at sea they do have certain characteristics similar to those ascribed to mermaids. The nearly hairless manatee is somewhat larger than the human female but the female ma-

5   natee's breasts which are forward near its flipperlike forelimbs are in a position similar to the human female's. The manatee has no other limbs and its blubbery body tapers to a horizontal flipper of a tail. The dugong is similar in shape to the manatee. It has a muzzle covered with bristly whiskers, and is said to suckle its

10   young with its upper body out of the water cradling the baby with one flipper.

27

Semicolons
and Colons

SEMICOLONS

27.1 Using Semicolons (*BHW* 27a–d)

In the following passages, decide whether semicolons are used correctly. If the semicolon is correct, write C in the space provided; if it is incorrect, write X. Be prepared to explain which mark of punctuation, if any, should replace each faulty semicolon.[5]

Example: Most of the dead animals you see on highways
near the cities are dogs; a few cats.   X

1. Out in the countryside, the forms and coloring of the
   dead are strange; these are the wild creatures.   _____

2. Seen from a car window, they appear as fragments,
   evoking memories of woodchucks, badgers, skunks,
   voles, snakes; sometimes the mysterious wreckage of
   a deer.   _____

3. It is always a queer shock, part a sudden welling of grief; part unaccountable amazement. _____

4. It is simply astounding; to see an animal dead on a highway. _____

5. The outrage is more than just the location; it is the impropriety of such visible death, anywhere. _____

6. You do not expect to see dead animals in the open; it is the nature of animals to die alone, off somewhere, hidden. _____

7. It is wrong to see them lying out on the highway; it is wrong to see them anywhere. _____

8. Everything in the world dies. We only know about it; however, as a kind of abstraction. _____

9. If you stand in a meadow, at the edge of a hillside, and look around carefully; almost everything you can catch sight of is in the process of dying, and most things will be dead long before you are. _____

10. If it were not for the constant renewal and replacement going on before your eyes; the whole place would turn to stone and sand under your feet. _____

27.2 Sentence Practice: Using Semicolons (*BHW* 27a–d)

Write two sentences of your own using semicolons to link closely related independent clauses. Then write three sentences in which you join independent clauses by using a semicolon and the sentence adverb given in parentheses. (Suggested topics: teachers, the perfect vacation, writing.)

Examples: (related clauses) *There were fifty people waiting in line; every one of them wanted to sign up for Ms. Tilka's first-year writing course.*

(moreover) *Ms. Tilka was an immensely popular teacher; moreover, her students usually finished her course well prepared to write in their other courses.*

1. (related clauses) _____

   _____

   _____

2. (related clauses) _____

   _____

   _____

3. (therefore) _____

   _____

   _____

4. (however) _____

   _____

   _____

5. (furthermore) _____

   _____

   _____

   _____

27.3 Using Semicolons as a Stylistic Device (*BHW* 27a–d)

Study the use of semicolons in the following passages—the first two from speeches, the third from an essay. Be prepared to discuss the effect each writer achieves by using semicolons. Rewrite one of the passages, removing all semicolons. How does your revision alter the impact of the passage? Finally, write a passage of your own using semicolons to achieve a particular rhetorical effect.

1. With malice toward none; with charity for all; with firmness in the right, as God gives us to see the right, let us strive on to finish the work we are in; to bind up the nation's wounds; to care for him who shall have borne the battle, and for his widow, and his orphan—to do all which may achieve and cherish a just, and a lasting peace, among ourselves, and with all nations.[6]

2. But one hundred years later, the Negro still is not free; one hundred years later, the life of the Negro is still sadly crippled by the manacles of segregation and the chains of discrimination; one hundred years later, the Negro lives on a lonely island of poverty in the midst of a vast ocean of material prosperity; one hundred years later, the Negro is still languishing in the corners of American society and finds himself in exile in his own land.[7]

3. It is almost always a greater pleasure to come across a semicolon than a period. The period tells you that is that; if you didn't get all the meaning you wanted or expected, anyway you got all the writer intended to parcel out and now you have to move along. But with a semicolon there you get a pleasant little feeling of expectancy; there is more to come; read on; it will get clearer.[8]

COLONS

27.4 Using Colons (*BHW* 27e–h)

In the following passages, decide whether colons are used correctly. If the colon is correct, write C in the space provided; if it is incorrect, write X.

Be prepared to explain which mark of punctuation, if any, should replace each faulty colon.

Example: Before deciding to major in English, I had tried: psychology, anthropology, and geography.   ✗ _____

1. As an academic discipline, anthropology has its attractions: an intriguing combination of book learning and field work.   _____
2. I was concerned, however: that a degree in anthropology might make it difficult for me to get a job after graduation.   _____
3. A degree in psychology, on the other hand, can lead to several careers, such as: social work, counseling, or teaching.   _____
4. The two "tracks" offered by the geography department were: physical geography and human geography, but neither appealed to me.   _____
5. I finally decided that the English department's program had the kind of variety I wanted: courses in literature, language, creative writing, and professional writing.   _____

27.5 Using Colons to Achieve Economy (*BHW* 27e–h)

Rewrite the following passages, using a colon and a list to make each passage more economical.

Example: Mrs. Goodnight's living room was legendary. It was a bizarre swirl of clashing colors. There were red drapes. On the drapes were chartreuse ties. The walls were a dingy orange. The carpet was a war between lavender and peach.

Mrs. Goodnight's legendary living room was a swirl of clashing colors: red drapes with chartreuse ties, dingy orange walls, and a carpet on which lavender battled with peach.

1. Professor Wilson planned to assign four novels in his pop-lit course. The class would read Owen Wister's *The Virginian*. They would also read Margaret Mitchell's *Gone with the Wind*. And they would read Harriet Beecher Stowe's *Uncle Tom's Cabin* and James Michener's *Poland.*

2. The mayor outlined three major problems that the town had to address. There was an inadequate sewer system. Also, the city needed to replace its outdated fire-fighting equipment. Finally, something had to be done to upgrade police protection.

3. In the 1960s the New York Stock Exchange established regulations to govern advertising by brokerage firms. Among other things, the regulations forbid overly superlative or promissory language. They also prohibit forecasts and predictions that are not clearly labeled as opinions. Other forbidden practices include the publication of testimonials and the use of unqualified boasts about past success.*

27.6   Sentence Practice: Using Colons
(*BHW* 27e–h)

Write three sentences using colons. (Suggested topics: shoes, popular magazines, ice cream flavors.)

Example: *Converse tennis shoes have the features that everyone wants: comfort, style, and the right price.*

1. _____

   _____

   _____

   _____

2. _____

3. _____

28

Dashes and Parentheses

DASHES

28.1 Sentence Practice: Using Dashes
(*BHW* 28a–f)

Write five sentences showing the correct use of dashes. Two of your sentences should contain paired dashes. (Suggested topics: books, inexpensive ways to travel, grandparents.)

Example: *John Blair's first novel—what an ending it has—earned high praise from science fiction buffs.*

1. (dash) _____

_____

_____

_____

2. (dash) _____

_____

_____

_____

3. (dash) _____

_____

_____

_____

4. (paired dashes) _____

_____

_____

5. (paired dashes) _____

_____

_____

28.2 Using Dashes as a Stylistic Device (*BHW* 28a–f)

Study the use of dashes in the following passages, and be prepared to discuss the effect each writer achieves by using them. Rewrite one passage without using dashes. How does your revision alter the impact of the passage? Finally, write a passage of your own using dashes to achieve a particular rhetorical effect.

1. American jazz emerged a little more than a century ago in the city of New Orleans. It was a fusion of the existing musical art forms of black America—the work songs, spirituals, and blues—combined with elements of white folk music, the rhythms of Hispanic America and the Caribbean, the melodies of French dances, and the instrumentation of the marching band.[9]

2. Walking down the sidewalk, under the canopy of tall trees, I'd warily notice the—suddenly—silent neighborhood kids who stood warily watching me. Nervously, I'd arrive at the grocery store to hear there the sounds of the *gringo*—foreign to me—reminding me that in this world so big, I was a foreigner. [10]

3. If our freedom means ease alone, if it means shirking the hard disciplines of learning, if it means evading the rigors and rewards of creative activity, if it means more expenditure on advertising than education, if it means in the schools the steady cult of the trivial and the mediocre, if it means—worst of all—indifference, or even contempt for all but athletic excellence, we may keep for a time the forms of free society, but its spirit will be dead. [11]

4. The endless primary season; the hyperbolic, carefully scripted, flag-waving conventions; the endless sound bites and TV spots; the charges and counter charges, the pandering and posturing; the wheedling and whining—American presidential campaigns have become costly, predictable rituals designed more to evade that to engage the issues.

PARENTHESES

28.3 Sentence Practice: Using Parentheses
(*BHW* 28g–l)

Write three sentences that illustrate the correct use of parentheses. (Suggested topics: sports fans, world leaders, your home state or province.)

Example: Canadian prime minister Lester
Pearson (1897–1972) received the
Nobel Peace Prize for his role in
mediating the 1956 Arab-Israeli War.

1. _____

   _____

2. _____

_____

_____

_____

3. _____

_____

_____

28.4 Using Parentheses as a Stylistic Device (*BHW* 28g–l)

Study the use of parentheses in the following passages, and be prepared to discuss the effect each writer achieves by using them. Rewrite one passage without using parentheses. How does your revision alter the impact of the passage? Finally, write a passage of your own, using parentheses to achieve a particular rhetorical effect.

1. A human adult is nearly two-thirds water (infants a boggy 80 percent) and all the water is murky, afloat with particles. [12]

2. If we agree that buying art is desirable but beyond the means of ordinary citizens, a tax deduction could be granted for money spent to participate in ''art clubs'' to buy art and circulate the works among members who share similar tastes, creating, in essence, fluid mini-museums in the private sphere. (This is how Ben Franklin launched what eventually became our system of lending libraries.) [13]

3. As we approached the ticket booth, we heard the thump, thump of a loudspeaker's bass. Overhead, large neon letters spelled out ''EM-PIRE'' (in pink) and ''ROLLERDOME'' (in green), but they in no

way prepared us for the Empire's interior, which is a huge, cavernlike space dominated by words. There were words of warning accompanied by drawings illustrating "THE CORRECT WAY TO FALL" (on your rear) and "THE WRONG WAY TO FALL" (on your hands); there were words that shimmered in the music ("Sweat/ Sweeaaat/Makes me feel right/Work me all night"); and there were a lot of neon shapes—orange lightning bolts, blue palm fronds, yellow squiggles—that amounted to words in another kind of language (a weak translation might be "Excitement"). [14]

28.5 Review Exercise: Using Commas, Semicolons, Colons, Dashes, and Parentheses (*BHW* Chapters 26–28)

For each blank space in the following passages, supply the necessary mark of punctuation: comma, semicolon, colon, dash, or parentheses. If no punctuation is needed, write an X in the space. The first sentence is done for you as an example. (In some cases, more than one mark of punctuation is correct; in others, punctuation is optional.)

PASSAGE 1

While the cowboy sat there quietly turning his guitar 1. __,__ I marveled at how rough 2. __X__ and weatherbeaten he was. His boots looked as if he had worn them a hundred years 3. _____ the color was faded 4. _____ the leather was scruffed 5. _____ and cracked 6. _____ and the heels were worn almost flat. One pant leg was half tucked into the tall leg of his boot 7. _____ the other extended all the way down to his heel. A dark piece of denim was sewn in place just above his right knee 8. _____ clashing with the dirty 9. _____ light blue color of his jeans. A brand new belt 10. _____ a real contrast to the rest of his outfit 11. _____ hung loosely around his waist 12. _____ practically useless because of the tight fit of his jeans.*

317

PASSAGE 2

The fact 1. _____ that Epson has sold more printers for more personal computers than all other manufacturers on earth 2. _____ is certainly important to us 3. _____ but why should it matter to you?

The reason we have continually outsold our competition is disarmingly simple 4. _____ we build a better printer for the money.

Epson makes a full line of high-quality printers for every home 5. _____ and business application 6. _____ which is no doubt why computer and software companies 7. _____ as well as other printer companies 8. _____ make their products "Epson-compatible." We're not only the world leader 9. _____ we're the world standard.

Coincidentally 10. _____ another good reason for buying such a widely available printer is that it is widely available.

What's more 11. _____ Epson-brand printers sold in the U.S. are backed by a full one-year warranty 12. _____ on all parts and labor.

And if you *were* to have a problem 13. _____ an unlikely occurrence 14. _____ you could have your Epson serviced at over 1,000 authorized Epson Service Centers 15. _____ from coast to coast. [15]

PASSAGE 3

Several different beverages are in the category of true meads. Strictly speaking 1. _____ mead is made with honey 2. _____ water 3. _____ and yeast. This type of mead may take up to a year to ferment 4. _____ and require up to three years to reach its peak flavor. There are other types of mead 5. _____ just as delicious 6. _____ which are made with fruits. These are known as melomels 7. _____ and they require the same amount of time to ferment 8. _____ and age as our

318

wines. The type of melomels 9. _____ which were once made 10. _____ are as follows 11. _____ pyment 12. _____ a honey wine produced by a combination of honey and grape juice 13. _____ hippocras 14. _____ which is the same as pyment, with spices and herbs added to enhance the flavor 15. _____ metheglin 16. _____ made with honey 17. _____ spices 18. _____ and herbs 19. _____ and cyser, made with honey 20. _____ and apple cider. [16]

29

Quoting

29.1 Using Quotation Marks (*BHW* 29d–e)

In the following passages, insert quotation marks where necessary.[17]

Example: "The following sentences," said the author, "are adapted from an article in *Saturday Review* called 'What Makes a Genius?'"

1. Just why, asked the law professor, do you say that Rossini was a genius?

2. That's easy, replied the general. He composed a wide variety of great music.

3. That doesn't make him a genius, retorted the editor. He has to have more than great talent and industry to qualify.

4. Well, protested the general, Thomas Wolfe said genius was ninety

percent energy and ten percent talent. [The general is paraphrasing Wolfe, not quoting him directly.]

5. Seems to me, remarked the host, that genius is more than what we call talent; genius adds something that wasn't there before.

6. At this point the hostess had found the right page in the dictionary. It says here, she put in, that genius is extraordinary power of invention or origination of any kind. [Beginning with the word *extraordinary,* the hostess quotes directly from the dictionary.]

7. Freud had something to say on the subject, but I'm not sure I can quote him accurately, said the psychoanalyst, blushing a little. As I recall it, he described a genius as something in the nature of one in an hypnotic state, who achieved great things without being really aware of it. [The psychoanalyst does not attempt to quote Freud.]

8. I might go along with that in the arts, said the professor, because I'm sure neither Beethoven nor Van Gogh nor Shakespeare, for example, ever said to himself: Now I'm going to create, now I'm going to perpetrate an act of genius.

9. The editor had been rummaging through his host's books. What about this? he asked. This man Amiel published a diary back in 1850, and he said: Doing easily what others find difficult is talent—doing what is impossible for talent is genius. [The editor quotes Amiel directly.]

10. It's clear enough, said the professor, that not one of us, when the argument started, had more than the foggiest idea of what he meant by the word genius.

29.2 Eliminating Errors in Quoting
(*BHW* 29d–e, o–r)

Some of the following sentences violate rules for using double and single quotation marks, ellipsis marks, and brackets. Cross out any punctuation that is unnecessary or incorrect. Then add punctuation where appropriate. Circle the number of any sentence that contains no errors.

Example: "The movie," said Floyd, "features an actress [sic] named Carroll O'Connor."

1. In order to annoy Helen, Tom said, "Shakespeare considered man the superior sex.

2. "In *Hamlet,* he continued, Shakespeare says that man is 'the beauty of the world, the paragon of animals.' "

3. Helen said, "Shakespeare no doubt intended to include women in his use of the generic term "man."

4. After she thought for a minute, Helen reminded Tom about *As You Like It:* "In that play Shakespeare makes Rosalind the sensible, level-headed heroine; her lover Orlando acts silly during much of the play."

5. "And in *A Midsummer Night's Dream,*" Helen added, "Bottom says, '*Man* is but an ass.' "

6. Outwitted, Tom decided to take Helen's advice: 'Read more Shakespeare.'

7. But instead of reading the plays, Tom found a book *about* Shakespeare which said that "the bard wrote more than fifty (*sic*) plays."

8. He also discovered a passage about Shakespeare's female characters:

323

"The bard did, indeed, create many strong . . . portraits of the weaker sex."

9. Helen decided that the book was inaccurate and pompous when she read the following passage: "Shakespeare, that 'sweet swan of Avon,' lived well into the early part of the seventeenth century, writing several novels (*sic*) in addition to his beloved plays . . ."

10. What amused Helen most was the author's statement that ". . . Shakespeare would probably be writing brilliant TV sitcoms if he were alive today."

29.3 Sentence Practice: Integrating Quoted Material (*BHW* 29k–l, o–r)

Using the following guidelines, write five sentences in which you integrate quoted material from a newspaper, magazine, or book.

1. A sentence in which you integrate a brief quotation so that it does *not* have to be introduced by a comma or a colon (29k)
2. A sentence in which you introduce a brief quotation using a comma (29l)
3. A sentence in which you introduce a brief quotation using a colon (29l)
4. A sentence using an ellipsis mark to show that material has been omitted from a quotation (29o–q)
5. A sentence using brackets to insert your own word or words into a quotation (29r)

29.4 Combining Quotation Marks with Other Marks of Punctuation (*BHW* 29g)

In some of the following sentences, quotation marks have been combined incorrectly with other punctuation. Circle each error; then, in the space provided, write the correct punctuation and the word preceding it. If a sentence contains no error, write C in the space. [18]

Example: In *The March of Folly,* historian Barbara Tuchman shows how governments throughout history have pursued "policies contrary to their own interests⟩.

interests."

1. "Misgovernment," writes Tuchman, "is of four kinds, often in combination."

2. Her book concerns the fourth kind: "folly or perversity".

3. "Wooden-headedness . . . plays a remarkably large role in government", says Tuchman.

4. In *A Distant Mirror,* Tuchman describes the fourteenth century as "a violent, tormented, bewildered, suffering and disintegrating age;" it was "a time, as many thought, of Satan triumphant."

5. Tuchman's chapter on the plague of 1348–1350 is called " 'This Is the End of the World:' The Black Death."

6. The Black Death had reduced the population of Europe "by nearly 50 percent at the end of the century." (Tuchman 119).

7. In the country, "peasants dropped dead on the roads, in the fields, in their houses" (Tuchman 98).

8. After reading *A Distant Mirror,* Phil asked his

history professor, "Is this Tuchman's first book?" _____

9. His professor said, "Don't tell me you've never heard of her other books"! _____

10. "Does the university library have them"? asked Phil. _____

30

Forming and Spacing Punctuation Marks

30.1 Forming and Spacing Punctuation Marks with a Typewriter or Word Processor (*BHW* Chapter 30)

In each of the following pairs, identify the sentence that violates the conventions for punctuating with a typewriter. Circle each error.

Example: (a) In two months ⊖ the hottest of the
year, I admit ⊖ we spent more than
$400 for air conditioning.

(b) In two months--the hottest of the
year, I admit--we spent more than $400
for air conditioning.

1. (a) Earl Warren served as Chief Justice of the United States (1953 - 1969) and as governor of California (1943 - 1953).

   (b) Earl Warren served as Chief Justice of the United States (1953–1969) and as governor of California (1943–1953).

2. (a) Some people considered the course a challenge; others thought it was merely impossible.

   (b) Some people considered the course a challenge; others thought it was merely impossible.

3. (a) The professor said that her course would strengthen the ill-prepared -- if they could survive the first test.

   (b) The professor said that her course would strengthen the ill-prepared--if they could survive the first test.

4. (a) Several of T.S. Eliot's poems have been set to music for the Broadway production Cats.

   (b) Several of T. S. Eliot's poems have been set to music for the Broadway production Cats.

5. (a) According to the brochure, ''the College was founded in 1886. . . . Its first student was graduated in 1892.''

(b) According to the brochure, ''the College was founded in 1886. . . . Its first student was graduated in 1892.''

6. (a) The columnist argued that the country ''would be better served by a single-term, six-year presidency...than by the present system of allowing two four-year terms.''

(b) The columnist argued that the country ''would be better served by a single-term, six-year presidency . . . than by the present system of allowing two four-year terms.''

7. (a) Shakespeare writes, ''Golden lads and girls all must,/As chimney-sweepers, come to dust.''

(b) Shakespeare writes, ''Golden lads and girls all must, / As chimney-sweepers, come to dust.''

8. (a) Dr. Lochman accused his opponent of using either/or reasoning.

(b) Dr. Lochman accused his opponent of using either / or reasoning.

9. (a) My neighbor's dog (a collie) looks like Lassie but has none of Lassie's charm.

(b) My neighbor's dog (a collie) looks like Lassie but has none of Lassie's charm.

10. (a) How many spaces follow a question
mark? How many follow a period?
(b) How many spaces follow a question
mark?   How many follow a period?

VII
CONVENTIONS

31

Verb Forms

31.1 Using Past-Tense and Past-Participle Verb Forms (*BHW* 31a–d)

Circle any incorrect past-tense or past-participle verb forms in the following sentences. Then write the correct form in the space provided. If a sentence contains no error, write C in the space. Consult a dictionary as necessary to determine the correct forms.

Example: Yesterday I (laid) on the beach for two

hours.   *lay*

1.   Unfortunately, I sat my beach umbrella at the

wrong angle; today I'm nursing a sunburn.   _____

2.   I done the same thing two weeks ago when my

friend Joe visited from Galveston.   _____

3.   We had gone to the beach planning to swim and

play volleyball.   _____

4.   Instead, we set around sunbathing most of the

day with a couple of my friends.   _____

5. If we had swam, my burn might have been
   less severe.

   _____

6. In order to observe wildlife last winter, I built
   a sturdy, wind-proof shelter in the woods.

   _____

7. But it didn't seem to help much; every time I
   used it, my feet and hands were nearly froze.

   _____

8. Maybe I should have wore warmer clothing.

   _____

9. But I suppose that after I had sat in near-
   freezing temperatures for several hours, even
   the warmest clothing and the best shelter
   wouldn't have helped.

   _____

10. Worst of all, I never seen more than a deer or
    two the entire season.

   _____

31.2 Using -s and -ed Verb Endings (BHW 31a–d)

Circle any verb in the following sentences that lacks a necessary -s or -ed
ending. Then write the correct form in the space provided. If a sentence
contains no error, write C in the space.

Example: Said Mr. Bunker, "I am not now,

nor have I ever been, (prejudice)"

prejudiced

1. Mr. Bunker was accustom to his daughter's
   frequent accusation that he was prejudiced
   against women.

   _____

2. "I admit that I use to be prejudiced," he argued, "but I've changed my attitudes."

   _____

3. "I suppose I owe you another chance," said his daughter.

_____

4. "I change my views last week," said Mr. Bunker, "after watching a Phil Donahue show that featured a bunch of women-libbers."

_____

5. "You're hopeless," his daughter concluded. "The very fact that you used a term like 'women-libbers' shows that you're bias."

_____

6. "What am I supposed to call them?"

_____

7. "They prefer to be call 'feminists,' and I think you should honor their wishes."

_____

8. Alex use to use oil-base paint whenever he painted the outside of his house.

_____

9. He now prefers latex because it spread more easily and dries more quickly.

_____

10. Having just finished a new paint job, he claims that he now see the advantage of aluminum siding.

_____

31.3 Identifying Active and Passive Verb Forms (*BHW* 31c–d)

For each of the following sentences, indicate whether the writer has used an active verb form (A) or a passive verb form (P). Then rewrite each sentence, converting active verbs to passive and passive verbs to active. For sentences that contain passive verbs, you may need to supply subjects (as illustrated in the first example).*

Examples: It is pointed out in the article that textbooks help teachers organize their courses. A/(P)

In the article, the author points out

that textbooks help teachers organize their courses.

Some teachers regard textbooks as needlessly restrictive. (A)/P

Textbooks are regarded by some teachers as needlessly restrictive.

1. Homemade teaching materials are preferred by some teachers. A/P

2. The author takes issue with instructors who want to eliminate textbooks. A/P

3. Because homemade teaching materials are bulky, they often cause storage problems. A/P

4. Teachers often find textbooks more accessible and simpler to use than homemade materials. A/P

5. Although textbooks have limitations, many objectives can be achieved by teachers who use them. A/P

_____

_____

_____

6. With thirty hours of English under my belt, I thought an advanced writing course would be a snap. A/P

_____

_____

_____

7. Errors that I have been making for years are now more easily seen when I edit. A/P

_____

_____

_____

8. In most of my high school English courses, a formal style of writing was encouraged. A/P

_____

_____

_____

9. Minor errors can be eliminated through careful proofreading. A/P

_____

_____

_____

10. I usually write my first drafts very quickly. A/P

_____

_____

_____

31.4 Converting Verb Forms from Passive to Active (*BHW* 31c–d)

Underline the passive verbs in the following passage. Then rewrite the passage, making all verbs active. The first two passive forms are underlined as an example. *Sample revisions:* It was midday. Passengers were getting into the bus. They were squashing each other together.

It was midday. The bus <u>was being got</u> into by passengers. They <u>were being squashed</u> together. A hat was being worn on the head of a young gentleman, which hat was encircled by a plait and not by a ribbon. A long neck was one of the characteristics of the

5   young gentleman. The man standing next to him was being grumbled at by the latter because of the jostling which was being inflicted on him by him. As soon as a vacant seat was espied by the young gentleman it was made the object of his precipitate movements and it became sat down upon. The young gentleman

10   was later seen by me in front of the gare Saint-Lazare. He was clothed in an overcoat and was having a remark made to him by a friend who happened to be there to the effect that it was necessary to have an extra button put on it. [1]

31.5 Using Subjunctive Verb Forms (*BHW* 31e)

Circle any verb in the following sentences that should be subjunctive but is not. Then write the correct subjunctive form in the space provided. If a sentence already contains a correct subjunctive form, write C in the space.

Examples: So be it.   *C*

        Jack wishes he (was) in the land of cotton.   *were*

338

1. If you have been born in the land of cotton, you too would want to live there. _____

2. The doctor recommended that Geneva cuts back on her smoking and drinking. _____

3. She later wished that she had been less forth-coming with the doctor about her vices. _____

4. The law requires that each eighteen-year-old male registers for the draft. _____

5. If she had been president, Jane would have vetoed the draft registration bill, a bill she still considers discriminatory. _____

6. I wish I was finished with this research paper. _____

7. The instructor requires that everyone submit each paper on or before the due date. _____

8. It is essential that you are here tomorrow at noon. _____

9. As Elvis Presley stepped out onto the lawn at Graceland, his fans shouted, "Long lives the king." _____

10. He is, as it was, a mouse learning to be a rat. _____

31.6 Review Exercise: Editing a Passage for Errors in the Use of Verb Forms (*BHW* Chapter 31)

Edit the following passage for errors in past-tense, past-participle, and subjunctive verb forms. Circle the errors and write your corrections in the space above the lines. The first sentence is done for you as an example.

planted

Last spring my family (plant) a vegetable garden for the first time. At first, everyone was enthusiastic, but since we had all plan a busy summer, we knew the garden would have to be a group effort if it was to succeed. We spent nearly a week planning the project.

5 After we had chose what to grow, we bought seeds and plants at the local feed store. Next, we carefully prepared the soil and lay out the rows using stakes and string. Finally, we planted the seeds and sat out the tomato seedlings. After we finish the planting, my father recommended that each member of the family is in charge

10 of the garden for one month during the summer. Through the end of July, the garden done very well. My brother was then suppose to care for it while the rest of us visited relatives in Idaho. When we return from the trip, we found the garden overgrowed with weeds and parched by the August heat. My brother—he lacked the

15 horticultural spirit to start with—had took off unexpectedly, quitting his job to spend the month, as he put it, "on the road getting my head together." He left the garden in charge of a friend who use to live next door. Unfortunately, the friend didn't know a garden hose from an artichoke.

20 My father was more disappointed than the rest of us; when he was young, his family use to rise their own produce every summer. He said that if he was to try a garden again, he would plan to spend the entire summer at home.

32

Plurals and Possessives

PLURALS

32.1   Forming Plurals (*BHW* 32a–j)

In the space provided, write the plural form of each word. Consult a dictionary as necessary.

Examples: army   *armies*

            speech   *speeches*

1. traitor   _____

2. warlord   _____

3. son-in-law   _____

4. ghetto   _____

5. baptism   _____

6. bar mitzvah _____

7. witch _____

8. hero _____

9. Jones _____

10. cupful _____

11. libretto _____

12. deer _____

13. syllabus _____

14. soprano _____

15. Wilson _____

16. reply _____

17. calf _____

18. child _____

19. datum _____

20. patio _____

POSSESSIVES

32.2 Forming Possessives (*BHW* 32k–s)

In the space provided, use a possessive noun or pronoun to form a phrase that is equivalent to the phrase on the left.

Examples: the budget of the city *the city's budget*

poetry written by Yeats *Yeats's poetry*

the car that belongs to you *your car*

	the property which they own	*their property*
1.	poetry written by Miles	
2.	photographs taken by Karsh	
3.	the fragrance it has	
4.	the idea conceived by Ms. Koepsel	
5.	the lyrics of Robert Burns	
6.	the speech of the president-elect	
7.	music composed jointly by Lennon and McCartney	
8.	music composed by John Lennon and by Beethoven	
9.	a night of a hard day	
10.	an orchard that is the joint property of Jack and Fern	
11.	the plight of the princess	
12.	the future that belongs to us	
13.	the machinery we own	
14.	the terror of the guillotine	
15.	the reaction of whom	
16.	the skill of Ms. Lombardo	
17.	the circulation of *The New York Times*	

18. the rights of everyone   _____

19. the bowling score of Jean John-
    son   _____

20. the nest in which it lives   _____

32.3 Proofreading for Apostrophe Errors (*BHW* 32k–t)

The following passages contain errors in the use of apostrophes to show possession and to indicate omissions. Add apostrophes where necessary and circle any that are misused.

Example: It's rare these days to find someone who isn't cynical about the job prospects of the class of '96.

PASSAGE 1

In the past month, there have been five robbery's at the local Sac n Pac grocery store. Its little wonder that the owner cant find people to work the night shift. The stores manager finally quit last week after his 57 Chevy was stolen from the parking lot. A week
5   earlier the owner's vicious German shepherd guard dog, Fluffy, lost it's life trying to protect a Wonder Bread delivery man during a hold-up.

PASSAGE 2

My uncle Claude is a true eccentric when it come's to food. He eats all his meals in bed at night—not ordinary meals, but little snacks and prepackaged treats that he hides in his room during the day. Aunt Pansy claims that she once found nearly fifty Chock
5   Full O Nuts bars under his bed. He's never eaten at restaurants because they serve "tainted" food—"tainted" with what he just

does'nt say. His mothers and fathers eating habits were equally eccentric. On her butchers recommendation, his mother ate only mutton. Her husbands preference was for pickled foods—mainly
10   vegetables—which he washed down with large quantities of rye whiskey. Throughout their marriage, they stored food in separate cupboards marked "her's" and "his."

PASSAGE 3

Popular sayings among household pet's: "Every dog will have it's day"; "Its a dog-eat-dog world"; "Well, thats a fine kettle of fish"; "Hes an odd fish"; "Shes a rare bird"; "Its raining cat's and dog's"; "Dog day's of summer"; "Its a dogs life"; "Dog is
5   mans best friend."

33

Spelling

33.1 Spelling Words That Look or Sound Alike (*BHW* 33c)

Examine each pair of words in parentheses and circle the correct one. Use a dictionary and *The Borzoi Handbook for Writers* as necessary.

Example: I plan to (waive, wave) my right (to, too) a jury trial, even though doing so will adversely (affect, effect) my chances for an acquittal.

1. Henry is (to, too) tired (to, too) listen to (your, you're) (advice, advise) about (weather, whether) he should go (forward, foreword) with his campaign for governor.

2. If (your, you're) unwilling to (accept, except) the settlement as (its, it's) now defined, (than, then) you should inform the (principal, principle) before you (precede, proceed) with (your, you're) legal challenge.

3. Judge Frolick is not (suppose, supposed) to be (prejudice, prejudiced)

(buy, by) such cheap theatrics, but after that last speech, I thought his (bias, biased) was obvious. Yesterday he said the case was (to, too) (miner, minor) for serious attention; now (its, it's) suddenly the most important case he's seen in (some time, sometime).

4. Ann had (all ready, already) written to Paul three times, but her letters seemed to have no (affect, effect) on him. Still, she was determined to (elicit, illicit) some sort of response, so she took out a fountain (pen, pin) and a piece of her best (stationary, stationery) and started a (forth, fourth) letter.

5. (Their, There, They're) were twenty students in the room at 8:00 A.M. waiting for (their, there, they're) test results; at 8:15 the dean entered and announced that everyone had (passed, past).

6. She (complemented, complimented) several people on the staff (who's, whose) work had deeply (affected, effected) (every one, everyone) in the village.

7. Once the missile left (it's, its) launch (cite, sight, site) in the California (desert, dessert), scientists used a sophisticated tracking (device, devise) (to, too) (altar, alter) (it's, its) (coarse, course).

8. (Everyday, Every day) the (personal, personnel) office processes fifty applications, (every one, everyone) of them from a well-quali-fied candidate.

9. The (ante-, anti-) nuclear group rented office space on the second floor of a converted (ante-, anti-) bellum home, but (their, there, they're) (presence, presents) didn't seem (to, too) (faze, phase) the other renters, (who's, whose) businesses were on the first floor.

10. (It's, Its) wheels are (loose, lose) and (it's, its) frame is rusty, but the children still ride the old tricycle (every day, everyday).

33.2 Editing for Commonly Misspelled Words (*BHW* 33d–f)

Circle the misspelled words in the following passages. Then write the correct spellings in the space above the lines. One of the errors in the first sentence is corrected for you as an example.

1. He put *a lot* of work into his vegtable garden, hopeing to sell part of his produce to a locale restaraunt.

2. Although she was only a sophmore, Allison decided to run for president of the student goverment. Much to her suprise, her canidacy was endorsed by one of the campus sororaties.

3. Last Wensday, five atheletes from Taiwan visited the campus for a gymnastic exibition. Amoung other things, they preformed a dicsiplined series of excercises on the paralell bars, probally one of the finest such preformences I've ever seen.

4. The instructer decided to develope a course calander listing the due dates for all major assignments. Than she revised her abscence policy, making it consistant with the new attendence regulations issued by the university during the preceeding semester.

5. We had alot of snow in Febuary, and on several ocassions the temprature dropped so low that even vetran Wisconsinites began to complain.

6. Nobody thought that the desparate, starving prisoners had the strenth

349

to excape, but through an extrordinary effort, they managed to make it accross fourty miles of mountainous terrain, arriving safely at the border where they were rescued by local police.

7. His poor judgement, his overly agressive style of managment, his lack of disipline, and his tendancy to exagerate his sucesses and ignore his failures—all these factors led the firm to a truely disasterous year. Embarassed and outraged, the board of directers fired him as soon as his incredable ineptitude came to light.

8. Michael O'Rear's newest novel is a study in the psycology of terror. By subtley manipulating the reader, he manages to make the villian seem monsterous without making him seem all together unrealistic.

9. During her campaign, the govorner made alot of promises about cleaning up the enviroment, but she now seems unable to fulfill those promises. She still seems knowlegeable about the key issues, but she no longer posesses the committment she once had.

10. Up until last week, things were going alright. Then I had my worst day of the semester: first, I caused a fire in the chemistry labratory; later that day, my English teacher returned a paper marked with twelve mispellings and several errors in grammer; then on Thursday, I had an arguement with my roomate about which of us should controll the thermostat in our room.

33.3 Spelling Words with *ie* and *ei* Combinations (*BHW* 33g)

Fill in the blanks with the correct *ie* and *ei* combinations. Use a dictionary or *The Borzoi Handbook for Writers* as necessary.

Examples: rec __*ei*__ ve

w __*ei*__ rd

1. bel_____ve
2. for_____gn
3. y_____ld
4. c_____ling
5. ach_____ve
6. th_____f
7. fr_____nd
8. s_____ze
9. _____ther
10. spec_____s

11. v_____n
12. w_____gh
13. pr_____st
14. th_____r
15. consc_____nce
16. effic_____nt
17. _____ght
18. l_____sure
19. sc_____nce
20. dec_____ve

33.4   Keeping a Spelling List (*BHW* 33a)

Add to your spelling list the words you missed in the three preceding exercises (33.1–33.3). As your essays are returned to you, add any misspellings marked by the instructor.

34

Hyphenation

34.1 Using Hyphens (*BHW* 34 a–f)

Insert hyphens as necessary in the following items, and circle hyphens that are not needed. If the item is already correct, write C in the space.

Examples: a dog‸eat‸dog world ⎯⎯⎯⎯⎯⎯⎯

a well-mannered child *C*⎯⎯⎯⎯⎯

a child who is well mannered *C*⎯⎯⎯⎯⎯

1. a well-guarded secret ⎯⎯⎯⎯⎯⎯⎯

2. a secret that is well-guarded ⎯⎯⎯⎯⎯⎯⎯

3. the well to do banker ⎯⎯⎯⎯⎯⎯⎯

4. a building that is seventy five years old ⎯⎯⎯⎯⎯⎯⎯

5. a fifty-five-year-old house ⎯⎯⎯⎯⎯⎯⎯

6. a convincingly-argued proposal ⎯⎯⎯⎯⎯⎯⎯

7. my ex professor ⎯⎯⎯⎯⎯⎯⎯

8. mayor-elect Farr ⎯⎯⎯⎯⎯⎯⎯

9. an exam that has three parts ⎯⎯⎯⎯⎯⎯⎯

10. a three part exam _____

11. a hotter than usual summer _____

12. right-to-work law _____

13. a pro-fascist organization _____

14. her stunningly brilliant mind _____

15. a price cut by one-half _____

16. un American activities _____

17. McCarthy like tactics _____

18. tactics similar to those that McCarthy-used _____

19. an ante bellum home _____

20. his uh oh here we go again look _____

34.2 Editing a Passage for Errors in Hyphenation (*BHW* 34a–f)

Insert hyphens as needed in the following passage. Take care to avoid unnecessary hyphenation. The first sentence is done for you as an example.

The four-part exam was carefully designed to test our knowledge of Shakespeare's *As You Like It*. We were responsible for identifying twenty five brief passages from the play and for completing thirty five fill in the blank questions. The short answer part of the

5   test, which accounted for one fifth of the total points, was a hard to follow series of questions about the plot. After the objective portion came the essays. The first one asked us to contrast the ill tempered Duke Frederick with his exiled brother, the ex Duke. The second question was about the ever melancholy Jaques and

10   his well known speech on the seven ages of man. The exam concluded with an open ended question about Shakespeare's multi faceted view of marriage in the play.

35

Capitals

35.1 Eliminating Errors in Capitalization (*BHW* 35a–r)

In the following sentences, circle any letters that should be capitalized, and strike through any that are capitalized unnecessarily.

Example: Professor ⓜyers, a noted ⓕreudian critic, concluded his lecture on *Sons Ⱥnd Lovers* by stating, "ɪ̶n the end, Paul must 'kill' his Ɱother to save himself."

1. I don't think mother will go to michigan, but she might visit uncle Leon in florida next Winter.

2. Serious presidential candidates can no longer afford to ignore the south or the west.

3. Gail's training in Chemistry had been minimal in High School, so she decided to attend Yakima Valley community college and enroll in chemistry 100.

4. On thursday, The Gormans traveled west to Cheyenne; they hoped to reach Tacoma by the end of the Month.

5. The Politician mustered his finest oratorical style and said, "ladies and gentlemen, the congress of the United States is taxing the Middle Class right out of existence."

6. Rosa's english paper, due this friday, is a discussion of Biblical allusions in Thomas Wolfe's story "Child By Tiger."

7. Asked to comment on a story about campus Environmentalists, dean Nardo said, "my official statement on the matter will be issued in the Spring."

8. During thanksgiving, Brian started his Term Paper, an analysis of marxist influences in Canadian Politics during the 1970s.

9. Living in an apartment as a Freshman (The dorms were full) put a serious strain on my academic performance: Shopping and cleaning took up a good part of saturday, and nearly every Weekday I ineptly cooked at least one meal.

10. Gary read two impressive books during the break: James Magner's *Rose Of My Flowering Night* and Charles Miller's *Auden: an American Friendship*.

35.2 Editing a Passage for Errors in Capitalization (*BHW* 35a–r)

The following passage contains numerous errors in capitalization. Circle any letters that should be capitalized, and strike through any that are capitalized unnecessarily. The first few errors have been corrected for you as an example.

Kate O'Flaherty was born in St. Louis in 1851. Her Father was a successful st. louis merchant who had married into an Aristocratic family of french origin. Kate attended the best school available to young women in the City, then spent two years busy with the
5   social activities appropriate to a person of her class; in 1870 she married oscar chopin, of a prominent Louisiana creole family, and moved with him to new orleans.

In the twelve years of their marriage, she bore him six children; and upon his sudden death in the early 1880s, she assumed
10   the management of the Family Plantation in natchitoches, Louisiana. In 1884 she returned to her Mother's home in st. louis, and only after her Mother's death the next year did she begin serious writing. Her first Novel, *at fault,* appeared in 1890 and was followed by two collections of Short Stories, *Bayou folk* in 1894 and
15   *A Night In Acadia* in 1897. By the time *the awakening* appeared in 1899, she was the well-known author of over a hundred Stories, Sketches, and Essays which had appeared in the popular and Literary Magazines of the period. She died in 1904.

Published in 1899 by herbert s. stone (chicago), *the awaken-*
20   *ing* met with widespread hostile criticism, and the book was removed from the Library shelves in st. louis. Chopin herself was refused membership in the st. louis fine arts club because of the novel. In 1906 it was reprinted by duffield (new york); but then it went out of print and remained so for more than half a Century
25   in this Country.[2]

357

36

Italics, Abbreviations, Numbers

36.1 Eliminating Errors in the Use of Italics, Abbreviations, and Numbers (*BHW* 36a–n)

Using *The Borzoi Handbook for Writers* as a reference tool, edit the following sentences. First underline words and phrases that should be italicized. Then cross out errors in the use of abbreviations and numbers, and make corrections in the space above the lines. (Assume that the sentences come from nontechnical prose—a college essay of the sort you would submit in your writing course.)

Example: <u>Bilker's Digest</u> ran a story last week about ~~2~~ two brothers from Punta Gorda, F~~l~~., *Florida* who made ~~twenty-six thousand dollars~~ $26,000 in a single day; they managed to sell nearly a hundred people on a bogus Caribbean cruise aboard the <u>Love Boat II</u>.

1. Most of Herman Melville's novel Moby-Dick takes place at sea, aboard the Pequod.

2. Mr. Wacker, the new football coach, warned the team: "Before this training session is over, you will all know the meaning of the word pain."

3. Aeschylus, the great Greek tragedian, probably wrote nearly 90 plays, including Prometheus Bound; he lived from 525–456 B.C.

4. In late Oct., Prof. Clifton D. Rodar, D.D.S., will give a lecture entitled, "Your Future in Dental School." Currently on leave from the Martindale College of Dentistry, Dr. Rodar is author of the bestselling book You and Your Teeth.

5. Asked to name 5 books of the Bible, Roger could name only three— Genesis, Job, and Ruth.

6. The house at 211 Harvard sold for an astounding two hundred and twenty-eight thousand dollars.

7. Honi soit qui mal y pense is the motto of the Order of the Garter.

8. Greta finally won the Scrabble game by using the word flocculus on a triple word score.

9. The U.S. Olympic team won 17 gold medals, thirty-six silver medals, and 14 bronze medals.

10. The CIA and FBI were notified about the incursion at 2:00 A.M. on the morning of Feb. 3rd.

36.2 Review Exercise: Editing a Passage for Errors—Plurals, Possessives, Spelling, Hyphenation, Capitals, Italics, Abbreviations, and Numbers (*BHW* Chapters 32–36)

Carefully proofread the following passages for misspellings and for errors in the use of plurals, possessives, hyphenation, capitals, italics, abbreviations, and numbers. First, underline words and phrases that should be italicized. Then cross out the other errors, and make corrections in the space above the lines. The first two sentences are done for you as an example. [3]

PASSAGE 1

Peter Weir is perhaps the *A*ustralian *d*irector who is most famous
abroad. His <u>Picnic *A*t Hanging *R*ock</u> (1975) became the first Australian film to ~~attrack~~ *attract i*nternational attention. His Gallipoli, released through paramount, and The year Of Living Dangerously,

5   to be released by mgm, were amoung the first australian films to
hook up with Hollywood for mass release worldwide.

Weir comes from a University background of Arts and Law.
He began to shoot 16-mm. underground movies while makeing a
living doing odd jobs in london and was then hired to make

10   documentarys. Now thirty-eight, he lives with his wife and children at palm beach, a geographically superier version of malibu,
about 50 miles North of sydney.

PASSAGE 2

Australias least pretintious but most financially rewarded direcster
is George Miller, who's Mad Max (1979) and this years The Road
Warrier are International blockbusters, earning more money then

any other australian film. The hero of both films is a loner named

5   max, who is more or less coerced into standing up to a viscious
gang of motorcycle riding thugs who are plagueing some oil
refinery people in post holocaust Australia.

A chubby, twinkly eyed gamin of thirty-six, Miller gloats, "I
make B pictures." He grew up in rural queensland and went on

10 to enter Medical School. In his last year there, he helped his twin
brother make a 1 min. film. This led to a month long University
course in film making, than some shorts depicting Millers cine-
matic preoccupation with the sinistor and the violant. For a while,
Miller was a practicing medical doctor, making house calls to

15 finance his entry into cinima.

VIII
RESEARCH
PAPERS

37

Conducting Research

37.1 Acquainting Yourself with a Research Library (*BHW* 37a, c–d)

Visit the library in which you plan to do your research. Then complete the following exercise. [1]

1. What are the library's hours? _____

2. For how long can a book be checked out? _____

3. What is the library's policy on renewals? _____

   _____

   _____

4. Can you recall a book from another reader if you need it immediately?

   _____

   What is the procedure for doing so? _____

   _____

   _____

5. Where are the library's card catalog and on-line catalog located?

_____

_____

Use one of these catalogs to find the title and call number of a book on each of the following topics:

A. World War II _____

_____

_____

B. The Egyptian pyramids _____

_____

_____

C. Clothing of the 1920s _____

_____

_____

D. Farming methods _____

_____

_____

E. Edgar Allan Poe _____

_____

_____

6. Does the library have an interlibrary loan service? _____
   If so, what is the procedure for using it? _____

   _____

   _____

   _____

7. Is there a special section for reserve books? _____
   If so, list the title and call number of one book currently on reserve.

8. Where is the reference room (or desk) located? _____

9. Where is the *New York Times Index* located? _____

   What color is the cover of the most recent volume? _____

10. Where is the *Readers' Guide to Periodical Literature* located?

   What color is the cover of the most recent volume? _____

11. Where is the *Book Review Digest* located? _____

   What color is the cover of the most recent volume? _____

12. Does your library have any electronic databases? _____

   If so, name one that looks promising for the topic you plan to research.

13. Does the library have a collection of microfilm and microfiche?

   If so, give the title and call number of a newspaper stored on microfilm.

   What is the headline story on the front page of this newspaper for the day you were born? _____

14. Where are the current periodicals located? _____

   How are they organized? _____

_____

_____

_____

What is the procedure for locating a periodical published before 1975?

_____

_____

_____

_____

15. Where are the current newspapers located? _____

_____

How are they organized? _____

37.2 Using Background Sources for a Broad Introduction to a Subject (*BHW* 37e)

Give the title of a reference source (other than a general encyclopedia) in which you could find a broad introduction to each of the following subjects. Look up one of the subjects, and briefly explain the type of information you found.

1. Ludwig van Beethoven _____

_____

2. The writings of Sigmund Freud _____

_____

3. The New York Stock Exchange _____

_____

4. Science fiction _____

_____

5. Major religions in the United States or Canada _____

_____

6. Type of information found in one of the five sources

_____

_____

_____

_____

_____

_____

37.3 Using Background Sources to Locate Specific Information (*BHW* 37e)

For each field listed below, locate a reference source other than a general encyclopedia. Then, in the space provided, write the title of the source and a *specific* item of information that you found in it.

Example: Music *American Popular Music: A Reference Guide/The first stereo long-playing records were marketed in the U.S. in 1958.*

1. Education _____

_____

_____

2. Literature _____

_____

_____

3. Business _____

_____

_____

4. Psychology _____

_____

_____

5. Science/technology _____

_____

_____

37.4 Conducting an Interview (*BHW* 37f)

On your campus or in your community, locate a person with expertise about the topic of your research paper or another issue that interests you. Using the guidelines given in *The Borzoi Handbook for Writers,* interview the person. Then write a brief report about what you discovered, drawing on the notes you took during the interview.

37.5 Using Notecards (*BHW* 37g)

Assume that you are conducting research for a paper about fetal alcohol syndrome. Read the following passages from an article by George Steinmetz, entitled "Fetal Alcohol Syndrome," which appears in the January 1992 issue of *National Geographic,* pages 36–39. Then write four notecards using the models given in *The Borzoi Handbook for Writers:*

1. A card giving bibliographic information about the source
2. A card quoting from one of the passages
3. A card summarizing the first passage
4. A card paraphrasing the second passage

PASSAGE 1 (p. 37)

First identified about 1970, fetal alcohol syndrome (FAS) is a term used to describe the damage some unborn children suffer when their mothers drink during pregnancy. Alcohol in the mother's bloodstream can be toxic to the developing fetus depending on the stage of pregnancy and how much she drinks. Damage can range from subtle to severe, causing clumsiness, behavioral problems, stunted growth, disfigurement, mental retardation.

PASSAGE 2 (pp. 38–39)

Little is known about the [p. 39 begins here] thresholds of alcohol that cause FAS. . . . Not all mothers who drink have FAS babies. Some doctors believe that any alcohol puts the baby at risk, while nearly all agree that binge drinking is perilous, especially during the first 12 weeks, when signs of pregnancy are few.

BIBLIOGRAPHY CARD

CONTENT CARD: QUOTATION FROM EITHER PASSAGE

CONTENT CARD: SUMMARY OF PASSAGE 1

CONTENT CARD: PARAPHRASE OF PASSAGE 2

38

Writing from Sources

38.1 Arriving at a Trial Topic (*BHW* 37b)

Select a subject area from the following list. Then, working alone or with a group of classmates, write down five topics for a brief research essay. State each topic in the form of a question. In arriving at the topics, use whatever prewriting method you wish—reviewing your experiences and reading, freewriting, brainstorming, asking questions.

Example: Subject: Pollution

Topics: How has smog affected Los Angeles in the past twenty years?

Are the Great Lakes more or less polluted today than they were in the 1960s?

What are the effects of acid rain on the environment?

Is noise pollution a serious problem or merely an annoyance?

Who should pay for the clean-up of toxic waste dumps—government or industry?

38.2 Testing a Trial Topic (*BHW* 37b)

Test the five topics you developed for the preceding exercise by answering these questions:

1. *Interest.* Is the topic interesting and significant enough to justify the writer's time in conducting research and the instructor's time in reading the results of the research?
2. *Limitation.* Is the topic too broad and complex to cover adequately in a brief research essay, or is it too narrow and simple for an essay of the assigned length?
3. *Sources.* Is the writer likely to find enough research material to support an essay on this topic? What types of sources are likely to be most useful?

38.3 Exploring a Trial Topic (*BHW* 37b)

Select one of the topics you tested in the preceding exercise (38.2), and jot down some preliminary questions that it raises. Does any question suggest a way to narrow the topic further, to move toward a possible thesis? Which questions are most likely to lead to fruitful research?

Example: Topic: What are the effects of acid rain on the environment?

Questions: What is acid rain? What causes it? Does everyone agree on the cause? Is the rain harmful to animals and plants? To people? Is there any way to prevent acid rain? Why are the Canadians (according to many newspaper reports) so concerned about acid rain?

Topic _____

Questions _____

_____

_____

_____

38.4 Evaluating Proposals for Research Papers (*BHW* 38a)

Evaluate the following proposals for ten-page research papers. Which of the four looks most promising? What advice would you give the students as they modify their topics or formulate new ones? Write your comments in the space provided.

PROPOSAL 1

I plan to study the use of vitamin supplements in the North American diet. First, I will describe the history of vitamin supplements, explaining when and why they developed and how they became popular. Second, I will describe how vitamins are made and what kinds of chemicals they contain. In the third part of the paper, I will discuss whether vitamin supplements are really necessary in the North American diet. I expect this to be the longest part of the paper. Judging from my preliminary reading, I will take the position that most vitamin supplements are unnecessary. In the final part of the paper, I will argue that misleading advertising by drug companies is responsible for the use of millions of unnecessary vitamins.

PROPOSAL 2

Was Lyndon B. Johnson a good president? I will attempt in my paper to answer this question by looking at both sides of the issue. First, I will present evidence showing that Johnson was an unsuccessful president. Then I will present the case of those who say that he was effective. In the final part of the paper, I will evaluate the two sides and present my conclusion that Johnson was a good president despite the many criticisms made against him.

_____

_____

_____

_____

_____

PROPOSAL 3

Because of my interest in dentistry as a profession, I intend to write a paper on the job-related stress experienced by dentists. In my preliminary reading, I found that dentists do experience a great deal of stress because of the way they are perceived by patients (painful, not healing) and because of the intense concentration, confined working areas, and high-pitched noises associated with their jobs. One source said that job stress may partly explain the unusually high rate of suicide among dentists. I plan to divide my paper into three main sections. First, I will explain the concept of job stress—its symptoms and its effects. Second, I will describe the reasons for the high levels of stress experienced by dentists. Finally, I will discuss the effects of this stress.

_____

_____

_____

_____

PROPOSAL 4

My paper will describe the process used to make home-brewed beer. Drawing from my own experience and from three books on the subject, I will first describe the various types of beer that can be made at home. This will take about one-third of the paper. In the rest of the paper, I will give step-by-step instructions for making beer and ale. This part of the paper will be organized around the five main steps in the beer-making process.

38.5 Evaluating Research Paper Outlines and Introductions (*BHW* 38a)

Compare the following student outlines and introductory paragraphs for ten-page research papers. The assigned general topic was "Early Developments in the Computer Industry." Which outline and introduction look more promising? Why? If the writers were submitting this work for your consideration *before* they continued to write their first drafts, what advice would you give them? Use the space provided to summarize your comments.

PAPER 1

```
Title: Early Computers

Tentative Thesis: The main computers which started

                  the age of data processing were

                  the ENIAC, EDVAC, UNIVAC, and

                  Whirlwind.


Outline:

  I.  Introduction

 II.  ENIAC

III.  EDVAC

 IV.  UNIVAC
```

V. Whirlwind

VI. Conclusion

Introduction:
The invention of the computer in the late 1940s
and early 1950s provided people with the ability
to do large calculations in a matter of seconds.
The first electronic digital computer was
invented in 1946. After its invention, many
people did not realize the potential ability of
computers. In the brief time we have had
computers, the rate of growth of this industry
has changed greatly. This growth began in the
early 1950s when computers were made for sale.
The most important and well-known early computers
were the ENIAC, EDVAC, UNIVAC I, and Whirlwind I.
Each of these computers has a different
importance in the history of computers, and each
will be discussed separately.

_____

_____

_____

_____

_____

PAPER 2

Title: Major Advances in the Computer Industry,

 1950-1955

Tentative Thesis: From 1950 to 1955, computer

 hardware became smaller and faster

 than it had been before, making

 possible the efficient handling of

scientific information and the
application of the computer to
growing business needs.

Outline:

I. Background

II. Developments in 1950
   A. REAC
   B. IBM Model 701
   C. Whirlwind I
   D. SEAC

III. Developments in 1951: improved memory
   A. UNIVAC
   B. Electrostatic memory

IV. Developments from 1952 to 1954: mainly in software

V. Developments in 1955: shift back to hardware
   A. TRANSAC
   B. IBM Model 702
   C. IBM Model 608
   D. Input/Output devices

VI. Summary of benefits
   A. Aircraft industry
   B. Military
   C. Business

Introduction:
One of these days all of us may be walking around
with tiny computers on our wrists, or we may at
least have computers in our homes. Even today the
computer is playing a major role in our lives.
Its importance can be attributed partially to the
advances that were made in the industry between
1950 and 1955. During this period, much of the
hardware that was developed became smaller and

faster than it had been before, making possible
the efficient handling of scientific information
and the application of the computer to growing
business needs.

38.6   Using Quotation, Paraphrase, and Summary (*BHW* 38c)

Drawing from the notecards you wrote in Exercise 37.5, write three brief
passages in which you demonstrate the following:

1.   The use of a quotation
2.   The use of summary
3.   The use of paraphrase

In each passage, make sure to introduce the borrowed material, indicating
clearly where it begins and ends.

38.7   Recognizing Plagiarism (*BHW* 38b)

Read the following passages. The writer of passage B has quoted and
paraphrased material from passage A. Put quotation marks around any
direct borrowings, and underline any paraphrased material that the writer
should have acknowledged.

PASSAGE A: THE SOURCE

What happens if you smoke during pregnancy? Briefly, smoking
during pregnancy stunts the baby's growth and possibly diminishes its IQ; it increases the risk of miscarriage; it can cause
serious complications in pregnancy and delivery, such as placental
5   separation, which can be fatal; and it increases the chances of a

child's dying just before or after birth. These are the disturbing
reports from two decades of studies conducted in many countries
throughout the world. One of the largest and most thorough inves-
tigations, the United States Collaborative Perinatal Project, exam-
10 ined more than five thousand pregnancies at twelve major hospitals in the United States and concluded that smoking during
pregnancy produces a long list of risks to the unborn and newborn
child. Researchers in the study noted an increased risk of fetal
death or damage, a delay in fetal growth, and an increased likeli-
15 hood of pregnancy-related complications for the mother.

[*Source:* Niels H. Lauersen, *Childbirth with Love,* New York:
Putnam's, 1983, p. 239]

PASSAGE B: THE WRITER'S PARAGRAPH

Women today are more aware than they were a few

years ago of the importance of prenatal care for

their babies. Until recently, the unborn child was

thought to absorb from the mother only the nutrients

needed for proper growth. Scientists now know that

whatever the mother takes into her body--food,

drink, drugs, cigarette smoke--is likely to have a

direct effect for good or for bad upon the health of

the fetus. Smoking during pregnancy, for example,

stunts the baby's growth and possibly diminishes IQ.

Most people assume that a smoker would give up her

habit during pregnancy once she learned these facts,

facts that are confirmed by two decades of studies

conducted in many countries throughout the world.

Yet many well-informed women do continue to smoke

during pregnancy, even when faced with evidence such

as that gathered recently by U.S. scientists who
studied thousands of pregnancies at a dozen
hospitals. These scientists discovered that smoking
mothers take great risks: a high rate of fetal death
or damage, retarded growth of the fetus, and a
greater chance of complications for themselves
during pregnancy.

38.8 Avoiding Plagiarism: Quoting, Summarizing, and Paraphrasing Fairly (*BHW* 38c)

Write one or two paragraphs explaining why women should avoid drinking alcohol and smoking cigarettes during pregnancy. Support your point by drawing from the source material given in Exercises 37.5 and 38.7. Put quotation marks around all direct borrowings, and underline any material you summarize or paraphrase.

38.9 Using a Checklist to Plan Your Research Paper

Use the following checklist as a guide for planning your paper. Your instructor may want to collect some of your work as you move through the various stages on the list; if so, indicate due dates in the left margin. Remember that the checklist is a general guide, not a detailed program for completing the essay. Be prepared to be flexible. For example, you may have to modify your thesis at any point in the project, or you may find yourself returning to the library for further research even as you draft the essay.

1. *Select a topic.* If your instructor suggests a general subject area, narrow it until you find a trial topic that interests you and falls within the limits of the assignment.

2. *Get an overview of the topic.* Formulate several questions about the topic and do some preliminary reading to see which questions look most promising. Take notes.

3. *Prepare a working bibliography.* List the books, articles, and other sources that appear to be most significant for the topic. Continue reading and taking notes.

4. *Formulate a trial thesis.* Based on your early reading and thinking about the topic, formulate a trial thesis and, if possible, a tentative outline.

5. *Take detailed notes.* With your trial thesis in mind, take detailed notes from the sources you have gathered. Be prepared to follow any new leads suggested by your research.

6. *Revise the thesis and outline.* Revise your thesis and outline to match the evidence you have gathered.

7. *Write a first draft.* Using your revised thesis and outline as a guide, write a first draft. Keep track of sources as you write, making notes in the margins to indicate where you quote or paraphrase the work of others.

8. *Revise.* If possible, get reactions to your draft. Acting on the suggestions of others, and on your own careful evaluation of the paper, make necessary conceptual, organizational, and editorial changes. Plan your revision using the Checklist for Revision in *The Borzoi Handbook for Writers,* inside front cover.

9. *Prepare a works cited list or reference list.* Double-check all citations; then compile a list of sources used in the paper. Follow MLA form, APA form, or another system of documentation as required.

10. *Prepare the final copy.* Following the manuscript conventions given in the handbook, type or handwrite the final copy of your paper. Proofread carefully before submitting.

39
Using MLA Documentation

39.1 Using MLA Parenthetic Citations
(*BHW* 39a)

Revise the paragraph(s) you wrote for Exercise 38.8, adding an MLA parenthetic citation for each quotation, summary, or paraphrase you included.

39.2 Writing an MLA Works Cited List
(*BHW* 39b)

For each of the following items, write a works cited entry using the appropriate MLA form. Then arrange the entries alphabetically.

1. A book by Nik Cohn called *The Heart of the World*. The book was published in 1992 by Alfred A. Knopf of New York, New York.

2. A book by three authors, listed on the title page in this order: Robert McCrum, William Cran, and Robert MacNeil. The book is called *The Story of English*, and it was published in 1986 by Viking Penguin of New York, New York.

3. A reference work called *The Chicago Manual of Style.* No author or editor is listed. The book, in its thirteenth edition, was published by the University of Chicago Press in 1982. The title page lists the location of the press as Chicago and London.

4. "Jewish Writers," an essay by Mark Shechner. The essay appears on pages 191 through 239 of the *Harvard Guide to Contemporary American Writing,* a book edited by Daniel Hoffman. The book was published in 1979 by the Harvard University Press. The title page lists the location of the press as Cambridge, Massachusetts, and London, England.

5. "Mary Oliver and the Tradition of Romantic Nature Poetry," an article by Janet McNew, which appears on pages 59 through 77 of the Spring 1989 issue of *Contemporary Literature.* The issue is also labeled Volume 30, Number 1. The journal uses continuous pagination through each year's volume.

6. "The Politics of Vigilance," an article by George F. Will, which appears on page 66 of the January 27, 1992, issue of *Newsweek* magazine. The issue is also labeled Volume 119, Number 4. *Newsweek* is published weekly, and each issue has separate pagination.

7. A quotation from "Stellar Physics," a book review on page 1139 of *Science* magazine, June 5, 1981, Volume 212, Number 4499. The reviewer is Sidney C. Wolff; the book reviewed is *The Brightest Star,* by Cornelis De Jager.

8. "East Germans Face World of Flux," an article by Francine S. Kiefer in *The Christian Science Monitor,* a daily newspaper. The article appears on page 3 of the Thursday, April 18, 1991, issue.

9. An unsigned newspaper editorial, "Personal Commitment Next Challenge on Gang Front," in the *Austin-American Statesman.* The editorial appears on page 18, Section A, of the May 11, 1991, issue.

10. "Coffee," an entry by William C. Struning in the 1976 edition of *Encyclopedia Americana.*

39.3 Analyzing a Completed Research Paper—MLA Style (*BHW* 39c)

Working alone or with a group of classmates, study the student research paper printed below. Then answer the questions that follow it.

Diana Hall

English 1320

Ms. McElyea

When It Rains It Pours

In recent years, Americans have become increasingly aware of the many pollutants damaging their environment. One of the most controversial of these is acid rain--rain which contains an abnormally high level of sulfates and nitrates (Tver). These acidic chemicals are released into the air from power plants and other sources. Once in the atmosphere, they mix with the moisture in the clouds and are carried hundreds of miles by the wind, eventually drifting down to earth in the form of rain, snow, or fog. One Canadian government publication, Fact Sheet on Acid Rain, points out that rain ''ten or more times as acidic as normal has been occurring frequently in the northeastern U. S. and Canada.'' This rain is a dangerous pollutant that continues to damage the environment and to strain political relations between the United States and Canada.

Acid rain is slowly destroying the ecosystems of many lakes in the northeastern United States and Canada. A lake's ecosystem is made up of many different plants and animals that work together to support one another. John T. Baccus, a biology professor at Southwest Texas State University, explains that when acid rain falls into these lakes, the acid level is increased beyond the tolerance of the organisms living there. David Tver reports that many lakes are already badly affected:

> According to Science News, February 2, 1979, the Adirondack lakes were becoming fishless because of acid rain and a 1978-79 survey of 85 lakes in the Boundary Waters Canoe Area along the Minnesota-Ontario border showed that two-thirds of them were near the brink of acidity where fish-life could not be supported.

Once acid rain destroys an ecosystem, that system cannot be put back into its original form. According to Professor Baccus, we do not have enough scientific knowledge to restore an ecosystem that has taken thousands of years to evolve.

Acid rain not only presents a major problem for the ecosystems found in lakes but also creates difficulties for plant-life and the soils in which they grow. Joseph A. Davis explains that the alkaline soils found in the upper regions of the United States and the lower eastern regions of Canada have a natural buffering capacity which can neutralize the acid up to a certain point (''Acid

Rain Still a Sore Point'' 1063). However, these
soils cannot buffer the large amount of acid rain
that falls on them. According to Robert Ostmann,
author of Acid Rain: A Plague Upon the Waters,

> many scientists believe that continuing or
> worsening acid deposition could reduce the
> productivity of vital forests and
> farmlands, disrupt the crucial,
> life-sustaining process of plant
> photosynthesis in large areas, and poison
> some drinking water supplies and food fish
> stocks. (13)

Professor Jack Corbett, a political scientist at
Southwest Texas State University, points out that
acid rain not only disrupts plant photosynthesis but
also hinders plant growth; Corbett explains that
when acid rain falls on a plant's new buds, it can
kill the buds, thwarting growth almost before it
begins (personal interview).

The serious consequences of acid rain are
clear, but its causes are less apparent. Some acid
rain comes from natural sources, such as volcanic
eruptions and plant photosynthesis (Tver). However,
scientists believe that much acid rain is caused by
the burning of coal with a high sulfur content.
Robert Ostmann supports this theory, stating that
''in one year the sulfur-dioxide emissions from a

large coalfired plant can equal the high amount released by the May 18, 1980, eruption of Mount St. Helens'' (11). And according to a report from the National Academy of Sciences, there is ''overwhelming'' circumstantial evidence linking acid rain to power plant emissions (Fact Sheet).

Many people, however, still dispute the theory that most acid rain is caused by the burning of high-sulfur coal. They argue that not enough evidence exists to prove the actual causes of acid rain and that scientists should not single out power plants. Once again, these people are proven wrong by Joseph A. Davis, who confirms that ''the region emitting the most sulfur dioxide is the Ohio River Valley, where states like Ohio, Indiana, and Kentucky burn large amounts of high-sulfur .coal'' (''No Reagan Acid Rain Legislation'' 2187). This high-sulfur coal is used to produce electrical energy and also to provide jobs for thousands of Americans.

While most scientists agree that acid rain is caused by the burning of high-sulfur coal, the United States government has claimed repeatedly that there is insufficient evidence to establish the sources of acid rain, a claim that has caused serious political friction between the United States and Canada. Joseph Davis sums up the situation, stating that ''acid rain is literally eating away the sandstone of Canada's Parliament buildings and showering diplomatic fallout on the U. S. Capital'' (''Acid Rain Still a Sore Point'' 1063).

Many Canadians believe that the United States is responsible for most acidic air pollution that falls in their country. Jack Corbett tends to agree with them. While admitting that it is difficult to determine which specific damage in Canada is done by which source, Corbett claims that more acid rain is produced in the United States than in Canada (personal interview). Canadians are frustrated at the United States for not acting promptly on what they consider an important environmental issue. Corbett explains that the Canadians' sense of urgency and frustration appears to be ''matched by a general U. S. reluctance to do anything beyond a moderate amount of research and release of press statements attesting to its continuing interest'' (''Acid Rain''). The United States' general reluctance seems to be the main cause of strained political ties between the two traditionally friendly countries.

Although the United States and Canada's political ties are strained, there is a continuing effort to make progress on the issue of acid rain. Several major scientific panels in the United States have studied the problem, including the National Research Council and the National Acid Precipitation Task Force (Davis, ''No Reagan Acid Rain Legislation'' 2187). The Canadian Embassy's Fact Sheet on Acid Rain lists many of the findings of these and other groups, findings that provide a basis for discussion between the two countries. Since 1976 Canada and the United States have conducted a series of formal and informal talks about acid rain; however, these talks have not led to dramatic progress. For example, in 1982 Canada proposed a plan in which each nation would reduce industrial emissions by twenty-five percent. After negotiations, the United States rejected the proposal because, as one newspaper put it, ''not enough is known about acid rain to justify the huge expense of Canada's proposal'' (''As Lakes Quietly Die'').

Cost estimates, however, vary greatly depending on the source. Corbett explains that ''research data on economic costs are somewhat sparse, and are frequently generated by those with a vested interest in a particular outcome'' (''Acid Rain''). If utility companies have to pay for clean-up costs, it would mean higher electric rates for consumers. And many people might have to pay with their jobs if companies decide to move elsewhere rather than pay the high cost of emission control. Corbett says that the United Mine Workers estimate that the most restrictive legislation to control acid rain would cost up to 89,000 jobs in coal mining in the Midwest and South (personal interview).

Although lost jobs and increased utility rates are important, one must also consider other losses that Americans and Canadians may face if the acid rain problem is not controlled in the near future: the loss of animal and plant life in the lakes of both countries.

There are ways in which the United States could control acid rain and improve its relations with Canada. Davis suggests that ''one of the cheaper ways to reduce sulfur dioxide is to burn low-sulfur Western coal'' (''No Reagan Acid Rain Legislation'' 2187). The burning of low-sulfur coal would be effective, but better legislation would also help. Currently, older power plants are not required to have the same emission-control standards as the newer plants. In fact, the older plants, according to Davis, are ''allowed higher emissions for years or decades until they are retired'' (''Acid Rain Still a Sore Point'' 1063). If a new law were passed ordering all power plants to have stringent emissions controls, then the amount of acid rain falling on the United States and Canada could be reduced considerably. Acid rain could also be controlled more efficiently if the Reagan administration showed more concern about the acid rain issue. Robert Ostmann describes the administration's policy as one of ''growth, expansion, using more energy and more resources to become powerful--these are the nation's priorities, not environmental integrity'' (184).

Although growth and expansion are important for our economy, the protection of the environment should also be a high priority. If acid rain is not reduced considerably, the United States and Canada may witness serious damage to their environment. This damage already threatens some of our valuable natural resources and may someday disrupt our environment seriously enough to affect our food supply. If the government takes action now, it can slow the irreversible damage of acid rain and ease the current strain on our relations with Canada.

Works Cited

''As Lakes Quietly Die, the U.S. and Canada Feud Over Acid Rain,'' Washington Post 27 Sept. 1982, sec. 1: 1.

Baccus, John T. Personal interview. 2 Mar. 1984.

Corbett, Jack. ''Acid Rain in Canadian-United States Relations: The Politics of Inaction,'' Canadian

Political Science Association Annual Meeting.
Vancouver, BC, 6-8 June 1983.

---. Personal interview. 2 Mar. 1984.

Davis, Joseph A. ''Acid Rain Still a Sore Point for
United States, Canada: But Both Sides Are
Optimistic,'' Congressional Quarterly 28 May
1983: 1063-1065.

---. ''No Reagan Acid Rain Legislation in Sight,''
Congressional Quarterly 22 Oct. 1983: 2186-2187.

Fact Sheet on Acid Rain, Washington, DC: Canadian
Embassy, n.d.

Ostmann, Robert, Jr. Acid Rain: A Plague Upon the
Waters. Minneapolis: Dillon, 1982.

Tver, David F. ''Acid Precipitation,'' Dictionary of
Dangerous Pollutants, Ecology, and Environment.
New York: Industrial, 1981.

**STUDY QUESTIONS FOR
"WHEN IT RAINS IT POURS"**

1. Identify Hall's thesis. Is the topic of the essay adequately limited for
   a brief research paper? Explain.
2. Is the first paragraph an effective introduction? Explain.
3. Is the paper well organized? Point out specific examples to support
   your answer. Then write a subordinated outline showing the main
   points developed in the paper.
4. Does Hall clearly explain the causes and effects of acid rain? Should
   any point be explained more fully?
5. Hall acknowledges that there is disagreement about the causes of acid
   rain. Does she give adequate consideration to those who disagree with
   her explanation of the causes? Explain.

6. In discussing the U.S.-Canadian conflict over acid rain, does Hall seem fair to both sides? Explain, pointing out specific examples.
7. Is Hall's conclusion effective? Why or why not?
8. Evaluate Hall's use of sources. Specifically, make a list of the different types of sources she uses. Do the number and variety of sources seem appropriate? What advantages does Hall gain by using personal interviews with two of her professors?

39.4 Using Endnotes (*BHW* 39d)

For each item in Exercise 39.2, write an endnote using "alternative MLA" style. Arrange the items consecutively on an endnote page. For each endnote, except item 10, include a reference to a specific page of the work (assume that items 1 through 3 each contain 300 pages).

40

Using APA Documentation

40.1 Using APA Parenthetic Citations (*BHW* 40a)

Revise the paragraph(s) you wrote for Exercise 38.8, adding an APA parenthetic citation for each quotation, summary, or paraphrase you included.

40.2 Writing an APA Reference List (*BHW* 40b)

For each item listed in Exercise 39.2, write a reference list entry using the appropriate APA form. Then arrange the entries alphabetically.

40.3 Analyzing a Completed Research Paper—APA Style (*BHW* 40c)

Working alone or with a group of classmates, study the student research paper printed below. Then answer the questions that follow it.

Stuart Leung

English 1A

Ms. Mahan

Clever Hans and His Effect:

Horse Sense about Communicating with Animals

At first the drama featured just two characters--a man and a horse--and its only spectators were jeering neighbors surrounding a courtyard in central Berlin. There each day the man, a retired schoolteacher named Wilhelm von Osten, would attempt to teach his Russian stallion Hans how to think and calculate like a human being. In his long white coat and floppy broad-brimmed hat, worn in every kind of weather, and with his teacher's slate and chalk at hand, urging Hans to tap out answers to math problems with a raised hoof, von Osten seemed ridiculous to his neighbors (Fernald, 1983, p. 7). Surely, they told each other, he had to be crazy to waste his time for months and finally years attempting to break through barriers established by nature itself.

Everything changed, however, in 1904, when word spread rapidly in Berlin, and then through all Europe and across the Atlantic, that Hans was not just another long-suffering pet with a crackpot master. He was Clever Hans, the equine genius. The visitors who now packed von Osten's courtyard,

without ever being charged for the privilege,
verified for themselves that the horse could manage
virtually any problem in arithmetic. As one observer
recalled,

> The four fundamental processes were
> entirely familiar to him. Common fractions
> he changed to decimals, and vice versa.
> . . . The following problems are
> illustrations of the kind he solved. ''How
> much is 2/5 plus 1/2?'' Answer: 9/10.
> . . . ''What are the factors of
> 28?''--Thereupon Hans tapped consecutively
> 2, 4, 7, 14, 28. ''In the number 365287179
> I place the decimal point after 8. How
> many are there now in the hundreds
> place?''--5. ''How many in the ten
> thousandths place?''--9. (Pfungst, 1911,
> pp. 20-21)

But that wasn't all. Hans, it turned out, could
read and spell German words; he appeared to have
memorized the calendar, so that he could supply the
date of any mentioned day; he could be told a German
sentence and, twenty-four hours later, correctly tap
out the code for its fifty-eight letters; and, still
using taps for letters, he could perform astounding
feats of musical analysis and judgment (Pfungst,
1911, pp. 21-23). Moreover, an investigative

committee headed by Carl Stumpf, the distinguished
director of Berlin's Psychological Institute,
disproved any deceptive intent on the part of the
trainer von Osten, whose passionate faith in Hans's
intelligence prompted him to cooperate fully with
the committee's tests for fraud.

It was this apparent scientific validation that
set Clever Hans apart from any number of other
performing animals dating back to the sixteenth
century (Mountjoy & Lewandowski, 1984, p. 27),
including ''composing and chess-playing dogs,
calculating cats, [and] a learned pig'' (Hövelmann,
1989, p. 203). The ruling out of deception, however,
only made Hans's powers more mysterious. Had he
truly, thanks to von Osten's extraordinary diligence
and patience, broken through to a human plane of
understanding? Or, as Sigmund Freud among others
suspected (Fernald, 1983, p. 213), was he receiving
messages through mental telepathy or some other
occult mechanism?

The bewildered Professor Stumpf, for one, felt
that the explanation must lie within the range of
commonly known phenomena, and so he directed one of
his graduate students, Oskar Pfungst, to seek for
such an answer (Fernald, 1983, p. 47). The choice
was inspired. Pfungst, not Hans or von Osten or
Stumpf, was destined to become the real hero of the

drama--the debunker of Hans's alleged gifts and the setter of enduring standards for rigor in the conduct of experimental psychology.

As he later recounted in his classic study Clever Hans, Pfungst (1911) began by putting Hans to a sterner test than any devised by Stumpf's committee. To determine whether the horse was actually capable of independent thought, he offered Hans problems whose answers were unknown to the questioner (p. 32). As Pfungst explains, the results were unequivocally negative:

> Hans can neither read, count nor make calculations. He knows nothing of coins or cards, calendars or clocks, nor can he respond, by tapping or otherwise, to a number spoken to him but a moment before. Finally, he has not a trace of musical ability. (p. 40)

Instead, reasoned Pfungst (1911), Hans must have acquired an exceptional responsiveness to unconscious cueing by those questioners who did know what answers to expect. By carefully watching von Osten and others in the act of interrogation, he discovered that ''as soon as the questioner gave the problem he bent forward--be it ever so slightly--in order to observe the horse's foot the more closely, for the hoof was the horse's organ of speech''

(p. 57). And when Pfungst himself succeeded, simply by inclining his torso, in making Hans start ''counting'' in the absence of any question, the whole mystery evaporated. Hans's talent was not for mathematics or music but for pantomime'' (p. 141), or a mimicry of human bowing in the hope of earning sugar cubes.

Yet along with Hans's demotion from a wizard to a well-trained horse came the birth of a fundamentally important concept. This was to become known as the ''Clever Hans effect''--the inadvertent communication from an experimenter to an experimental subject through what Pfungst (1911) called ''the tension of expectation'' (p. 147). After Pfungst, no experiment dealing with animal or human intelligence could be considered trustworthy unless it showed strict precautions against the Clever Hans effect.

This is not to say, however, that later scientists have always kept the Clever Hans effect in mind. In the 1970s several celebrated researchers in what Thomas A. Sebeok (1969) has named ''zoosemiotics'' (p. 200), or animal communication, based far-reaching conclusions about primate language acquisition on studies that failed to match Pfungst's rigor in 1904. One such researcher,

Herbert A. Terrace (1984), eventually came to see that ''the teacher's coaxing and cueing have played much greater roles in so-called 'conversations' with chimpanzees than was previously recognized'' (p. 196). And according to Gerd H. Hövelmann (1989), ''not a single ape language study'' has as yet taken sufficient precautions against cueing (p. 207).

One need only read Pfungst's Clever Hans (1911) to see why, for example, no faith should be invested in Francine Patterson's ''talking gorilla'' Koko, sponsored and publicized in the seventies by the National Geographic Society. Koko, writes Patterson (1978), is not just ''the focus of [her] career'' but also her ''dear friend'' (p. 438); in other words, the experimenter has a strong emotional investment in her subject's success at learning American Sign Language. Predictably, both photographs (Patterson, pp. 442–443) and film clips (Terrace, 1984, p. 196) of Koko's ''speech'' show Patterson unmistakably cueing the gorilla's signs. And if Patterson had taken Clever Hans to heart, she might have thought twice about interpreting even Koko's mistakes as proving a knack for ''lies,'' ''brattiness,'' and ''jokes'' (Patterson, pp. 440, 449, 462).

Significantly, an increasing number of

researchers now challenge the whole strategy of removing animals from their habitats and turning them into human ''artifacts'' (Hediger, 1981, p. 5). ''In neither the natural nor domesticated state,'' as one expert on the body language of horses has remarked, ''has [a horse] any occasion to push buttons or turn labyrinthine corners in quest of a snack'' (Ainslie & Ledbetter, 1980, p. 27). What one species can learn from being forced to use another's language may, after all, be of relatively minor scientific interest (Walther, 1984, p. 371). The future of studies in animal intelligence probably lies in the wild, where communication systems reflect not the impoverished stimulus-response model of the laboratory but ''social organization involving many speakers and many listeners of different age-sex classes'' (Todt, Goedeking, & Symmes, 1988, p. v; Bright, 1984, p. 233).

To be sure, efforts to impart human language to animals continue in the 1990s. Some of them, it is thought, may actually have demonstrated a limited capacity of imprisoned dolphins, seals, and apes to handle symbolic concepts (Crowley, 1988, p. 54). Yet Oskar Pfungst would have wanted to remind us of the gulf separating the performing of conditioned stunts and the active use of words to express ideas. As the

parlor magician James Randi (1981) has said,
scientists who think they cannot be deceived by
apparent human language on the part of captive
animals ''should listen more carefully. From a
distance of many decades comes a sound that they
should heed; it is the sound of that ubiquitous
horse, and he is laughing'' (p. 296).

References

Ainslie, T., & Ledbetter, B. (1980). The body
language of horses. New York: Morrow.

Bright, M. (1984). Animal language. Ithaca: Cornell
University Press.

Crowley, G. (1988, May 23). The wisdom of animals.
Newsweek, pp. 52-59.

Fernald, D. (1983). The Hans legacy: A story of
science. Hillsdale, NJ: Erlbaum.

Hediger, H. K. P. (1981). The Clever Hans phenomenon
from an animal psychologist's point of view. In
T. A. Sebeok & R. Rosenthal (Eds.), The clever
Hans phenomenon: Communication with horses,
whales, apes, and people (pp. 1-17). Annals of
the New York Academy of Sciences, 364.

Hövelmann, G. H. (1989). Animal ''language''

research: The perpetuation of some old mistakes. Semiotica, 73 199-217.

Mountjoy, P. T., & Lewandowski, A. G. (1984). The dancing horse, a learned pig, and muscle twitches. Psychological Record, 34 25-38.

Patterson, F. (1978). Conversations with a gorilla. National Geographic, 154 438-465.

Pfungst, O. (1911). Clever Hans (the horse of Mr. von Osten): A contribution to experimental animal and human psychology. New York: Holt.

Randi, J. (1981). Semiotics: A view from behind the foot lights. In T. A. Sebeok & R. Rosenthal (Eds.), The clever Hans phenomenon: Communication with horses, whales, apes, and people (pp. 291-298). Annals of the New York Academy of Sciences, 364.

Sebeok, T. A. (1969). Semiotics and ethology. In T. A. Sebeok & A. Ramsay (Eds.), Approaches to animal communication (pp. 200-231). The Hague: Mouton.

Terrace, H. S. (1984). ''Language'' in apes. In R. Harré & V. Reynolds (Eds.), The meaning of primate signals (pp. 179-203). London: Cambridge University Press.

Todt, D., Goedeking P., & Symmes, D. (Eds.). (1988). Primate vocal communication. Berlin: Springer-Verlag.

Walther, F. R. (1984). <u>Communication and expression in hoofed mammals</u>. Bloomington: Indiana University Press.

STUDY QUESTIONS FOR "CLEVER HANS AND HIS EFFECT: HORSE SENSE ABOUT COMMUNICATING WITH ANIMALS"

1. The focus of Leung's paper—the importance of the "Clever Hans effect"—is not stated explicitly until his eighth paragraph. Is this delayed announcement of the thesis justified? What effect does Leung gain by leading up to his main point rather than announcing it near the beginning?

2. What does Leung do in the first paragraph to engage the reader's interest? Is the strategy effective? Why?

3. Is the essay well organized? Write a formal outline showing Leung's main and subordinate points.

4. Study the development of Leung's ideas. Does each paragraph follow logically from the one before? How is each paragraph related to Leung's thesis?

5. In his sixth, seventh, and eighth paragraphs, Leung relies heavily on Oskar Pfungst's book *Clever Hans*. Given the topic and thesis of the paper, is the extensive use of a book published more than sixty years ago justifiable? Explain.

6. In his last four paragraphs, Leung uses eleven different sources, most of them published in the past twenty years. Given the points developed in this part of the paper, why do you suppose Leung decided to incorporate a range of current sources?

7. Evaluate Leung's closing paragraph. Does it adequately reinforce his thesis? How? Is the quotation from Randi an effective way to end the paper? Explain.

Notes

PART I (CHAPTERS 1–6)

1. "Pluto," *The Concise Columbia Encyclopedia*, 1983.
2. Robert Jastrow, *Red Giants and White Dwarfs*, rev. ed. (New York: Warner, 1979) 154.
3. Rodney Zaks, *The CP/M Handbook* (Berkeley: Sybex, 1980) 1.
4. *An Introduction to CP/M Features and Facilities* (Pacific Grove: Digital Research, 1978) 1.
5. My thanks to Elvin Holt, who supplied the material for this exercise.
6. Physician Task Force on Hunger in America, *Hunger in America: The Growing Epidemic* (Middletown: Wesleyan UP, 1985): 175.
7. John Leo, "What's in a Nickname?" *Time* 19 Jan. 1987: 82.
8. Louisa M. Alcott, *Little Men* (1871; Cleveland: New World, 1950) 189–190.
9. Pierre Szamek, "Teachers' Tests," *Harper's* Feb. 1984: 42.
10. Robert B. Reich, "The Unprepared American," *Christian Science Monitor* 11 April 1991: 19.
11. Lynne V. Cheney, *Tyrannical Machines* (Washington: National Endowment for the Humanities, 1990) 34.
12. Jane E. Brody, *Jane Brody's Good Food Book* (New York: Norton, 1985) 5.
13. Martin Luther King, Jr., "Letter from a Birmingham Jail, April 16, 1963," *Why We Can't Wait* (New York: Harper, 1963) 84–85.
14. Sam Iker, "Death from the Sky," *International Wildlife* Sept.–Oct. 1983: 46.
15. Information from "The Cleveland Story" and "Downtown Cleveland Facts," Cleveland Growth Association, Cleveland, OH.
16. Letter to the author from a correspondent in Minneapolis, MN, 19 Feb. 1991.
17. Mary Robertson, "MADD Helps Crack Down on Drunk Driving," *The University Star* (Southwest Texas State University) 26 Jan. 1984: 3.
18. "Letters," *The University Star* (Southwest Texas State University) 26 Jan. 1984: 4.
19. Timothy Titcomb, *Titcomb's Letters to Young People* (New York: Scribner, Armstrong, 1875) 40.
20. Mary Wood-Allen and Sylvanus Stall, *What a Young Woman Ought to Know* (Philadelphia: Vir, 1898) 225.
21. "New Utility Billing System No Good," "Letters to the Editor," *San Marcos Daily Record* 19 Sept. 1991: 4.

22. David A. Noebel, *Rhythm, Riots and Revolution* (Tulsa: Christian Crusade, 1966) 24.
23. William R. Brown, "Why I Don't Let Students Cut My Classes," *The Chronicle of Higher Education* 28 Jan. 1987: 88.

PART II (CHAPTERS 7–10)

1. Adapted from Joseph Alper, "The Stradivarius Formula," *Science 84* Mar. 1984: 37–38.
2. Alison Lurie, *The Language of Clothes* (New York: Random, 1981) 3.
3. Adapted from "Nestworks," *Natural History* Sept. 1982: 80–81.
4. Judith Murray, "Pumpkin beyond Pie," *Gourmet* Oct. 1983: 52.
5. "Types of Pliers," *Reader's Digest Complete Do-It-Yourself Manual* (Pleasantville: Reader's Digest, 1973) 22.
6. Some information adapted from *Elephants* (San Diego: Wildlife Education, 1980).
7. Eudora Welty, *One Writer's Beginnings* (Cambridge: Harvard UP, 1984) 14.
8. Jon N. Leonard, Jack L. Hofer, and Nathan Pritikin, *Live Longer Now* (New York: Grosset, 1974) 8–9.
9. This paragraph is based on information from Jan Adkins, "The Evolution of Jeans," *Mother Earth News* July-Aug. 1990, and Iain Finlayson, *Denim: An American Legend* (New York: Simon, 1990).
10. Philip K. Chiu, "The Myth of the Model Minority," *U.S. News and World Report* 16 May 1988: 7.
11. Adapted from "W. H. Auden," *Critical Survey of Poetry* (Englewood Cliffs: Salem, 1983) 1: 71.
12. Ernest Hemingway, *Death in the Afternoon* (New York: Scribner's, 1960) 105.
13. Joan Brooks McClane and Gillian Dowley McNamee, *Early Literacy* (Cambridge: Harvard UP, 1990) 23.
14. Alan Devoe, *Lives Around Us* (New York: Creative Age, 1942) 208–209.
15. Pico Iyer, "In Praise of the Humble Comma," *Time* 13 June 1988: 80.
16. Richard Hofstadter, *Anti-Intellectualism in American Life* (New York: Knopf, 1963) 310.
17. William O. Douglas, *The Right of the People* (New York: Doubleday, 1958) 158.
18. Stephen Jay Gould, "Sex and Size," *The Flamingo's Smile: Reflections in Natural History* (New York: Norton, 1985) 59.
19. Annie Dillard, *Teaching a Stone to Talk: Expeditions and Encounters* (New York: Harper, 1982) 56–57.
20. Grace Lichtenstein, "Rocky Mountain High," *New York Times Magazine* 28 Dec. 1975: 13.
21. Frank Gibney, "The Japanese Presence in the U.S.," *Time* (Special Advertising Section) 13 June 1988: unpaginated.

22. Peter Philip, *Furniture of the World* (New York: Galahad, 1974) 28.

23. E. D. Hirsch, Jr., *Cultural Literacy: What Every American Needs to Know* (Boston: Houghton, 1987) 116.

24. My thanks to John D. Hennessy, who supplied some of the information for this paragraph.

25. Richard Olney, *The French Menu Cookbook* (revised and updated) (Boston: Godine, 1985) 43–44.

26. Witold Rybczynski, *Home: A Short History of an Idea* (New York: Penguin, 1987) 204.

27. Tania Bayard, *Sweet Herbs and Sundry Flowers* (New York: Metropolitan Museum of Art, 1985) 20–21.

28. Rob Mairs, "How the Storm Developed," *Yachting* Nov. 1979: 120.

29. Jeff Greenfield, "The Black and White Truth About Basketball," *Esquire* Oct. 1975: 170.

30. Frances Fitzgerald, *Cities on a Hill: A Journey Through Contemporary American Cultures* (New York: Simon and Schuster, 1986) 203–204.

31. Noel D. Vietmeyer, "The Captivating Kiwifruit," *National Geographic* May 1987: 682.

32. James P. Degnan, "Masters of Babble," *Harper's* Sept. 1976: 37.

33. "Is There a Nurse in the House?" *Ms.* June 1988: 66.

34. William Zinsser, "No Stomach for the Undercover Chickenfurter," *Life* 3 Oct. 1969: 24B.

35. Sharon Begley and Daniel Glick, "A Safety Net Full of Holes," *Newsweek* 23 Mar. 1992: 56.

36. R. Monastersky, "Hot Year Prompts Greenhouse Concern," *Science News* 19 Jan. 1991: 36.

37. David Stern, "The Supreme Fictionalist," *New Republic* 4 Feb. 1991: 34.

PART III (CHAPTERS 11–13)

1. William E. Leuchtenburg et al., *The Age of Change,* vol. 12 of *The Life History of the United States* (New York: Time-Life, 1974) 12: 112–113.

2. Sing Lau, "The Effect of Smiling on Person Perception," *The Journal of Social Psychology* 117 (1982): 66.

3. Adapted from Michael Hutchins and Victoria Stevens, "Olympic Mountain Goats," *Natural History* Jan. 1981: 62, 63, 65.

4. Adapted from "Currents," *Science 84* Mar. 1984: 10, 14.

5. Adapted from Millicent E. Selsam and Jerome Wexler, *The Amazing Dandelion* (New York: William Morrow, 1977) 5, 6, 10, 13, 42, 43, 44.

6. John F. Kennedy, Inaugural Address, 20 Jan. 1961.

7. May Sarton, *Journal of a Solitude* (New York: Norton, 1973) 13.

8. Malcolm Cowley, *The View from 80* (New York: Viking, 1980) 8.

9. Robert McCrum, William Cran, and Robert MacNeil, *The Story of English* (New York: Viking, 1986) 163.

10. My thanks to Nora, Kevin, and Bridget Hennessy for supplying the passages.
11. John Jarolimek and Ruth Pelz, "People Build Communities," *Adventuring,* ed. Virginia A. Arnold and Carl B. Smith (New York: Macmillan, 1987) 257–258.
12. Larry K. Olsen, Richard W. St. Pierre, and Jan M. Ozias, *Being Healthy* (Orlando: Harcourt, 1990) 214.
13. Leonard Martinelli et al., *The World* (New York: McGraw, 1983) 131.

PART IV (CHAPTERS 14–16)

1. Samuel Langhorne Clemens (Mark Twain), *Adventures of Huckleberry Finn* (New York: Norton, 1977) 18.
2. Tom Wolfe, *The Kandy-Kolored Tangerine-Flake Streamline Baby* (New York: Farrar, 1965) 167.
3. Elaine Tyler May, "Myths and Realities of the American Family," *Riddles of Identity in Modern Times,* ed. Antoine Prost and Gérard Vincent (Cambridge: Harvard UP, 1991) 592, vol. 5 of *A History of Private Life.*
4. Jeanette Covert Nolan, *The Story of Martha Washington* (New York: Grosset, 1954) 174.
5. Joyce Carey, *The Horse's Mouth* (London: Michael Joseph, 1951) 11.
6. Henry David Thoreau, "from *Journal,*" *The Norton Reader,* 8th ed., ed. Arthur M. Eastman (New York: Norton, 1992) 78.
7. Ernest Hemingway, *In Our Time* (New York: Macmillan, 1986) 146.
8. Howard Fineman, "Rx for the Veep," *Newsweek* 20 May 1991: 22.
9. William Zinsser, *On Writing Well,* 3rd ed. (New York: Harper, 1985) 7.
10. Virginia Woolf, *A Room of One's Own* (New York: Harcourt, 1957) 60.
11. Donald Hall, *Writing Well,* 5th ed. (New York: Harper, 1985) 71–72.
12. James Critchfield, "Stretching Earth's Oil," *World Monitor* Sept. 1990: 29.
13. Paul Fussell, *Wartime: Understanding and Behavior in the Second World War* (New York: Oxford UP, 1989) 3.
14. E. B. White, "Once More to the Lake," *Essays of E. B. White* (New York: Harper, 1977) 198.
15. Eldridge Cleaver, *Soul on Ice* (New York: McGraw, 1968) 67.
16. Charles H. Miller, *Auden: An American Friendship* (New York: Scribner's, 1983) 100–101.
17. John Simpson, "The Rare Stone That Buys Guns," *World Monitor* Sept. 1990: 14.
18. Brock Yates, "The Love Affair Connection," *The American Spectator* Dec. 1987: 52.
19. Lance Morrow, "The Five-and-Dime Charms of Astrology," *Time* 16 May 1988: 100.
20. Abigail Zuger, "Acrophobia in the Ivory Tower," *Harper's* Oct. 1975: 4.

PART V (CHAPTERS 17–24)

1. Adapted from "Beaver," *Encyclopaedia Britannica*, 1974, *Micropaedia*.
2. Adapted from Linda Grant De Pauw, *Founding Mothers* (Boston: Houghton, 1975) 12–15.
3. Adapted from "Geosphere," *Geo* Oct. 1982: 118.
4. Adapted from "Geosphere," *Geo* July 1983: 106.
5. Thanks to Kevin Hennessy, who supplied the information for this paragraph.
6. Joan Didion, "On the Mall," *The White Album* (New York: Pocket, 1979) 179.
7. Kenneth Clark, *Civilization* (New York: Harper, 1969) 300.
8. Adapted from Dirk van Loon, *Small-Scale Pig Raising* (Charlotte: Garden Way, 1978) 38–40.
9. Adapted from Ingeborg S. MacHaffie and Margaret A. Nielsen, *Of Danish Ways* (Minneapolis: Dillon, 1976) 17.
10. Items 3–5, Colman Andrews, "Confessions of a Potato Head," *Metropolitan Home* May 1991: 118.
11. Adapted from Fritz Müller, *The Living Arctic* (Toronto: Methuen, 1981) 79.
12. Adapted from Ken Croswell, "Stars Too Small to Burn," *Astronomy* Apr. 1984: 15.
13. Passages 1 and 2 adapted from "Geosphere," *Geo* Nov. 1982: 128, 116.
14. Adapted from Wayne Lynch, "Great Balls of Snakes," *Natural History* Apr. 1983: 65–66.
15. Henry David Thoreau, *Walden and Civil Disobedience*, ed. Sherman Paul (Boston: Houghton, 1960) 1.
16. Lillian Hellman, *Pentimento* (Boston: Little, 1973) 265.
17. Adapted from "Cucumber," a card published by the Chas. C. Hart Seed Co., 1980.
18. Thomas Jefferson et al., A Declaration by the Representatives of the United States of America, in General Congress Assembled, 4 July 1776.
19. Some information adapted from David Wallechinsky, Irving Wallace, and Amy Wallace, *The Book of Lists* (New York: Bantam, 1978) 317–318.
20. Muriel Spark, *The Driver's Seat* (New York: Knopf, 1970) 109–110.
21. My thanks to Miles Wilson, who supplied material for this exercise from his unpublished novel, *Fire Season*.
22. Adapted from Alexander Petrunkevitch, "The Spider and the Wasp," *Scientific American* Aug. 1952: 22.

PART VI (CHAPTERS 25–30)

1. Adapted from *Reader's Digest Complete Do-It-Yourself Manual* (Pleasantville: Reader's Digest, 1973) 160.
2. Adapted from "Geosphere," *Geo* Jan. 1983: 120.

3. Adapted from Mary Wood-Allen and Sylvanus Stall, *What a Young Woman Ought to Know* (Philadelphia: Vir, 1898) 35.
4. Adapted from Carrol B. Fleming, "Maidens of the Sea Can Be Alluring, but Sailor, Beware," *Smithsonian* June 1983: 86, 88, 89, 90, 92.
5. Adapted from Lewis Thomas, *The Lives of a Cell* (New York: Viking, 1974) 96.
6. Abraham Lincoln, Second Inaugural Address, 4 Mar. 1865.
7. Martin Luther King, Jr., "I Have a Dream," March on Washington, 28 August 1963, in *The McGraw-Hill Reader,* ed. Gilbert H. Muller (New York: McGraw, 1991) 266.
8. Lewis Thomas, *The Medusa and the Snail* (New York: Viking, 1979) 126.
9. James A. Inciardi, *The War on Drugs: Heroin, Cocaine, Crime, and Public Policy* (Palo Alto: Mayfield, 1986) 1.
10. Richard Rodriguez, *Hunger of Memory* (Boston: Godine, 1982) 17.
11. Adlai Stevenson, speech to the National School Boards Association, San Francisco, California, 26 Jan. 1959.
12. Sallie Tisdale, *Lot's Wife: Salt and the Human Condition* (New York: Henry Holt, 1988) 20.
13. André Ryerson, "Abolish the NEA," *Policy Review* Fall 1990: 32.
14. "The Frimbonians," *New Yorker* 22 April 1991: 30.
15. Adapted from an Epson advertisement appearing in *Science 84* June 1984: 77.
16. Adapted from Leigh P. Beadle, *Brew It Yourself* (New York: Farrar, 1971) 96.
17. Adapted from Delbert Clark, "What Makes a Genius?" *Saturday Review* 12 November 1955: 9.
18. Quoted material from Barbara W. Tuchman, *The March of Folly* (New York: Knopf, 1984) 4, 5, 7 [example and items 1–3] and *A Distant Mirror* (New York: Knopf, 1978) xiii, 98, 119 [items 4–7].

PART VII (CHAPTERS 31–36)

1. Ramond Queneau, *Exercises in Style,* trans. Barbara Wright (New York: New Directions, 1981) 72–73.
2. Adapted from Margaret Culley, "Preface," Kate Chopin, *The Awakening,* ed. Margaret Culley (New York: Norton, 1976) vii.
3. Adapted from Stephen MacLean, "Moviemakers from Down Under," *Geo* Nov. 1982: 59, 61, 64.

PART VIII (CHAPTERS 37–40)

1. My thanks to Robert O'Connor, who supplied some of the material for this exercise.

Acknowledgments

Pp. 6–7: "Pluto" from *Concise Columbia Encyclopedia,* 1983, © Columbia University Press, New York. Reprinted with the permission of the publisher.

P. 31: Reprinted from *The CP/M Handbook* by Rodnay Zaks, by permission of SYBEX, Inc. Copyright 1980 Sybex, Inc. All rights reserved.

P. 32: Excerpt from *An Introduction to CP/M Features and Facilities,* Digital Research Inc., 1978.

P. 33: From Elvin Holt.

Pp. 35–36: "What's in a Nickname?" by John Leo, in *Time,* January 19, 1987. Copyright 1987 Time Inc. Reprinted by permission.

Pp. 39–40: "Teachers' Tests," by Pierre Szamek. Copyright © 1984 by *Harper's Magazine.* All rights reserved. Reprinted from the February issue by special permission.

Pp. 41–42: Reprinted from *Jane Brody's Good Food Book, Living the High-Carbohydrate Way,* by Jane Brody, by permission of W. W. Norton & Company, Inc. Copyright © 1985 by Jane E. Brody.

P. 43: Excerpt from "Letter from Birmingham Jail" from *Why We Can't Wait* by Martin Luther King, Jr. Copyright © 1963, 1964 by Martin Luther King, Jr. Reprinted by permission of HarperCollins Publishers. and Joan Daves.

Pp. 45–46: Excerpt from "Death from the Sky" by Sam Iker. Copyright 1983 by the National Wildlife Federation. Reprinted from the September–October 1983 issue of *International Wildlife* magazine.

Pp. 52–53: "Why I Don't Let Students Cut My Classes," by William R. Brown, in *The Chronicle of Higher Education,* January 28, 1987. Reprinted by permission of the author.

Pp. 97–98: Reprinted by permission of *Science 84* Magazine, copyright © 1984 the American Association for the Advancement of Science.

P. 99: Excerpt from *The Language of Clothes* by Alison Lurie. Copyright © 1981 by Alison Lurie. Used by permission of Melanie Jackson Agency.

P. 99: Excerpt from "Nestworks" by Douglas J. Preston. Reprinted with permission from *Natural History,* Vol. 91, No. 9; Copyright The American Museum of Natural History, 1982.

P. 102: Excerpt from "Types of Pliers," *Reader's Digest Complete Do-It-Yourself Manual,* copyright © 1973 The Reader's Digest Association, Inc. Reprinted by permission.

Pp. 102–103: Excerpt from "Elephants," reprinted by permission of Wildlife Education, Ltd.

Pp. 106–107: Reprinted by permission of the publishers from *One Writer's Beginnings* by Eudora Welty, Cambridge, Mass.: Harvard University Press, Copyright © 1983, 1984 by Eudora Welty.

Pp. 111–112: Entry on W. H. Auden reprinted from *Critical Survey of Poetry,* volume 1, page 71. By permission of the publisher, Salem Press, Inc. Copyright, 1982, by Frank N. Magill.

P. 112: Reprinted with permission of Charles Scribner's Sons, an imprint of Macmillan